A PERSPECTIVE ON

CRYSTAL GROWTH

A PERSPECTIVE ON
CRYSTAL GROWTH

An Historical Collection in Celebration of 25 Years of the
Journal of Crystal Growth

Principal Editor
D.T.J. HURLE

1992
NORTH-HOLLAND

North-Holland

Elsevier Science Publishers B.V.

P.O. Box 211
1000 AE Amsterdam
The Netherlands

ISBN: 0 444 89707 9

The figures on the front cover have kindly been made available by B.T. Murray, National Institute of Standards and Technology, USA and A.A. Wheeler, University of Bristol, U.K.; NIST International Report number 4894 (see page [viii] for the caption).

Printed on acid-free paper

Printed in The Netherlands

ACKNOWLEDGEMENTS

Acknowledgement is gratefully made to the publishers of the journals in which the articles in this book originally appeared for their kind permission to reprint the articles:

Académie des Sciences
for A. Verneuil, "Production Artificielle du Rubis par Fusion", C.R. Acad. Sci. Paris C135 (1902) 791–794.

American Institute of Physics
for R.S. Wagner and W.C. Wellis, "Vapour-Liquid-Solid Mechanism of Single Crystal Growth", Appl. Phys. Lett. 4 (1964) 89–90;
and for W.C. Dash, "Growth of Silicon Crystals Free From Dislocations", J. Appl. Phys. 30 (1959) 459–474;
and for W.W. Mullins and R.F. Sekerka, "Stability of a Planar Interface During Soldification of a Dilute Binary Alloy", J. Appl. Phys. 35 (1964) 444–451;
and for J.R. Arthur, Jr., "Interaction of Ga and As_2 Molecular Beams with GaAs Surfaces", J. Appl. Phys. 39 (1986) 4032–4034;
and for J.A. Burton, R.C. Prim and W.P. Slichter, "The Distribution of Solute in Crystals Grown from the Melt. Part I. Theoretical", J. Chem. Phys. 21 (1953) 1987–1991;
and for D.E. Temkin, "Kinetics of Growth of a Crystal Needle in a Supercooled Binary Melt", Sov. Phys. Crystallogr. 7 (1962) 354–357.

American Society for Metals
for K.A. Jackson, "Mechanism of Growth", in: Liquid Metals of Soldification (1958) pp. 174–186.

Electrochemical Society, Inc.
for H.C. Theuerer, "Epitaxial Silicon Films by the Hydrogen Reduction of $SiCl_4$", J. Electrochem. Soc. 108 (1961) 649–653;
and for H.M. Manasevit and W.I. Simpson, "The Use of Metal-Organics in the Preparation of Semiconductor Materials: I. Epitaxial Gallium-V Compounds", J. Electrochem. Soc. 116 (1969) 1725–1732;
and for M.B. Panish, "Molecular Beam Epitaxy of GaAs and InP with Gas Sources for As and P", J. Electrochem. Soc. 127 (1980) 2729–2733.

Macmillan Magazines Ltd.
for F.P. Bundy, H.T. Hall, H.M. Strong and R.H. Wentorf, Jr., "Man-Made Diamonds", Nature 176 (1955) 51–55.

Munksgaard International Publishers Ltd.
for P. Hartman and W.G. Perdok, "On the Relations between Structure and Morphology of Crystals, I", Acta Crystallogr. 8 (1955) 49–52.

National Research Council of Canada
for J.W. Ruttter and B. Chalmers, "A Prismatic Substructure Formed during Soldification of Metals", Canad. J. Phys. 31 (1953) 15–39.

R. Oldenbourg Verlag GmbH
for J. Czochralski, "Ein neues Verfahren zur Messung der Kristallisationsgeschwindigkeit der Metalle", Z. Phys. Chem. 92 (1918) 219–221;
and for M. Volmer, "Zum Problem des Kristallwachstumms", Z. Phys. Chem. 102 (1922) 267–275;
and for I.N. Stranski, "Zur Theorie des Kristallwachstumms", Z. Phys. Chem. 136 (1928) 259–278;

Royal Society of Chemistry
for W.K. Burton and N. Cabrera, "Crystal Growth and Surface Structure: Part I", Discuss. Faraday Soc. 5 (1949) 33–39;
and for F.C. Frank, "The Influence of Dislocations on Crystal Growth", Discuss. Faraday Soc. 5 (1949) 48–51.
Society of Mining Engineers of the American Institute of Mining, Metallurgical and Petroleum Engineers, Inc.
for W.G. Pfann, "Principles of Zone-Melting", Trans. AIME 194 (1952) 747–753.
Taylor & Francis Ltd.
for K.F. Hulme and J.B. Mullin, "Facets and Anamalous Solute Distributions in Indium-Antimonide Crystals", Philos. Mag. 4 (1959) 1286–1288.

EDITORIAL

This book has been produced to celebrate 25 years of the Journal of Crystal Growth. As a science, the study of crystals and their growth has a long history, and emerged as commercially important with the invention of the transistor.

Following the First International Conference on Crystal Growth in Boston, USA, in 1966, the Journal of Crystal Growth was conceived and launched in 1967. Its aim was to provide a focus for the scientific sub-discipline of crystal growth and for its application to the production of single crystals and epitaxial layers for research and for commercial exploitation. Since then it has grown steadily to become the principal international journal in the field which attracts high quality papers covering a wide range of disciplines from laboratories worldwide. Being located at the interface of so many disciplines – physics, chemistry, bio-chemistry, metallurgy and ceramic technology, electrical and mechanical engineering, etc. – it is a fertile area of research.

The interdisciplinary nature of the subject has required a large board of editors and associated editors to maintain the high standards which have been set. Two individuals have been associated with the Journal since its inception and have played pivotal roles in its steady and successful development. They are Professor Michael Schieber, who founded the Journal and has been its Principal Editor throughout its life, and Mrs. F.Y. Verploegh Chassé, who has been its Technical Editor.

The Journal came into being when the commercial importance of crystal growth was emerging, so much of the underlying science predates it. The papers reproduced in this book have been selected by the Editorial Board, with benefit of suggestions and advice from the Associate Editors, to give perspective on the subject. We have sought to portray the historical evolution of the techniques, experimental science and theory of crystal growth. Several external constraints such as restriction to English, French and German languages, length of the paper and overall length of this book have limited the choice. Nonetheless, we hope that the publication will be recognized as a selection of key papers in the development of the subject.

Every anthology is subjective and each reader will no doubt feel that we have failed to include certain important papers. This is inevitable. We strongly resist any idea that we have attempted to compile "the best papers" in crystal growth; that has not been our purpose. Rather we ask that the selection be judged by the degree to which it properly illuminates the historical development of the subject.

During the past twenty-five years crystal growth has developed from a largely academic subject to one of the key science disciplines. Materials, both in the research and factory production stages, are the key to progress and competitiveness in many fields, but none more than in electronic devices and systems. To a very large degree progress has depended and will continue to depend increasingly upon our ability to prepare high quality single crystals in a cost-effective manner. The Journal of Crystal Growth has played a key role in bringing about the realisation that scientific understanding must be a part of materials preparation and that crystal growth is at the core of electronics and materials technology. It is our hope that during the next twenty-five years crystal growth will continue to advance in scientific depth, industrial application and impact on society and it is our promise that the Journal of Crystal Growth will be dedicated to these goals.

Finally we wish to offer this book as a tribute to the skilled and conscientious efforts of the hundreds – or perhaps thousands – of our colleagues who have helped to establish and maintain the standards of the journal in their unrewarded capacity as referees. Thank you all.

The Editors

FRONT COVER FIGURES

The front cover shows the evolution in time of a crystal with six-fold symmetry, into an highly undercooled melt. The computation was performed using a phase field model with physical parameters typical of a metal. The dimension of the side of each square box is approximately 20 μm and the times of the plots are at 0.029, 0.058, 0.116 and 0.174 μs, respectively, the upper plot being the earliest time. Further details can be found in "Computations of Dendrites Using the Phase Field Method", NIST IR 4894 (1992) by A.A. Wheeler, B.T. Murray and R.J. Schaefer.

CONTENTS

CHIMIE MINÉRALE. — *Production artificielle du rubis par fusion.*
Note de M. A. **Verneuil**, présentée par M. H. Moissan.

« Malgré ses persévérantes recherches, A. Gaudin n'a pas obtenu l'alumine fondue à l'état transparent.

» La cause de cet insuccès résidait dans l'emploi d'une température trop élevée, car, si l'on dépasse sensiblement son point de fusion, cet oxyde cristallise en donnant un produit opaque.

» De là résulte l'impossibilité d'affiner une masse d'alumine sur une profondeur un peu notable, à l'aide du chalumeau oxhydrique, puisque ce n'est qu'en surchauffant la couche supérieure que l'on peut liquéfier les parties plus profondes. Si l'on remarque enfin que l'alumine transparente obtenue est toujours sillonnée d'une multitude de craquelures, dues au contact de l'enduit fondu avec l'alumine sous-jacente, il faudra conclure de ces données que le problème posé ne peut se résoudre qu'en observant les conditions suivantes :

» 1° Maintenir le produit fondu dans une région de la flamme toujours identique.

» 2° Produire l'accroissement par couches superposées de bas en haut afin de réaliser l'affinage sur une série de couches minces;

» 3° Obtenir la fusion dans des conditions où le contact du produit fondu avec le support soit réduit à une surface extrêmement petite.

» La première de ces conditions se trouve réalisée par l'emploi d'un chalumeau oxhydrique vertical dont la flamme est dirigée sur un support mobile de haut en bas et qui peut être abaissé par le jeu d'une vis à pas très serré, permettant ainsi d'éloigner du chalumeau le produit fondu à mesure qu'il s'élève et de le ramener dans la zone convenable de fusion, lorsque celle-ci se sera éloignée du bout du chalumeau par l'augmentation progressive donnée à l'intensité de la flamme.

» J'ai réalisé la formation de la masse fondue constituée par des couches minces superposées de bas en haut, conformément à la deuxième condition énoncée, à l'aide d'une méthode que l'on peut appeler procédé de *semage* et qui consiste à entraîner la poudre d'alumine chromée ou le rubis naturel pulvérisé par le courant d'oxygène qui alimente le chalumeau. La matière, placée dans un panier en toile métallique suspendu dans une chambre qui surmonte le tube central du chalumeau, est lancée dans le courant d'oxygène par l'effet des chocs d'un petit marteau actionné mécaniquement. Les grains d'alumine (1) ou de rubis, ainsi distribués dans toutes les parties de la flamme, subiront la fusion dès qu'ils parviendront dans la zone suffisamment chaude, coïncidant dès l'origine du travail avec le support destiné à recevoir la masse fondue.

» Ce support, formé d'un petit cylindre d'alumine agglomérée au rouge avec quelques centièmes de carbonate de potasse, est placé très exactement dans l'axe du chalumeau, et sa surface est portée, par la flamme convenablement réglée, à une température un peu inférieure à celle de la fusion de l'alumine afin d'agglomérer seulement les grains qui tombent sur cette surface et forment bientôt un cône dont le sommet parvient peu à peu dans la partie de la flamme suffisamment chaude pour en effectuer la fusion. A partir de ce moment, tous les grains qui tombent sur la pointe fondue s'y liquéfient, et le filament obtenu, qui réduit ainsi à une très petite surface le contact de la matière avec le support, augmente peu à peu de diamètre à mesure qu'il s'élève et gagne une zone plus chaude et plus large de la flamme, en se transformant à son sommet en une sphère dont il faut maintenant accroître le diamètre le plus possible,

(1) L'alumine précipitée avec 2,5 pour 100 d'oxyde de chrome et calcinée est la meilleure forme sous laquelle on puisse l'employer.

ce que l'on obtient en augmentant progressivement l'arrivée de l'oxygène dont le débit est commandé par un robinet à vis d'un pas très serré.

» Le gaz d'éclairage ayant été admis en grand excès dès le début de la fusion, l'augmentation du débit de l'oxygène entraîne le déplacement de la zone convenable de fusion qui s'éloigne progressivement du *bout* du chalumeau; il faut donc, en abaissant le support qui porte la masse, ramener dans cette zone la partie supérieure de la sphère fondue : le bouillonnement caractéristique qui s'opère sous l'influence de la flamme trop chaude ou trop riche en oxygène est un indice qui permet de ramener toujours le produit dans la région voulue.

» Pour maintenir la fixité de la flamme et régulariser le rayonnement, l'opération s'exécute au milieu d'un petit four cylindrique en argile portant un regard permettant de suivre les phases de la fusion. En employant un chalumeau possédant un *bout* de $\frac{12}{10}$ de millimètre (dimension au-dessus de laquelle il devient difficile de former à l'origine une pointe fondue suffisamment fine), il est possible d'obtenir en 2 heures une masse ovoïde parfaitement affinée et d'une coloration bien homogène pesant $2^{g},500$ à 3^{g}, c'est-à-dire environ 12 ou 15 carats. Une telle masse présente 5^{mm} à 6^{mm} de diamètre lorsqu'elle est sphérique.

» Dès que l'on est parvenu à obtenir ces dimensions, vers la fin du travail, on supprime brusquement l'arrivée des deux gaz afin d'obtenir une trempe énergique du produit. A cette condition seulement et si la masse a été bien centrée et également chauffée, elle se fend exactement en deux parties suivant un plan vertical. Chacune de ces deux demi-sphères, taillées à l'aide des procédés employés par les lapidaires, donne un rubis semblable à celui que je soumets à l'Académie.

» Ces rubis, qui possèdent une magnifique fluorescence rouge, ont pour densité 4,01, et tous les lapidaires auxquels ils ont été soumis ont trouvé qu'ils présentaient la même dureté que le rubis naturel et pouvaient prendre son beau poli.

» Lorsqu'ils sont parfaitement réussis, il me paraît impossible de les distinguer des plus beaux rubis naturels, mais souvent, et surtout dans le cas des grosses pierres, ils présentent deux défauts qui indiquent leur origine artificielle et qui tiennent à la réelle difficulté qu'on éprouve à conduire correctement une fusion : l'affinage imparfait en quelques points se traduit par des groupes de petites bulles que l'on distingue avec une forte loupe. Leur formation est due soit à un *semage* exagéré, soit à l'emploi d'une flamme trop oxygénée.

» Le second défaut, plus caractéristique encore, réside dans la présence de zones rubannées dues à la décoloration de certaines portions, par la volatilisation du chrome, lorsque le *semage* a été trop ralenti. Ces défauts, qui n'altèrent pas sensiblement, du reste, la beauté de ces pierres lorsqu'elles sont montées, s'atténuent et peuvent même disparaître lorsque, par un travail convenablement suivi, il est devenu possible de se rendre tout à fait maître du *semage* (1). »

CHIMIE. — *Sur les alliages de cuivre et de magnésium.* Note de M. O. Boudouard, présentée par M. Troost.

« D'après Parkinson (2), en fondant 200^g de cuivre et 50^g de magnésium pendant 7 minutes, on obtient un alliage rouge jaunâtre ou couleur or, selon la proportion centésimale de magnésium (la perte est environ 1,75 pour 100). Cet alliage s'oxyde lentement; lorsqu'on le rompt, il a une apparence vitreuse; il est très cassant : 1 pour 100 de magnésium rend le cuivre cassant; le métal à 15 pour 100 de magnésium, dont la densité est 5,95, peut être pulvérisé au mortier. J'ai repris l'étude des alliages de cuivre et de magnésium et j'ai l'honneur de présenter à l'Académie les résultats relatifs à leur fusibilité et à leurs propriétés mécaniques.

» Quoique le point de fusion du cuivre soit assez élevé (1085°), j'ai pu employer le procédé qui m'avait servi dans les recherches sur les alliages du magnésium avec l'aluminium et le cadmium pour déterminer le point de solidification des mélanges contenant jusqu'à 75 pour 100 de cuivre (3); le Tableau ci-dessous montre en effet que ces mélanges fondent au-dessous de 600°. Ponr les teneurs supérieures à 75 pour 100, j'ai fondu les métaux sous le sel marin, le tube en verre destiné à protéger le couple thermoélectrique étant remplacé par un tube semblable en porcelaine. Voici les résultats obtenus :

Magnésium pour 100 en poids.	Cuivre pour 100 en poids.	Températures.
100	»	635°
90	10	610
80	20	560
70	30	475
60	40	530
50	50	550
45	55	550
40	60	545

(1) Je suis heureux de remercier mon élève M. Marc Paquier de l'aide très active qu'il m'a donnée pendant ce long travail.

(2) *Chemical Society*, 2e série, t. V, p. 117.

(3) *Comptes rendus*, t. CXXXII, p. 1325.

Ein neues Verfahren zur Messung der Kristallisationsgeschwindigkeit der Metalle.

Von

J. Czochralski.

(Mit 3 Figuren im Text.)

(Eingegangen am 19. 8. 16.)

Die Bestimmung der Kristallisationsgeschwindigkeit (KG) geht, wie Tammann gezeigt hat[1]), bei den nichtmetallischen Stoffen in der Regel glatt von statten. Bei den Metallen konnte dagegen infolge deren Undurchsichtigkeit das Tammannsche Verfahren nicht angewandt werden. Einige Untersuchungsergebnisse des Verfassers legten es nahe, die Messung der Kristallisationsgeschwindigkeit von Metallen auf einfache Weise durchzuführen. Das Verfahren beruht auf der Messung der Höchstgeschwindigkeit, mit der man einen dünnen Kristallfaden des betreffenden Metalles aus seiner Schmelze kontinuierlich ziehen kann, ohne dass ein Abreissen des Fadens erfolgt.

Die erforderliche, in Fig. 1 wiedergegebene Vorrichtung besteht aus dem Stativ S, der Führungsscheibe F'' mit den beiden Führungen F' für den Seidenfaden F, an dem ein Mitnehmer M aus Glas für den Kristallfaden K befestigt ist. Die Schmelze *Sch* befindet sich in einem Holzkohlentiegel H mit einer seitlichen Bohrung für das Thermometer. Durch ein leicht regulierbares Uhrwerk U kann der Seidenfaden F leicht aufwärts und abwärts bewegt werden. Zur Messung der Geschwindigkeit dient der Zeiger Z und die Millimeterskala MS. Um das Anhaften der Schmelze an dem Mitnehmer M zu erleichtern, versieht man dessen Spitze a (Fig. 2) durch Reiben in dem halberstarrten breiigen Metall mit einem dünnen Metallüberzug.

Für die Versuchsausführung wird der Mitnehmer M in das flüssige, etwas überhitzte Metall getaucht und der Apparat, nachdem sich die Temperatur des Schmelzpunktes eingestellt hat, in Tätigkeit gesetzt. Infolge der Kapillarkraft zieht der Mitnehmer M zunächst eine kleine

[1]) G. Tammann, Kristallisieren und Schmelzen 1903.

Menge des flüssigen Metalles empor, das beim Passieren der Kristallisationsgrenze $e - e$ (Fig. 3) in einer gewissen gleichbleibenden Entfernung von der Schmelze erstarrt und neue Mengen des flüssigen Metalles nach sich zieht. Bei übereinstimmender Geschwindigkeit werden lange zylindrische Fäden erzielt, während Unterschiede in der Ganggeschwindigkeit und der Geschwindigkeit der Kristallisation ein Verdicken, bzw. bei zurückbleibender Kristallisationsgeschwindigkeit ein

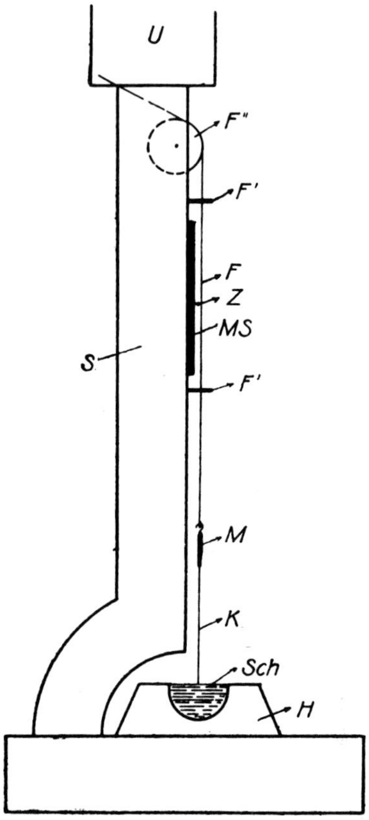

Fig. 1.

Fig. 2.

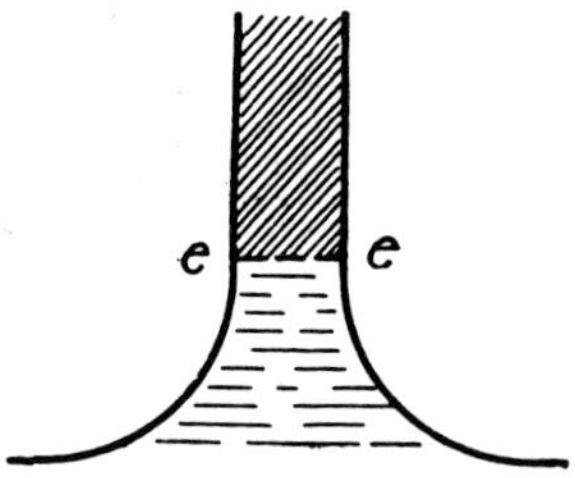

Fig. 3.

Verjüngen und Abbrechen des Kristallfadens zur Folge haben. Durch geeignete Ätzverfahren konnte man nachweisen, dass es sich in der Tat um homogene langgestreckte Kristallnadeln handelte.

In der Zahlentafel ist die Kristallisationsgeschwindigkeit einiger Metalle in der Nähe des Schmelzpunktes wiedergegeben. Unterkühlungen wurden nur bei Zinn, und zwar nur in einem Fall beobachtet; die Unterkühlung erstreckte sich bis auf 2° unterhalb des Schmelzpunktes.

eine Erhöhung der Kristallisationsgeschwindigkeit innerhalb dieses Gebietes war nicht zu beobachten[1]).

Zahlentafel.

Metall	Schmelzpunkt	KG in mm pro Minute etwa	Durchmesser des zylindrischen Metallfadens in mm	Länge der erhaltenen Kristallfäden in mm	Ätzmittel
Zinn	232°	90	0·2, 0·5, 1·0	bis 150	Kaliumchlorat-Salzsäure (1 + 1000)
Blei	320°	140	0·2, 0·5, 1·0	bis 120	Salzsäure 1·12
Zink	416°	100	0·2, 0·5, 1·0	bis 190	Salzsäure 1·12

[1]) Über die allgemein-theoretischen Schlussfolgerungen s. auch J. Czochralski, Veränderung der Korngrösse und der Korngliederung in Metallen, Zeitschrift des Vereins deutscher Ingenieure 1916 (im Erscheinen).

Principles of Zone-Melting

by W. G. Pfann

In zone-melting, a small molten zone or zones traverse a long charge of alloy or impure metal. Consequences of this manner of freezing are examined with respect to solute distribution in the ingot, with particular reference to purification and to prevention of segregation. Results are expressed in terms of the number, size, and direction of travel of the zones, the initial solute distribution, and the distribution coefficient.

IF a charge of binary solid-solution alloy is melted and then frozen slowly from one end, as for example in the Bridgman method of making single crystals,[1] coring usually occurs, with a resulting end-to-end variation in concentration. Such coring, or normal segregation, is undesirable where uniformity is an object. On the other hand, for certain systems, it can be utilized to refine a material by concentrating impurities at one end of the ingot.[1, 2]

In the present paper a different manner of freezing will be examined with respect to the distribution of solute in the ingot. A number of procedures will be indicated which have in common the traversal of a relatively long charge of solid alloy by a small molten zone. Such methods will be denoted by the general term *zone-melting*, while the process described in the preceding paragraph will be called *normal freezing*. It will be shown that, in contrast to normal freezing, zone-melting affords wide latitude in possible distributions of solute. Segregation can either be almost entirely eliminated or it can be enhanced so as to provide a high degree of separation of solute and solvent.

A number of simplifying assumptions will be invoked which, while not entirely realizable in practice, nevertheless provide a suitable point of departure for more refined treatments. Moreover, our own experience with zone-melting has shown that, for certain systems at least, the analysis holds quite well. The present paper will be confined to a discussion of principles and a general description of procedures. Comparison with experiment is planned for later publication.

Normal Freezing

Before considering zone-melting, segregation during normal freezing will be reviewed briefly. If a cylinder of molten binary alloy is made to freeze from one end as in Fig. 1, there usually will be a segregating action which will concentrate the solute in one or the other end of the ingot. If the constitutional diagram for the system is like that of Fig. 2, then the distribution coefficient k, defined as the ratio of the concentration in the solid to that in the liquid at equilibrium, will be less than one and the solute will be concentrated in the last regions to freeze. If the solute raises the freezing point, then k will be greater than one and the solute will be concentrated in the first regions to freeze.

W. G. PFANN, Member AIME, is associated with Bell Telephone Laboratories, Murray Hill, N. J.

Discussion on this paper, TP 3326E, may be sent, 2 copies, to AIME by Dec. 1, 1952. Manuscript, Jan. 9, 1952; revised, April 24, 1952. Philadelphia Meeting, October 1952.

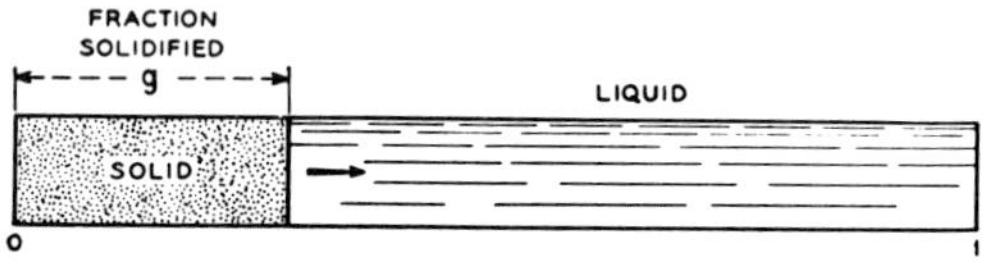

Fig. 1—Solidification by normal freezing (schematic).

The concentration in the solid as a function of g, the fraction which has solidified, can be expressed by the relation:

$$C = k C_o (1-g)^{k-1} \quad [1]$$

where C_o is the initial solute concentration in the melt. Eq 1 is based on the following assumptions:

1—Diffusion in the solid is negligible. 2—Diffusion in the liquid is complete (i.e., concentration in the liquid is uniform). 3—k is constant.

Concentration curves representing eq 1 for k's from 0.01 to 5.0 are plotted in Fig. 3. This equation, in one form or another, has been treated by Gulliver,[3] Scheuer,[4] Hayes and Chipman[5] for alloys and by McFee[2] for NaCl crystals. It is derived in Appendix I. It should be pointed out that the k which is calculated from the phase diagram will be valid only in the ideal case for which the stated assumptions are correct. In all actual cases, the effective k will be larger than this value for solutes which lower the melting point, smaller for solutes which raise the melting point, and will probably vary during the beginning of the freezing process. For simplification it will be assumed that the ideal k is valid.

Zone-Leveling Processes

The processes of this part are designed to produce a uniform, or level, distribution of solute in the ingot.

Single Pass: Consider a rod or charge of alloy whose cross-section is constant and whose composition, C_o, is constant, although permissibly varying on a microscopic scale.* Such a charge might be a rapidly frozen casting or a mixture of crushed or powdered constituents. Cause a molten zone of

* More accurately, C_o must be invariant with x, but the concentration may vary throughout a given cross-section.

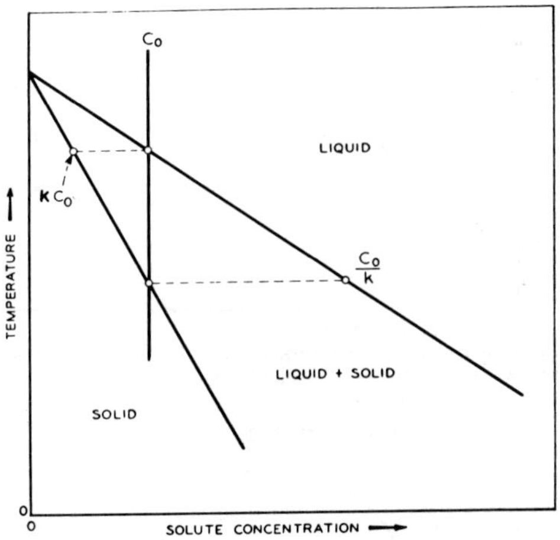

Fig. 2—Portion of constitutional diagram for a solute which lowers the freezing point of the solvent (schematic).

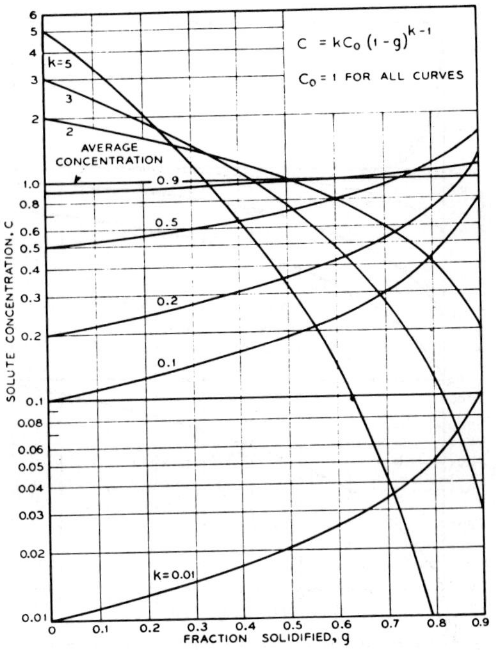

Fig. 3—Curves for normal freezing, showing solute concentration in solid as a function of *g*, the fraction solidified, calculated from eq 1 for various values of *k*, the distribution coefficient.

length l to traverse the charge, as shown in Fig. 4, l being constant and small compared to the length of the charge.

The course of segregation during this process may be visualized by reference to Fig. 2. As the molten zone advances it freezes out a layer dx of solid and melts a layer dx of the charge. The first solid to freeze, at $x=0$, is of concentration kC_o. For $k<1$, kC_o is less than C_o and hence the liquid is enriched. As the zone progresses the liquid continues to be enriched, although at a decreasing rate, until it attains concentration C_o/k. When this condition is attained the concentrations of solids entering and leaving the zone are the same and hence no further change of concentration occurs in the zone or in the solid freezing from it until the zone reaches the end of the charge. The remaining liquid then solidifies by normal freezing, as described by eq 1.

Thus, as shown in Fig. 5, simple zone-melting of a uniform charge results in an initial transition region; a region of uniform concentration which may have any desired length and an end region of length equal to one zone, in which normal freezing prevails. The concentration C at any length x in the zone-melted bar (except in the last zone) is given by:

$$C/C_o = 1 - (1\text{-}k)e^{-kx/l} \qquad [2]$$

where x is the length solidified, measured from the starting end, and not the fraction solidified. The derivation of eq 2 was made by W. T. Read and appears in Appendix II. The underlying assumptions are those of normal freezing, with the addition that l is assumed to be constant.

Calculated curves of C vs. x/l according to eq 2 are plotted in Fig. 6 for k's from 0.01 to 5.0, for the particular case of a charge ten units long, unit zone-length, and unity C_o. Nine zone-lengths are depicted; the tenth solidifies by normal freezing. In connection with the curves of Fig. 6 it should be noted that:

1—As k increases, C approaches equality with C_o at lower values of x/l. For a given k, the percentage yield of uniform material can be increased by increasing the rod-length and by reducing l.

2—The difference between the mean and initial concentrations is proportional to $(1\text{-}k)$ as in normal freezing.

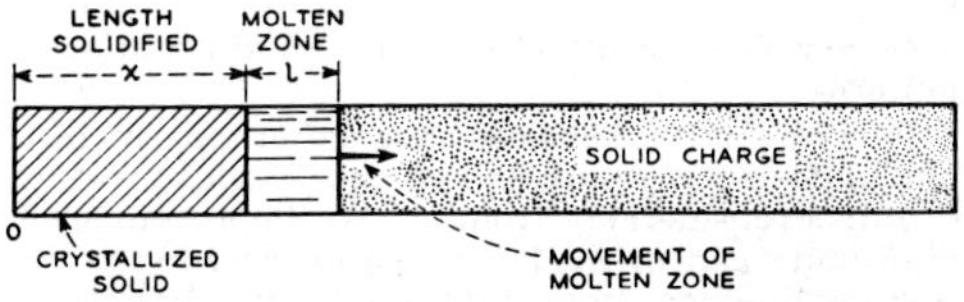

Fig. 4—Solidification by zone-melting (schematic).

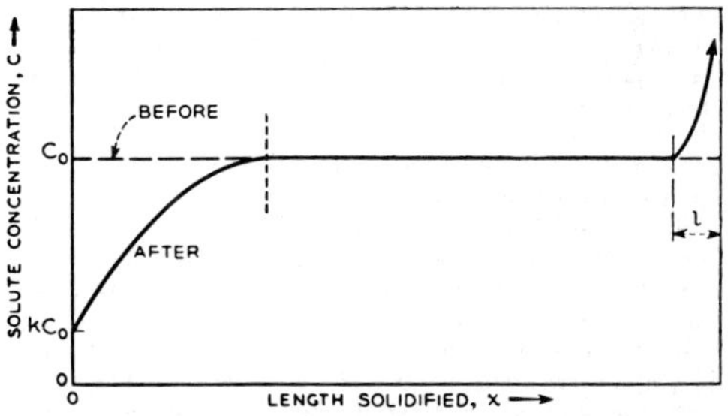

Fig. 5—Approximate concentrations before and after single-pass zone-melting. Note region of uniform concentration after zone-melting.

3—While eq 2 and the curves of Fig. 6 are based on the four stated assumptions, *the basic feature of the zone-melting process, that is, the attainment of a limiting composition* C_o, *is relatively independent* of these assumptions. (Of course, fluctuations in k

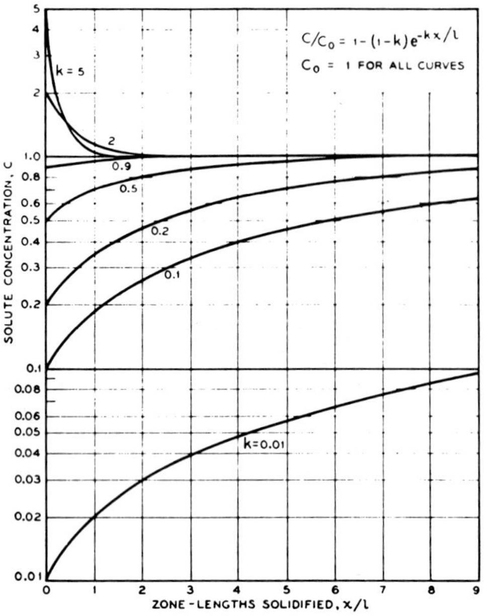

Fig. 6—Curves for zone-melting, showing solute concentration in solid as a function of x/l, the zone-lengths solidified, calculated from eq 2, for various k's. Nine zone-lengths are shown.

or l after C_0 has been reached will cause changes in C.)

4—For k's of about 0.2 or less the rod is not at all uniform.

Reverse Pass: It has been shown that zone-melting of a uniform rod results in two end-regions in which C differs considerably from C_0. An improvement in uniformity can be made by re-zone-melting in the reverse direction, from right to left. If C has essentially attained the value C_0 at some point in the first pass, as in curve a of Fig. 7, then the distribution of solute after the reverse pass will be as shown qualitatively in curve b. The deviation at the right will be eliminated; that at the left will be re-reduced. Even if k is very small, ~0.01, and C_0 is not attained in the first pass, it is found that reverse zone-melting results in substantially uniform composition in all but the last zone.

Repeated Pass: If a sufficient number of back-and-forth passes is made in a straight bar, all deviations from a uniform composition can be eliminated, except in the last zone to freeze. In this respect the molten zone may be likened to a weighted drag moved across soil in order to level it. The drag picks up soil at high spots, drops it at low spots. Similarly, the molten zone equalizes points of high and low concentration in the charge, the action being particularly effective if k is small. For a starting charge of mean composition C_0, not assumed to be uniform, and a charge of total length d, the final concentration, C_r, of the uniform rod is given by:

$$C_r/C_0 = \frac{dk}{dk + L(1-k)} \qquad [3]$$

The final concentration in the molten zone will be C_r/k.

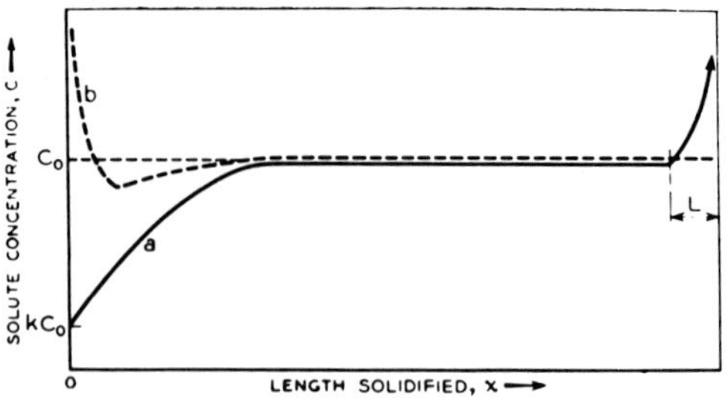

Fig. 7—Approximate concentrations after: (a) single-pass zone-melting; (b) reverse zone-melting of (a).

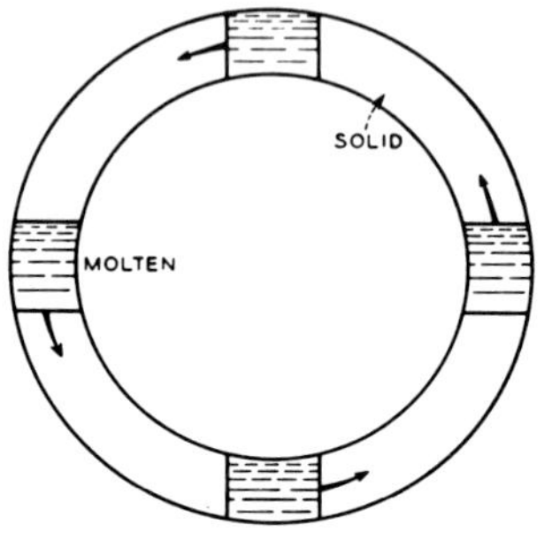

Fig. 8—Repeated-pass zone-melting of circular charge. The final state is a uniform solute concentration in the solid equal to k times that in the molten zones.

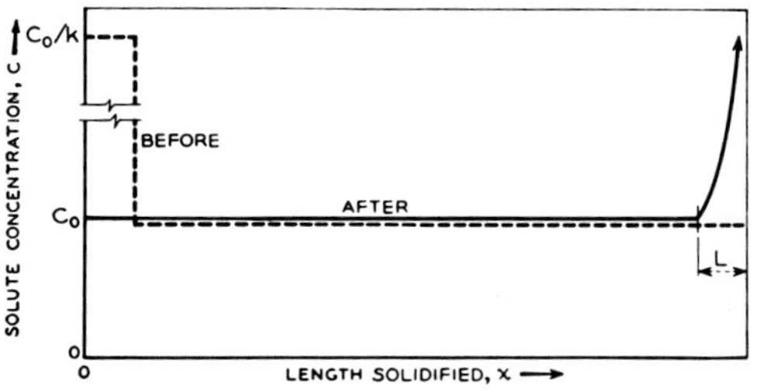

Fig. 9—Zone-melting with starting charge, to eliminate initial transition region.

An alternate means of achieving the result expressed by eq 3 is to arrange the charge in the form of a closed ring, as in Fig. 8, and to cause one or more molten zones to travel around it. In the ring method, if more than one zone is used, l, in eq 3, should be the sum of their lengths.

Starting Charge: The initial transition region in single-pass zone-melting is a result of the fact that the molten zone must travel some distance before it accumulates enough solute to attain concentration C_0/k. This region can be eliminated by arranging the charge to have a concentration C_0/k in the first zone and C_0 in the remainder,† as shown in Fig. 9.

† This fact was pointed out by W. Shockley (private communication).

Starting Charge into Pure Solvent: It may be seen from Fig. 6 that the initial transition region is

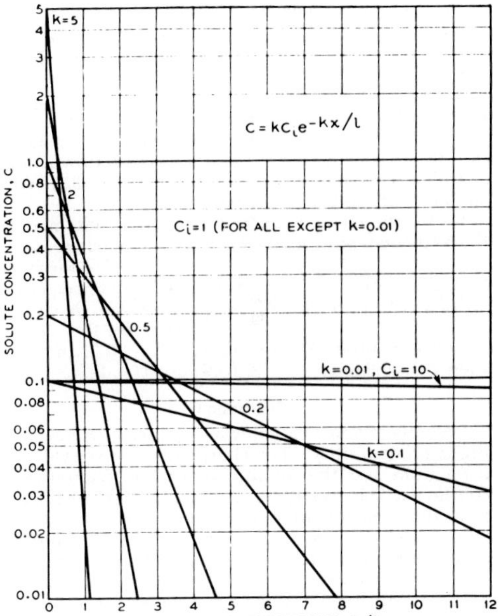

Fig. 10—Curves for zone-melting into pure solvent, showing solute concentration in solid as a function of x/l, the zone-lengths solidified, calculated from eq 4 for various k's.

extremely long for values of k of about 0.1 or less, and that segregation is quite severe in single-pass zone-melting. A method of zone-melting which is particularly effective in such instances is to place solute in the first zone only, the remainder of the charge being pure solvent. The concentration of the solid after one pass is given in all except the last zone by:

$$C = kC_i e^{-kx/l} \qquad [4]$$

where C_i is the concentration of the charge in the first zone. Calculated concentration curves for a range of k's are shown in Fig. 10. It may be seen that for k equal to 0.01 the concentration decreases only about 10 pct in ten zone-lengths.

Even such decrease can be entirely prevented by reducing the volume of the zone as it travels through the charge. For a charge of constant cross-sectional area, a, the concentration will remain constant, at the value kC_i, if the zone-length l is decreased in accordance with the equation:

$$l = l_o - kx \qquad [5a]$$

where l_o is the initial zone-length. If it is desired to maintain l at a constant value and decrease a, then a must vary in accordance with the equation:

$$a = a_o e^{x/D} \qquad [5b]$$

where:

$$D = \frac{l}{\log_e (1-k)}$$

and a_o is the cross-sectional area at $x = 0$. It may be noted that eq 5a is applicable only to a charge of finite length, l_o/k, for at that value of x the zone-length becomes zero. Eq 5b in principle at least is applicable to a charge of infinite length. Both equations are valid only if $k<1$. Derivations of eqs 4, 5a, and 5b appear in Appendix III.

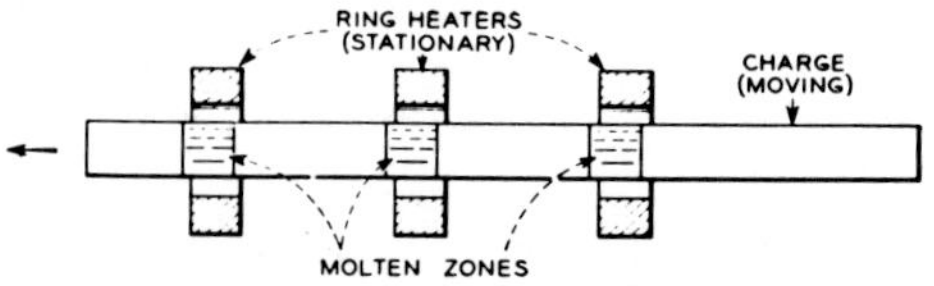

Fig. 11—Multiple-zone-refining, using a straight charge. For $k < 1$, the solute becomes concentrated in the end of the ingot, at the right.

Zone-Refining Processes

The processes of this part have the object of purifying a solvent material, or separating solute from solvent.

Utilization of segregation during normal freezing to purify part of an ingot is well known.[1, 2] The process is particularly effective where k is small and diffusion in the solid is limited. A glance at the curves of Fig. 3 indicates that for k's less than about 0.1 most of the solute is concentrated in the last tenth of the ingot. Further purification can be obtained by cropping the solute-rich tip, remelting and refreezing. In principle any desired degree of purification can be obtained by a repetition of such steps.

Refinement can also be accomplished by zone-melting. A comparison of Figs. 3 and 6 shows that for small k's a considerable purification is effected by single-pass zone-melting, although on the average it is less than for normal freezing, for any given fraction of the charge. The particular merit of zone-refining becomes evident when repeated crystallizations are desired. By passing a bar through a series of heaters a number of molten zones can be made to traverse the charge in a single operation. Each zone picks up solute on its way through the charge and deposits it at the end of the charge. Thus, any desired number of refining steps can be obtained in a single operation, and without resort to the intermediate steps of cropping. Figs. 11 and 12 illustrate multiple-zone-refining for a straight and for a circular charge.

It is of interest to know the distributions of solute after two, three, or more zones pass through an initially uniform charge and also the ultimate distribution after a large number of passes. The latter is more easily determined and will be discussed first.

Consider a charge of length d and of mean composition C_m, with no restriction being placed on the distribution of the solute. Assume for purposes of

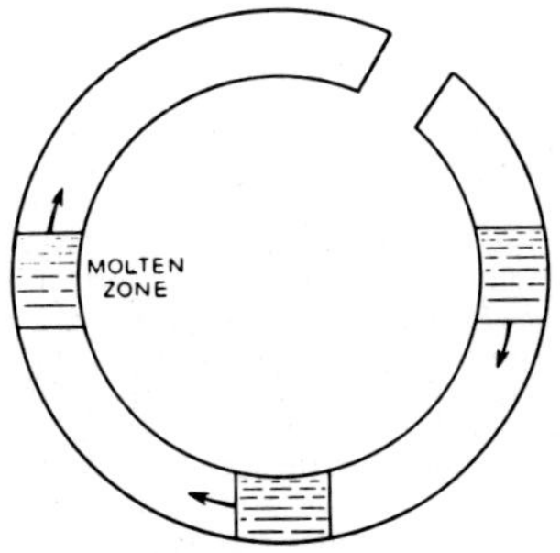

Fig. 12—Multiple-zone-refining, using a charge in the form of an open ring.

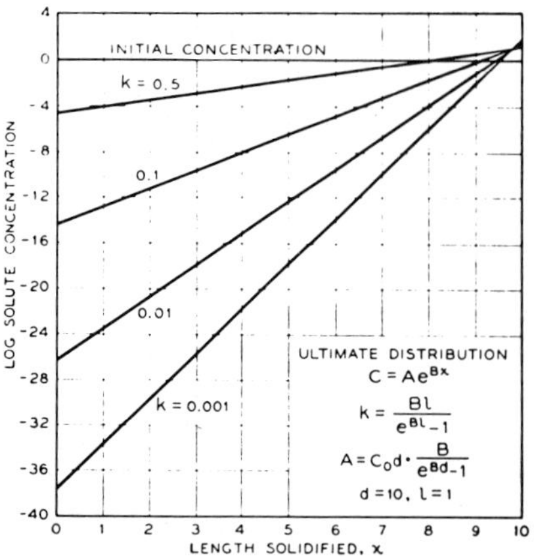

Fig. 13—Solute concentration curves showing the ultimate distribution after multiple-zone-refining, calculated from eq 8, for various *k*'s.

exposition that k is less than one. It is instinctively seen that after repeated passes in one direction a distribution will be reached which cannot be further changed. (The effect may be likened to piling a given amount of sand against a vertical wall—there will be a maximum attainable height.) Let this ultimate distribution be:

$$C = F(x) \qquad [6]$$

If a molten zone of length l is to pass through the bar without changing this distribution then the concentration of the solid freezing out of the zone at any point x must be given by eq 6. The concentration of the liquid in the zone is:

$$C_l = \frac{1}{l}\int_x^{x+l} C\,dx = \frac{1}{l}\int_x^{x+l} F(x)\,dx$$

assuming unit cross-sectional area. The concentration which freezes out at x is kC_l, from which:

$$F(x) = \frac{k}{l}\int_x^{x+l} F(x)\,dx \qquad [7]$$

The solution of eq 7 is:

$$C = Ae^{Bx} \qquad [8]$$

where:

$$k = \frac{Bl}{e^{Bl}-1} \qquad A = \frac{C_0 dB}{e^{Bd}-1}$$

Ultimate distributions calculated from eq 8 are plotted in Fig. 13 and it is seen that for small k's these are extremely steep. For example, if $k = 0.1$, $d = 10$, $l = 1$, the ultimate concentration at $x = 0$ is less than C_0 by a factor of about $10^{[illegible]}$. Eq 8 is actually an approximation because it cannot apply in the last zone, where normal freezing prevails, and the effect of the distribution in the last zone is reflected back into the preceding zones. However, this effect is small, especially at the pure end of the bar.

Since the concentration at the starting end is decreased by a factor of the order of k in each pass, it is evident from an inspection of Fig. 13 that at least 14 passes are required to approach the ultimate distribution.

A good approximation to the actual distribution after each of a number of successive single-zone passes readily can be obtained by a computation procedure suggested by R. W. Hamming in which the molten zone is assumed to advance in discrete steps of convenient size, say 0.5 zone-length, the concentration frozen out at each step being k times that in the zone. The result of such a computation is shown in Fig. 14 for three successive passes through an initially uniform charge, assuming $k = 0.1$. Also shown is the ultimate distribution.

Both refining and uniformity can be obtained by the repeated-pass methods described earlier in the paper, the purification being more effective for small k's. The ratio C_l/C_0 in eq 3 may be defined as the refinement ratio, R. For a given system R can be varied by controlling the fraction of the charge which is molten. For example, if $k = 0.01$, $d = 10$, then $R = 0.048$ for $l = 2$, 0.091 for $l = 1$.

Discussion

Possibly the most significant feature of zone-melting is its flexibility. The charge may be regarded as a medium and the molten zone as a distributor of solutes in the medium. Subject to the restriction that the concentration freezing out of the molten zone is k times that in the zone, and to certain other restrictions on solidification conditions, an operator can produce a large variety of useful distributions of solute in an ingot. Among the tools at his disposal are the arrangement of the starting charge, and the size, number, and direction of travel of the molten zones.

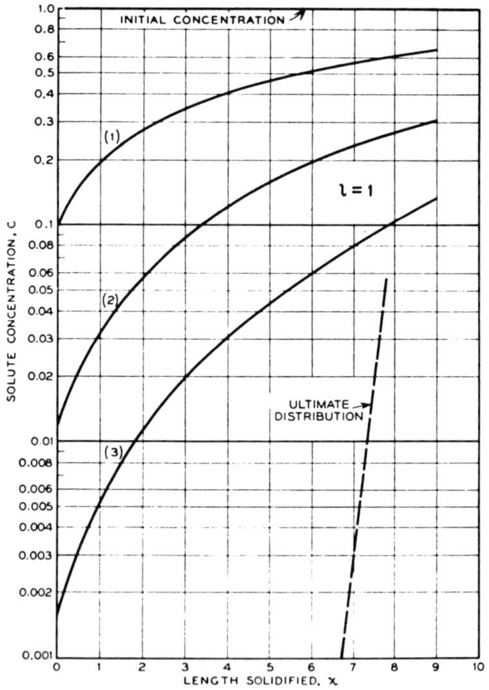

Fig. 14—Concentration curves, showing concentration of solute in solid as a function of x, the length solidified, after 1, 2, and 3 successive single-zone passes from left to right, through an initially uniform charge ten units in length, for unit zone-length.

While this paper is directed to metallurgists, the principles discussed in it are applicable to the freezing of any solid-solution system in which diffusion occurs much more readily in the liquid than in the solid. These methods may also be applied to solid-state transformations if the rates of diffusion of solute in the respective phases differ considerably.

The discussion of zone-melting has been confined to the categories of zone-leveling and zone-refining and a number of illustrative examples have been given in each. These by no means form a complete listing and many other variations are possible. For example, except in the part described under the subheading "Starting Charge into Pure Solvent," it has been assumed that l, the zone-length, is constant. However, by varying l as the zone travels, corresponding changes can be introduced in concentration. The descriptions have been confined to binary systems and ingots of bar form, either straight or ring shaped, but such restrictions are unnecessary.

Acknowledgments

The writer is greatly indebted to E. E. Schumacher and J. H. Scaff for discussions, advice and encouragement which have been important factors in bringing this work to fruition. He is indebted also to a number of colleagues at Bell Telephone Laboratories for valuable discussions, in particular to W. T. Read whose contributions to the mathematics have helped to crystallize much of the thinking.

Appendix I
Derivation of Eq 1

Freeze a unit volume of solution. Assume that during the freezing process there is no diffusion in the solid and complete diffusion in the liquid. Assume also that k the distribution coefficient is constant. Let:

g = the fraction of the original volume which has frozen.

s = the amount of solute remaining in the liquid.

s_o = the total amount of solute.

C = the solute concentration in the solid at the liquid-solid interface, in units of solute per unit volume of solution.

C_l = the solute concentration in the liquid.

By definition:

$$C = kC_l$$

Since $C_l = s/1-g$

$$C = \frac{ks}{1-g}$$

After a fraction g has frozen, freeze an additional amount, dg. The concentration C in the frozen layer of volume dg is:

$$C = -\frac{ds}{dg}$$

Eliminating C and integrating gives:

$$\int_{s_o}^{s} \frac{ds}{s} = \int_{o}^{g} -\frac{k}{1-g}\, dg$$

From which:

$$s = s_o\,(1-g)^k$$

and:

$$c = -\frac{ds}{dg} = ks_o\,(1-g)^{k-1}$$

Since the original volume was unity, $s_o = C_o$, where C_o is the original solute concentration, and hence:

$$C = kC_o\,(1-g)^{k-1} \qquad [1]$$

This treatment neglects the change of density during freezing. It places no restrictions on the shape of the molten or solid portion during freezing.

Appendix II
Derivation of Eq 2, after W. T. Read

Assuming k, the distribution coefficient, and l, the zone-length to be constant, the concentration, C, of the freezing solid at any length x, measured from the beginning of the ingot, may be found as follows:

Let C_o = mean concentration of solute in charge, assumed to be invariant with x, and expressed in units of solute per unit volume of solution.

s = quantity of solute in zone at any x.

s_o = quantity of solute in zone at $x = 0$.

Advance the zone a distance dx. An incremental volume dx of solid will form, an equal volume dx of charge will melt (see Fig. 4). The quantity of solute frozen out is:

$$kC_l\, dx$$

where C_l is the solute concentration in the molten zone. But $C_l = s/l$, assuming unit cross-sectional area. The quantity entering the zone is $C_o dx$. The net change in s is therefore given by:

$$ds = (C_o - \frac{ks}{l})\, dx \qquad [A\text{-}1]$$

From which:

$$\frac{ds}{dx} + \frac{k}{l}s = C_o \qquad [A\text{-}2]$$

The solution of eq A-2 is:

$$se^{\frac{k}{l}x} - s_o = C_o \int_o^x e^{\frac{k}{l}x} dx = \frac{C_o l}{k}\left(e^{\frac{k}{l}x} - 1\right)$$

Since $s_o = C_o l$ then:

$$s = [C_o l + \frac{C_o l}{k}(e^{\frac{k}{l}x} - 1)]\, e^{-\frac{k}{l}x}$$

$$= C_o l \frac{k\text{-}1}{k} e^{-\frac{k}{l}x} + \frac{C_o l}{k}$$

Since $C = \frac{ks}{l}$:

$$C = C_o\,(k\text{-}1)\, e^{-\frac{k}{l}x} + C_o$$

or:

$$C/C_o = 1 - (1\text{-}k)\, e^{-\frac{k}{l}x} \qquad [2]$$

Appendix III
Derivations of Eqs 4, 5a, 5b

Eq 4: The conditions are the same as in Appendix II except that all of the solute is in the first zone at the start. The concentration C_l, in the zone at $x = 0$ is therefore s_o/l. Advance the zone, at any x, a distance dx. Then:

$$ds = -\frac{ks}{l}\, dx$$

$$\int_{s_o}^{s} \frac{ds}{s} = -\int_{o}^{x} \frac{k}{l}\, dx$$

$$s = s_o\, e^{-kx/l}$$

Since:

$$C = -\frac{ds}{dx} \text{ and } C_l = \frac{s_o}{l}$$

$$C = kC_l\, e^{-kx/l} \qquad [4]$$

Eq 5a: Given that the cross-sectional area a is constant, find the dependence of l on x which will result in a constant value of C:

$$C = -\frac{ds}{a\,dx} = \frac{ks}{al} = \text{constant} \qquad [A\text{-}3]$$

Since a and k are constant, then:

$$d\frac{(s)}{(l)} = 0$$

$$\frac{ds}{l} - \frac{sdl}{l^2} = 0$$

$$\frac{ds}{s} = \frac{dl}{l}$$

From eq A-3:

$$\frac{ds}{s} = -\frac{k}{l}dx$$

hence:

$$\frac{dl}{l} = -\frac{k}{l}dx$$

$$l = l_o - kx \qquad [5a]$$

Eq 5b: Given that l is to be constant, find the dependence of a on x which will result in constant C. Let a be designated $a(x)$; let v = zone volume:

$$C = -\frac{ds}{a(x)dx} = \frac{ks}{v} = \text{constant} \qquad [A-4]$$

where:

$$v = \int_x^{x+l} a(x)dx$$

and:

$$\frac{dv}{dx} = a(x+l) - a(x) \qquad [A-5]$$

Since k = constant:

$$d\frac{(s)}{(v)} = 0$$

$$\frac{ds}{v} - \frac{sdv}{v^2} = 0$$

$$\frac{ds}{s} = \frac{dv}{v}$$

From eq A-4:

$$\frac{ds}{s} = -\frac{ka(x)dx}{v}$$

hence:

$$dv = -ka(x)dx$$

$$\frac{dv}{dx} = -ka(x)$$

From eq A-5:

$$\frac{dv}{dx} = a(x+l) - a(x)$$

hence:

$$a(x+l) - a(x) = -ka(x)$$

$$\frac{a(x+l)}{a(x)} = 1-k \qquad [A-6]$$

The solution of eq A-6 is:

$$a = a_o e^{x/D} \qquad [5b]$$

where:

$$D = \frac{l}{\log e\,(1-k)}$$

References

[1] P. W. Bridgman: *Proc.* Amer. Acad. Arts and Sciences (1925) **60**, p. 305.

[2] R. H. McFee: *Journal of Chemical Physics* (1947) **15**, p. 856.

[3] G. H. Gulliver: *Metallic Alloys* (Appendix) (1922) London. Chas. Griffin & Co.

[4] E. Scheuer: *Ztsch. Metallkunde* (1931) **23**, p. 237.

[5] A. Hayes and J. Chipman: *Trans.* AIME (1939) **135**, p. 85.

Journal of Crystal Growth 13/14 (1972) 560–565 © North-Holland Publishing Co.

ACCELERATED CRUCIBLE ROTATION: A NOVEL STIRRING TECHNIQUE IN HIGH-TEMPERATURE SOLUTION GROWTH

H. J. SCHEEL

IBM Zurich Research Laboratory, 8803 Rüschlikon, Switzerland

The role of diffusion and convection in conventional flux growth is compared with the strong stirring effect of the accelerated crucible rotation technique (ACRT). ACRT allows fast solution flow rates at the growing crystal faces. By this and by homogenization of the solution many problems in flux growth are solved. Control of nucleation in a closed crucible is achieved by combination of ACRT with localized cooling. Large inclusion-free crystals with applications in solid state physics and technology have been grown.

1. Introduction

This paper describes a new technique of stirring and its application to crystal growth from high-temperature solutions[1]).

In crystal growth from melts and from solutions, stirring and, to a lesser extent, convection, reduce the thickness of the boundary layer in front of the growing crystal[2–7]). In a well-stirred system, surface diffusion and particle integration (including the desolvation processes) dominate as rate-limiting growth processes over volume diffusion through the unstirred layer if supersaturation is high enough. Also fast motion of melt or solution relative to the growing crystal surface prevents the adverse effect of constitutional supercooling on the interface stability[8–10]).

By stirring, the solution is homogenized with respect to temperature and concentration. Therefore further nucleation after the first nucleation or after insertion of a seed crystal can be minimized or prevented altogether.

For these reasons stirring is employed in crystal growth wherever possible. But in high-temperature solution growth stirring by seed crystals is extremely difficult because generally volatile solvents like PbO, PbF_2, Bi_2O_3, or mixtures of these with B_2O_3 are used. Rotating seed crystals were applied only in a few exceptional cases which are listed, with the obtained maximum stable growth rates in table 1.

In the following it will be shown that an adequate stirring effect and growth rates as listed in table 1 can be achieved in a closed crucible by accelerated crucible rotation.

Compared to diffusion and convection which are

TABLE 1

Maximum stable growth rates in high-temperature solution growth (from experiments)

Crystal	Solvent	Linear growth rate (Å/sec)	Remarks	Reference
$GdAlO_3$	$PbO–PbF_2–B_2O_3$	~200	ACRT	This work
$NiFe_2O_4$	$Na_2Fe_2O_4$	200	Pulling from solution	11
$NiFe_2O_4$	$BaO–B_2O_3$	~500	Pulling from solution	12
$NiFe_2O_4$	$PbO–PbF_2$	~260	Seeded growth from solution	13
YIG	$BaO–B_2O_3$	120	Seed crystal on stirrer	14
YIG	$BaO–B_2O_3$	150	Pulling from solution	15
YIG	$BaO–B_2O_3$	260	Garnet film growth in a temperature gradient	16
YIG	$BaO–B_2O_3$	~150	Pulling from solution	17
$Ba_2Zn_2Fe_{12}O_{22}$	$BaO–B_2O_3$	200	Pulling from solution	18

slow material transport mechanisms in conventional flux-growth experiments, the Accelerated Crucible Rotation Technique (ACRT) reduces the thickness of the stagnant boundary layer and therefore allows faster stable growth rates. In addition, homogenization of the solution by ACRT combined with localized cooling permits control of nucleation. These statements are supported by estimates of the boundary-layer thickness and the maximum stable growth rate, by simulation experiments, and by successful crystal-growth experiments.

2. The role of convection in high-temperature solution growth

In the conventional flux-growth practice by the slow-cooling technique one relies exclusively on natural convection as the mechanism for material transport and homogenization. By comparison, heat conductivity and diffusion are significant processes only if there are appreciable temperature or concentration gradients. Thus they contribute to heat and material transport at boundary layers, but only very little within the bulk of the solution where, by the crystallization process, by inhomogeneous heating and by flux evaporation, relatively small concentration and temperature gradients are constantly generated. Therefore convection is generally present in crystal-growth experiments*.

The flow velocity of thermal convection is low and amounts to the order of 1 to 5×10^{-2} cm sec^{-1} for typical flux-growth conditions[19]). Even for a low viscosity liquid of 1 centipoise and the high thermal expansion coefficient of 10^{-3} °C^{-1}, the flow velocity will reach only 10^{-1} cm sec^{-1} for a temperature difference $\Delta T = 10$ °C. The width of the metastable Ostwald–Miers region imposes a limit on the permitted temperature difference of roughly this order of magnitude. For these flow velocities the stable crystal growth rate is limited by volume diffusion through the relatively thick boundary layer of approximately 5×10^{-2} cm and lies in the order of 50 Å sec^{-1}. Because of constitutional supercooling only small inclusion-free crystals have been obtained so far.

By the presence of convection cells, pockets with high supersaturations are probably formed locally and cause nucleation of many crystals instead of one or two which then may grow to large sizes. Localized cooling and convection generated by asymmetric temperature distribution increased only slightly the size and quality of the flux-grown crystals. In their crystal-growth experiments with a 2 gallon crucible, Van Uitert et al.[20]) combined crucible rotation with localized cooling at the bottom. Despite the expected improvement in convection the authors reported multinucleation. The resulting YIG and YAG crystals were very large when compared to crystals obtained from smaller crucibles, while the ratio of crystal-to-crucible size seems to have been comparable for large and small crucibles.

3. The accelerated crucible rotation technique (ACRT) in high-temperature-solution growth

Convection alone or in combination with uniform rotation is far from optimum as a material transport mechanism. In high-temperature solution growth a mechanism is required which agitates the solution in much the same way as conventional mechanical stirring in crystal growth from aqueous solutions. Accelerated and decelerated crucible rotation is proposed to achieve such a stirring effect in flux growth. Consider a crucible which is initially at rest. Then constantly accelerate the crucible to rotation about its vertical axis. The outer region of the solution follows the change in crucible motion with little delay. The center of the melt, however, continues to remain at rest due to inertia. Thus a shearing of solution rings is produced. Slowly the center of the solution begins to move, too, until, after a considerable time, it rotates at the same rate as the crucible.

By the laminar slip of the solution around the rotation axis a spiral is formed which, for typical flux-growth conditions and acceleration to 60 rpm, has the order of a thousand arms. Therefore any local variation in solute concentration or in temperature is distributed along this spiral. Since the spiral arms have a radial distance of less than a tenth of a millimeter, the concentration and temperature differences disappear by diffusion and heat conduction in a time of less than a second. The hydrodynamics of convection and of ACRT will be presented in the paper by Schulz-DuBois[21]).

Alternating accelerated and decelerated crucible ro-

* Convection flow rates due to thermal and concentration differences are believed to be of the same order of magnitude generally, depending on the material parameters and the growth conditions.

TABLE 2

Comparison of the influence of diffusion, convection, and ACRT on thickness of boundary layer and on maximum linear growth rate for volume-diffusion-limited growth

	Mean velocity of solution (or particles) at the crystal surface (cm sec^{-1})	Thickness of boundary layer[a] (cm)	Maximum linear growth rate (Å sec^{-1})
Diffusion	(5×10^{-5})	(1.7)	(0.5–3)
Convection[b]	4×10^{-2} [c]	6×10^{-2}	20–80
ACRT	1	1.2×10^{-2}	100–500
ACRT	10	4×10^{-3}	(300–1500)[d]
ACRT	100	1.2×10^{-3}	(1000–5000)[d]

[a] Calculated from formulas of Carlson[4]) and of Bennema[6]).
[b] For $T = 1400$ °K, $\Delta T = 10$ °C, $l = 5$ cm, $\eta = 2$ cp, $\rho = 7.5$ g cm^{-3}, $c_p = 0.15$ cal g^{-1} deg^{-1}, $\beta = 8\times10^{-4}$ deg^{-1}, $K = 0.02$ cal cm^{-1} sec^{-1} deg^{-1}.
[c] After Cobb and Wallis[19]), we get the same value for our conditions.
[d] Surface reactions are rate-limiting processes.

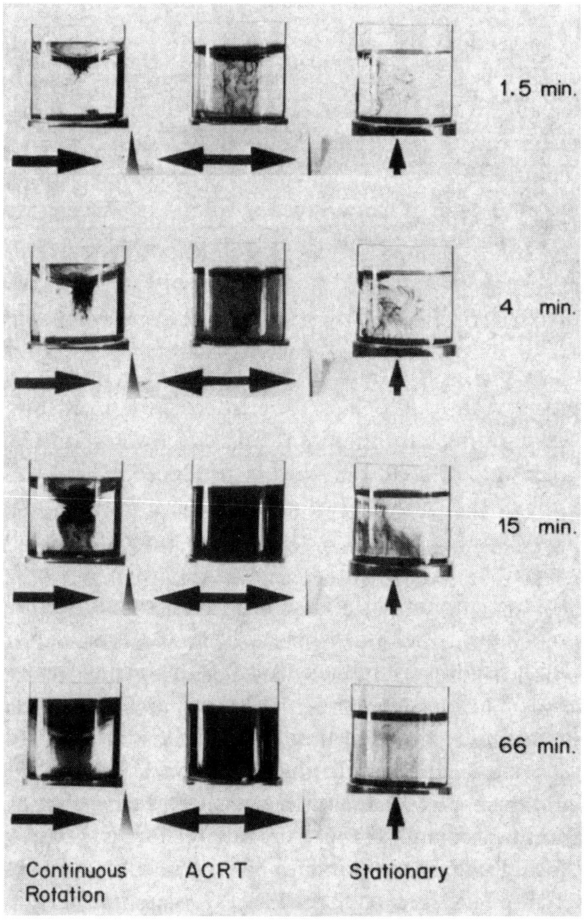

Fig. 1. Simulation experiment demonstrating the strong mixing effect of ACRT.

tation acts much the same way as a stirrer acting in the laminar regime. In addition to this rotational stirring effect, mixing in vertical and radial directions is provided by the Ekman flow and by the deformation of the liquid due to centrifugal forces, which is demonstrated by the parabolic surface at high rotation rates and the nearly flat surface of the liquid at rest. And, of course, there will be the relatively small mixing effect of the superimposed natural convection.

If the ACRT stirring technique is combined with localized cooling, control of nucleation is possible and only one or two nuclei are formed. Similarly, if a seed crystal is arranged in the crucible and all conditions are properly controlled, there is no additional spontaneous nucleation.

A forced flow of solution is produced along the crystal surface. The flow rate is determined by the properties of the solute-solvent system, by the crucible (and crystal) geometry and dimensions, and by acceleration and rotation rates. Flow velocities of 1 or even 100 cm sec^{-1} relative to the crystal are not difficult to

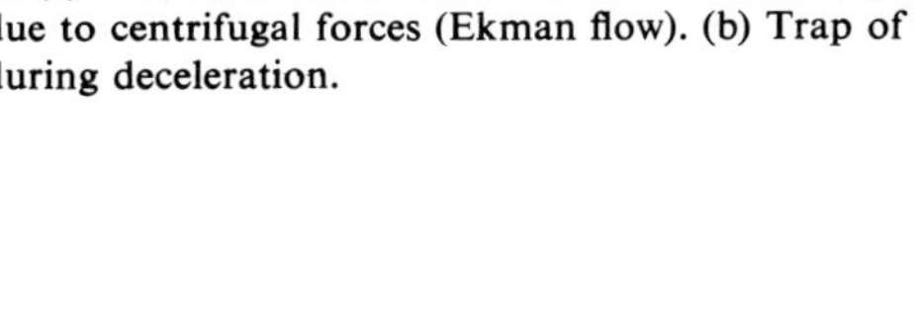

Fig. 2. (a) Direction of radial and vertical flow during acceleration due to centrifugal forces (Ekman flow). (b) Trap of crystallites during deceleration.

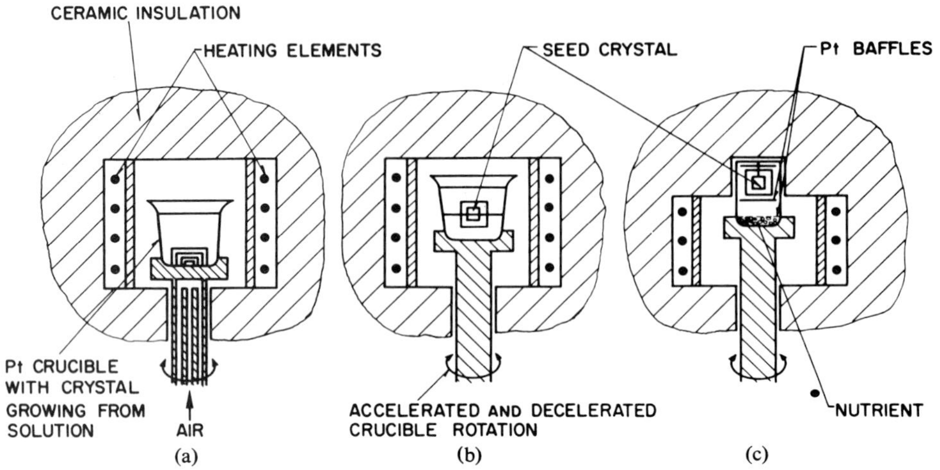

Fig. 3. (a) ACRT with localized cooling for nucleation control (slow cooling technique). (b) ACRT with a seed crystal under iothermal conditions (slow cooling technique). (c) ARCT with as seed crystal in constant temperature gradient.

realize. These reduce the thickness of the stationary boundary layer[4,6]) surrounding the crystal to the order of 10^{-2} to 10^{-3} cm, which, in turn, permits greater stable growth rates. In table 2 a comparison of the boundary layer thicknesses and the corresponding stable growth rates calculated for volume-diffusion-controlled growth are shown for the flow rates of convection and of ACRT, respectively. The data for pure diffusion are also shown and are somewhat hypothetical since one would expect convection to be present generally in flux-growth experiments. Crystal growth by convection requires an extremely low cooling rate in order to maintain a stable crystal growth rate of approximately 50 Å sec^{-1} only. In ACRT a flow rate of 1 cm sec^{-1} is adequate for a stable growth rate of 100 to 500 Å sec^{-1}. From table 1 it appears that no growth rates higher than this order of magnitude have ever been observed experimentally. This evidence suggests that by application of ACRT the diffusion through the boundary layer is no longer the main growth-rate limiting process.

4. Simulation experiments and crystal-growth results

The ACRT stirring effect can be easily demonstrated by a simulation experiment. Three glass beakers containing a liquid of a viscosity of 2 centipoise ($H_2O+H_2SO_4$) are heated from below in order to establish convection. Equal amounts of $KMnO_4$ as a coloring agent are placed at the center of the liquid surface where they float due to surface tension. The left beaker is continuously rotated, the right one remains at rest, while the center one is subjected to accelerated and decelerated rotation by a motor which is switched on and off for about a minute at a time. Fig. 1 shows the situation at times of 1.5, 4, 15, and 66 min, respectively, after the beginning of the experiment. In the center beaker the $KMnO_4$, as far as it is dissolved, is distributed homogeneously over the entire beaker volume in a time of one or two cycles of acceleration. After 15 min all the $KMnO_4$ is completely dissolved and a homogeneous solution is obtained.

In the uniformly rotated beaker there are stable unmixed regions with no coloration at all. This agrees with the observations by Carruthers and Nassau[22]). Due to Taylor–Proudman cells in the uniformly rotated beaker there seems to be even less mixing than in the stationary one.

In fig. 2 the directions of Ekman flow and the deformation of the liquid body due to centrifugal force are shown. The most simple experiment for demonstration of the Ekman flow is a cup of tea containing tea leaves. These tea leaves float to the circumference, when the tea is stirred, and back to the center when the stirring action is stopped.

Figs. 3a–3c show examples of experimental arrangements for flux growth by ACRT. To date, the greater part of our experience is with the method of fig. 3a. The 500 cm^3 platinum crucible with its special mechan-

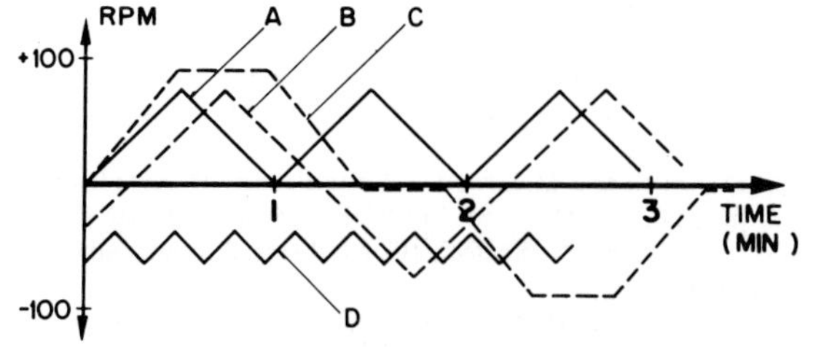

Fig. 4. Examples of cycles of accelerated crucible rotation.

ical stable shape is sealed by argon-arc welding, and is supported by a suitably shaped ceramic disk which in turn is placed on a ceramic tube. The latter is rotated about its vertical axis with periodically alternating acceleration and deceleration. Several useful cycles are illustrated in fig. 4. For flux growth, cycles A, B, C are appropriate. Cycle D may be useful in the Czochralski technique, when corresponding accelerated counter rotation of the crystal is used additionally.

Initial experience with the ACRT was gained by growing gadolinium aluminate, $GdAlO_3$, an orthorhombic perovskite-type compound, from $PbO\text{-}PbF_2\text{-}B_2O_3$ solution. Many experiments without ACRT in crucibles of 30 to 1000 cm^3 yielded crystals of $GdAlO_3$ up to 20 g weight with flux inclusions and inclusion-free crystals up to 8 mm in size (approx. 4 g). For ACRT experiments the mixture of the starting materials of highest purity was premelted in the 500 cm^3 platinum crucible, which was sealed and heated to 1300 °C for 15 hr. Then it was cooled to 900 °C at a rate which increased from 0.3 to 0.5 °C hr^{-1}. Faster cooling rates than these caused interface instability (flux inclusions) by stronger constitutional supercooling (large faces, higher viscosities, decreasing diffusion coefficients). At the end of the run the crucible with the one or two crystals formed was allowed to cool slowly to room temperature.

The first two runs yielded just one crystal of $GdAlO_3$ each, of 210 g and 104 g weight, respectively. Another run in a small 140 cm^3 crucible yielded just two crystals with a total weight of 44 g. Fig. 5 shows the abovementioned crystal of 210 g weight in the interior of which the light from behind is reflected. The overall dimensions of the crystal are $3.5 \times 3 \times 2.5$ cm^3. Like other spontaneously nucleated crystals, this crystal shows a central region of dendritic growth. However the outer portions of these crystals of about 1 cm

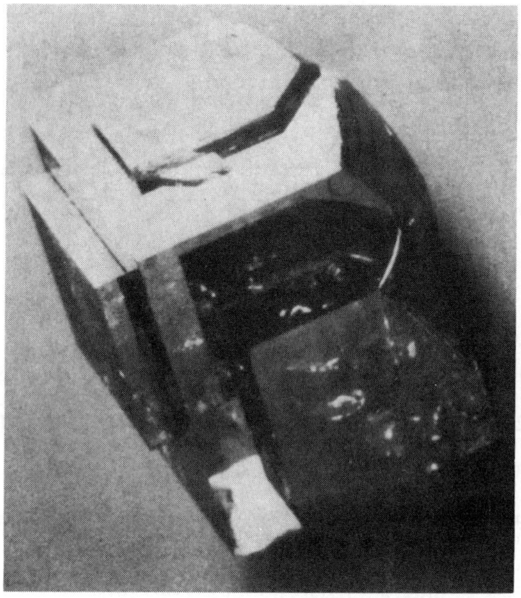

Fig. 5. Gadolinium aluminate crystal of 210 g weight showing internal light reflection through clear portion.

thickness are optically clear and free of inclusions. In crystal growth from aqueous solutions dendritic growth can be prevented by use of seed crystals. First experiments with seed crystals and ACRT in crystal growth from high-temperature solutions are promising. Other work is directed to magnetic materials, and large inclusion-free garnets have been grown.

Subsequent to our preliminary description of ACRT at national crystal growth conferences[23]), other laboratories had similar success with crystal growth of magnetic garnets and of manganese telluride by ACRT[24]).

5. Conclusions

The accelerated crucible rotation technique (ACRT) has been demonstrated to have a strong stirring effect in crystal growth from high-temperature solutions by successful crystal-growth runs and by simulation experiments. Specifically, ACRT accomplishes control of nucleation, it suppresses the adverse effects of constitutional supercooling and convection, and it permits the realization of stable crystal-growth velocities in the range of several hundred Å sec^{-1}. The method is believed to be especially useful in the growth of large crystals for the magnetic bubble domain technology, for laser rods, and for electrooptic or nonlinear optical materials. Simulation and preliminary crystal-growth experiments indicate that ACRT is a valuable aid also for crystal growth from melts, from the vapor phase, and from hydrothermal solutions.

Acknowledgement

The author thanks Dr. D. Elwell, Dr. E. O. Schulz-DuBois, Dr. W. V. Smith, Prof. W. A. Tiller and Dr. E. A. D. White for valuable discussions.

References

1) H. J. Scheel and E. O. Schulz–DuBois, J. Crystal Growth **8** (1971) 304.
2) W. K. Burton, N. Cabrera and F. C. Frank, Phil. Trans. Roy. Soc. London A **243** (1951) 299.
3) J. A. Burton, R. C. Prim and W. P. Slichter, J. Chem. Phys. **21** (1953) 1987.
4) A. Carlson, in: *Growth and Perfection of Crystals*, Eds. R. H. Doremus, B. W. Roberts and D. Turnbull (Wiley, New York, 1958) p. 421.
5) J. C. Brice, J. Crystal Growth **1** (1967) 161.
6) P. Bennema, J. Crystal Growth **5** (1969) 29.
7) W. A. Tiller, J. Crystal Growth **2** (1968) 69.
8) W. A. Tiller, K. A. Jackson, J. W. Rutter and B. Chalmers, Acta Met. **1** (1953) 428.
9) H. J. Scheel and D. Elwell, J. Crystal Growth **12** (1972) 153.
10) S. O'Hara, L. A. Tarshis, W. A. Tiller and J. P. Hunt, J. Crystal Growth **3, 4** (1968) 555.
11) W. Kunnmann, A. Ferretti and A. Wold, J. Appl. Phys. **34** (1963) 1264.
12) S. H. Smith and D. Elwell, J. Crystal Growth **3, 4** (1968) 471.
13) J. Kvapil, V. Jon and M. Vichr, in: *Growth of Crystals*, Vol. 7, Ed. N. N. Sheftal, (Consultants Bureau, New York, 1969) p. 233.
14) R. A. Laudise, R. C. Linares and E. F. Dearborn, J. Appl. Phys. **33** (1962) 1362.
15) R. C. Linares, J. Appl. Phys. **35** (1964) 433.
16) R. C. Linares, R. B. McGraw and J. B. Schroeder, J. Appl. Phys. **36** (1965) 2884.
17) M. Kestigian, J. Am. Ceram. Soc. **50** (1967) 165.
18) T. R. AuCoin, R. O. Savage and A. Tauber, J. Appl. Phys. **37** (1966) 2908.
19) C. M. Cobb and E. B. Wallis, Report AD 655388 (1967).
20) W. H. Grodkiewicz, E. F. Dearborn and L. G. Van Uitert, in: *Crystal Growth*, Ed. H. S. Peiser (Pergamon, Oxford, 1967) p. 441.
21) E. O. Schulz–DuBois, J. Crystal Growth **12** (1972) 81.
22) J. R. Carruthers and K. Nassau, J. Appl. Phys. **39** (1968) 5205.
23) Talks at National Conferences on Crystal Growth at Bristol, U.K. (Sept. 11, 1970), Zurich (Sept. 22, 1970) and Munich (Oct. 16, 1970).
24) Dr. W. Tolksdorf (Philips Zentrallaboratorium, Hamburg), private communication; see also the papers of W. Tolksdorf and D. Mateika at this Conference.

Epitaxial Silicon Films by the Hydrogen Reduction of SiCl

H. C. Theuerer

Bell Telephone Laboratories, Incorporated, Murray Hill, New Jersey

ABSTRACT

Epitaxial films of silicon with controlled thickness and resistivity either n- or p-type may be grown using the hydrogen reduction of silicon tetrachloride appropriately doped with PCl_3 or BBr_3. The basic chemistry and reaction kinetics pertinent to the growth of these films are discussed in detail in this paper.

The new epitaxial mesa transistors (1) and other semiconductor devices utilize silicon single crystal films grown on low resistivity silicon substrates. The hydrogen reduction of silicon tetrachloride is well suited to the preparation of these films since this reaction is surface catalyzed and has a readily controllable rate. For epitaxial growth, n- or p-type substrates having a $\langle 111 \rangle$ orientation with resistivities between 0.01 and 0.001 ohm-cm are normally used. The reduction of undoped silicon tetra-

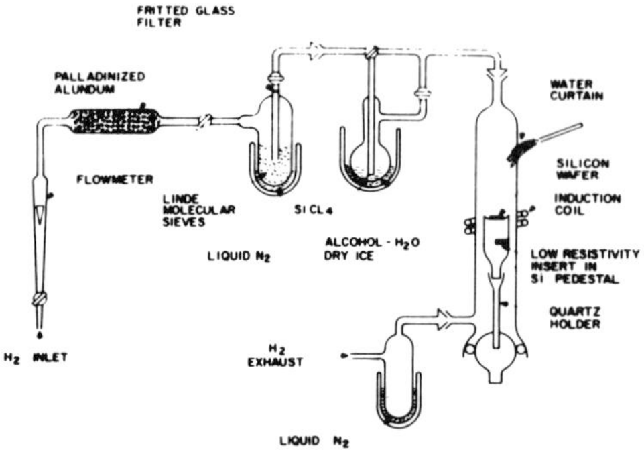

Fig. 1. Apparatus for silicon film preparation by the H_2 reduction of $SiCl_4$.

chloride purified by adsorption techniques (2) results in n-type films with resistivities between 20 and 100 ohm-cm. As required, the film thickness, resistivity, and conductivity type can be controlled by variations in the basic procedures. N- or p-type films with desired resistivities are obtained by doping the silicon tetrachloride with appropriate amounts of phosphorus trichloride or boron tribromide, respectively.

The reaction kinetics and basic chemistry pertinent to the growth of epitaxial films are discussed in detail in this paper.

Experimental Requirements for Film Deposition

The apparatus used to prepare epitaxial films by the hydrogen reduction of silicon tetrachloride is shown schematically in Fig. 1. Essentially, it consists of a source of pure hydrogen, a halide saturating system, the reduction chamber, and a radio-frequency generator for external heating. To purify the hydrogen, tank gas is passed through a trap containing palladinized alundum pellets to remove oxygen. The gas is then passed through a second trap containing No. 5A Molecular Sieves[1] refrigerated with liquid nitrogen for the purpose of removing water and other condensable gases from the hydrogen. The purified gas may then be passed into the reduction chamber either directly or first through the $SiCl_4$ saturator by manipulation of the stopcocks. Control of the $SiCl_4$-H_2 ratio is obtained by refrigerating the saturator with alcohol-water-dry ice mixtures.

The reduction is carried out in a water-cooled quartz tube 1-in. OD x 12-in. long within which the wafer to be treated is supported in a silicon pedestal for heating. The pedestal is mounted in a quartz holder from a nickel end closure. The heating pedestal is made from a high-purity silicon rod ½ in. diameter x 1½ in. long dished out at the top for a depth of 1/16 in. For rf coupling, a low resistivity insert is fused into the silicon ⅝ in. from the top of the pedestal.

The silicon substrates used for epitaxial growth, consist of 6 mil wafers 0.310 in. square with <111> faces. The wafers are ground flat with 1800 alundum and are given a bright etch to expose an undamaged crystal surface. A 5-min etch in a mixture of 30 ml HNO_3, 5 ml HF, and 10 ml acetic acid, followed by washing with deionized water and drying at 110°C was the usual procedure in this work. Prior to film deposition, the silicon wafer is treated in dry hydrogen at 1295°C for ½ hr to remove residual surface oxide. In this treatment the silicon reacts with SiO_2 to form SiO which evaporates and condenses on the tube walls. Following this treatment, the wafer is brought to deposition temperature, and the $SiCl_4$-H_2 mixture is introduced for prescribed times. The variables controlling the deposition rate are temperature, $SiCl_4$-H_2 ratio, flow rate, and time of treatment.

[1] This material may be obtained from the Linde Air Products Co.

Film Evaluation Methods

In this work conductivity type was determined by the hot probe method (3). The resistivity was determined from the film thickness and the sheet resistance obtained using the four point probe method (4). With this method it is necessary that the substrate wafer be of opposite conductivity type to that of the film being measured. In cases where the films are prepared on substrates of the same conductivity type, it is possible to determine resistivity and film thickness from measurements of capacitance as a function of voltage. Film thickness (5) was normally measured by polishing a 2° or 5° bevel on the coated surface of the wafer. The bevel was then stained with HF-HNO_3 100:1 which delineated the film region at the top of the bevel. The thickness can then be determined by counting interference fringes produced along the beveled film using an optical flat and sodium light for illumination. The weight gain of the wafers was also used as an index of thickness. Results by this method are semiquantitative, however, since it has been found that the underside of the wafers are also coated. In general, it has been found that the weight gains are somewhat larger than would be expected for a double film of uniform thickness. The film at the underside of the wafer is produced by transfer from the pedestal silicon by a process not directly related to the hydrogen reduction process under discussion herein.

Effect of Various Reaction Variables on Film Growth

Using a $SiCl_4$-H_2 mole fraction of 0.02 achieved by refrigerating the saturator at −30°C and treating the silicon wafer for 5 min at 1270°C with a hydrogen flow of 1 l/min results in a film 8μ thick. The thickness obtained can be controlled over a wide range by variations in the operating parameters. Most conveniently with other variables fixed, the film thickness may be varied linearly with time of treatment. As shown in Fig. 2, the thickness may also be varied by changes in flow rate for low hydrogen flows but at rates much above 1 l/min a further increase in deposition rate is not observed. Figure 3 gives the dependence of deposition rate on temperature. The data indicate an activation energy for the over-all reaction of 37 kcal, and for the temperature range of interest the deposition rate doubles with an 80°C rise in temperature. Figure 4

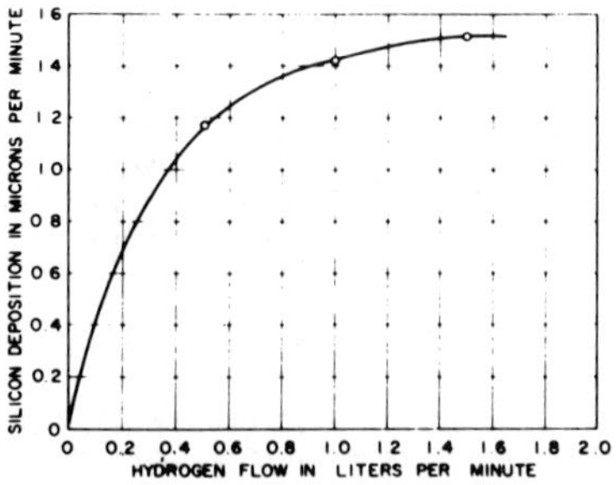

Fig. 2. Effect of gas flow rate on silicon deposition

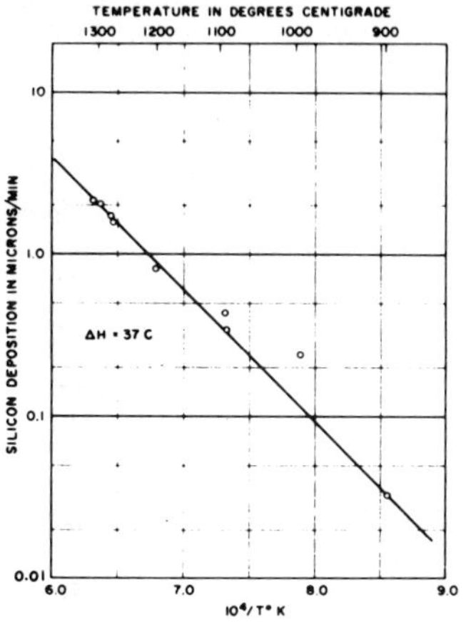

Fig. 3. Temperature dependence of silicon deposition

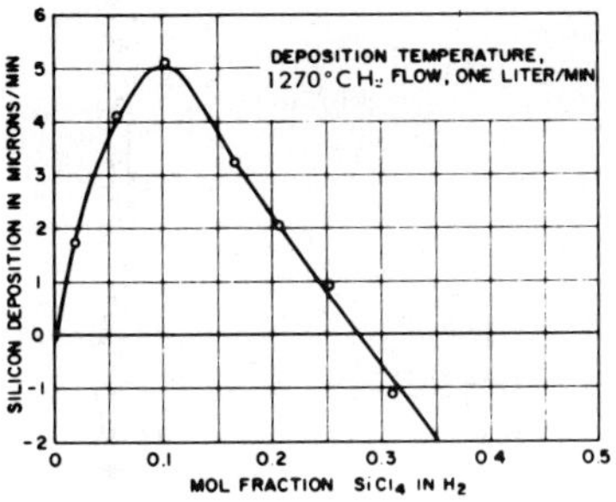

Fig. 4. Effect of $SiCl_4$-H_2 ratio on silicon deposition

shows the effect of variations in the mole fraction of $SiCl_4$ on deposition rate at the normal reduction temperature of 1270°C. It will be seen that the rate of deposition initially increases with increasing $SiCl_4$ concentration, peaks at a mole fraction of 0.10, and then diminished for further increases in $SiCl_4$. Above a mole fraction of 0.28, etching of the silicon substrate occurs.

Reaction Mechanism

The hydrogen reduction of silicon tetrachloride is a more complex reaction than is indicated by the basic equation

$$SiCl_4 + 2H_2 \rightleftharpoons Si + 4HCl$$

This equation does not predict the observed 20% yield of $SiHCl_3$ for a corresponding silicon yield of 10%, or the smaller amounts (< 1%) of high molecular weight polymers, typically (6) $Si_{10}Cl_{20}H_2$, found as a condensate on the reaction tube walls. The reduction mechanism, although not completely understood, undoubtedly occurs by way of intermediate reactions involving subchlorides, possibly the free radical $SiCl_2$. The relatively high activation energy of 37 kcal and the reduction in silicon yield with increasing $SiCl_4$-H_2 ratio suggest that the reaction involves activated adsorption and diffusion mechanisms. One can postulate that $SiCl_2$ is adsorbed on the substrate with the loss of chlorine by reaction with hydrogen which results in the formation of silicon This is followed by diffusion of the HCl from the substrate. At the same time $SiCl_2$ reacting in the gas phase with hydrogen results in the formation of $SiHCl_3$.

Control of Resistivity and Conductivity Type

Using silicon tetrachloride purified by adsorption techniques (2) epitaxial films are n-type with resistivities between 20 and 100 ohm-cm. This silicon tetrachloride is probably capable of producing silicon of much higher resistivity. However, using the described etching techniques an upper limit of about 100 ohm-cm is imposed on the process due to the incomplete removal of impurities from the surface. After etching, residual amounts of a fast diffusing donor impurity (7) to the extent of 0.005 monolayers are found on the surface. During the heat treatment and film deposition, this donor diffuses through the substrate and film resulting in a donor concentration of 5 x 10^{13} atom/cm^3 ~ 100 ohm-cm.

The resistivity obtained with pure $SiCl_4$ is adequate for most semiconductor requirements. Where lower resistivity films are desired, these can be obtained by appropriate doping using either BBr_3 or PCl_3 for p- and n-type films, respectively. These dopants have been chosen because they are liquids with similar vapor pressures to $SiCl_4$ as shown in Fig. 5. In the case of phosphorus doping, for a saturation temperature of −30°C it has been found that

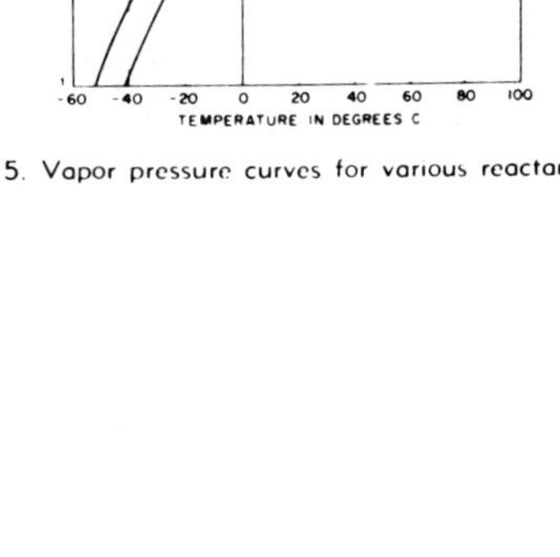

Fig. 5. Vapor pressure curves for various reactants

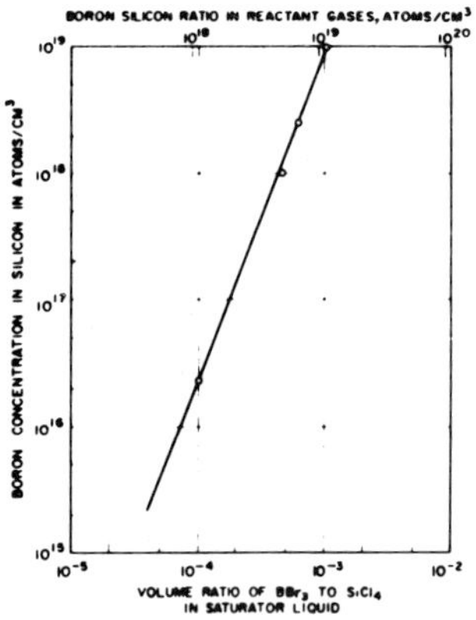

Fig. 6. BBr_3 concentration required in $SiCl_4$ for various doping levels in silicon.

good results are obtained using the following equation

$$\frac{V_{PCl_3}}{V_{SiCl_4}} = 3.9 \times 10^{-23} \times N_D .$$

where V is the volume in ml and N_D is the concentration of donors in atoms/cm³ of Si. In the derivation of the above equation Raoult's law was used, and it was assumed that the mole ratio of dopant to silicon in the $SiCl_4$ vapor is equal to that obtained in the reduced material. In the case of boron doping, as shown in Fig. 6, it has been found that more BBr_3 is required at concentration below 10^{18} atoms/cm³ than that calculated by the above method. Also, observed with heavy boron doping is a considerable increase in the deposition rate of silicon from the normal 8μ to 18μ, for a 5-min treatment at 1270°C. These findings indicate a marked change in the reduction kinetics, probably involving the oxidation of boron by $SiCl_4$ through the reaction

$$4B + 3SiCl_4 \rightarrow 4BCl_3 + Si$$

In using the above method of doping, since the composition of the gas phase differs from that in the solution, it is obvious that the concentration of the dopants will change as the silicon tetrachloride solution is evaporated. In theory, the change in concentration of the doped solution will vary as follows:

$$C_v = C_o k (1 - x)^{k-1}\ [2]$$

C_v is the mole fraction of dopant in $SiCl_4$ vapor, C_o the mole fraction of dopant in initial $SiCl_4$ liquid, k the distribution coefficient, and x the fraction evaporated. In the above expression for an ideal solution

$$k = \frac{p_{dopant}}{p_{SiCl_4}}$$

where p is vapor pressure of pure constituents. Figure 7 shows the curves for BBr_3 and PCl_3 when evaporated from $SiCl_4$. It will be seen that in the case of BBr_3 the change in concentration is negligible for the first 50% evaporated. In the case of PCl_3, a variation in concentration from 0.37 to 0.6 would be anticipated for 50% evaporation of the $SiCl_4$

[2] The derivation of this equation is similar to that for normal freezing of a liquid (8).

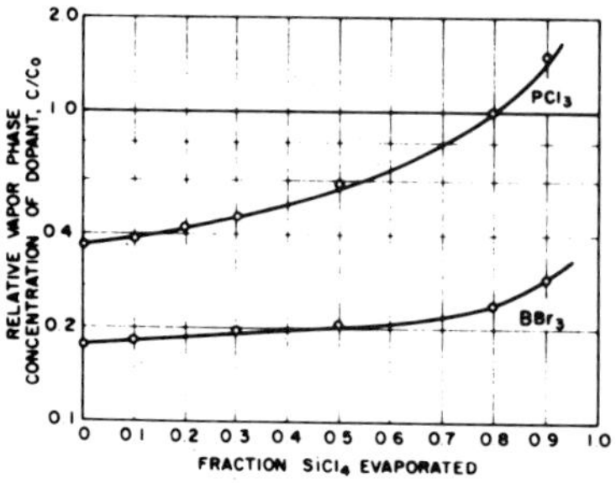

Fig. 7. Change in concentration of dopants as a function of $SiCl_4$ evaporation.

Fig. 8. Effect of deposition temperature on film perfection

solution. These variations can be tolerated for most applications, but where closer control is required, metered aspiration of the doped silicon tetrachloride into the hydrogen stream would be desirable.

Film Perfection

Epitaxially grown films prepared by deposition at 1270°C show specular reflection and replicate the contours of the etched substrate surface. Electron diffraction patterns of such films have the orientation of the <111> substrates and show Kikuchi lines indicating a high order of perfection. At lower deposition temperatures, the films are less perfect. Deposition at 1175°C results in films with the terraced structure shown in Fig. 8.

These films are basically single crystals with the <111> orientation of the substrate. However, triangular <111> faces appear at the corners of the terraces and with continued growth these faces twin and become grossly polycrystalline. At a deposition temperature of 895°C gray films are deposited characteristic of polycrystalline silicon. These results suggest that, during deposition, the high mobility of silicon atoms attained at temperatures above 1175°C is essential for good film perfection. It is probable that high surface mobility is the controlling factor in the deposition of single crystal films irrespective of the reaction used as a source of silicon.

Acknowledgments

The author gratefully acknowledges the aid obtained from his colleagues in much of this work. These include: H. H. Loar, J. J. Kleimack, A. D. Lopez for film evaluation, R. D. Heidenreich and Mrs. M. A. Read for electron diffraction studies, E. E. Thomas for the microscopic photographs, and D. D. Bacon for assistance in film preparation.

Manuscript received Jan. 30, 1961; revised manuscript received March 13, 1961. This paper was prepared for delivery before the Houston Meeting, Oct. 9-13, 1960.

Any discussion of this paper will appear in a Discussion Section to be published in the June 1962 JOURNAL.

REFERENCES

1. H. Theuerer, H. Loar, J. Kleimack, and H. Christensen, *Proc. IRE*, **48**, 1642 (1960).
2. H. Theuerer, *This Journal*, **107**, 29 (1960).
3. G. Pearson, *Trans. AIEE*, **60**, 209 (1947).
4. F. Smits, *Bell System Tech. J.*, **37**, 711 (1958).
5. W. Bond and F. Smits, *ibid.*, **35**, 1209 (1956).
6. R. Schwarz and R. Thiel, *Z. anorg. u. allgem. Chem.*, **235**, 247 (1938).
7. H. Theuerer, J. Whelan, H. Bridgers, and E. Buehler, *This Journal*, **104**, 721 (1957).
8. W. G. Pfann, *Trans. AIME*, **194**, 747 (1952).

The Use of Metal-Organics in the Preparation of Semiconductor Materials

I. Epitaxial Gallium-V Compounds

H. M. Manasevit and W. I. Simpson

Autonetics Division of North American Rockwell Corporation, Anaheim, California

ABSTRACT

Single-crystal GaAs, GaP, $GaAs_{1-x}P_x$ and $GaAs_{1-x}Sb_x$ films have been grown on GaAs and a number of insulating substrates by the decomposition of alkyl-gallium compounds in the presence of arsine, phosphine, arsine-phosphine, and arsine-stibine mixtures. Both triethylgallium and trimethylgallium have been used successfully in the preparation of GaAs. This process makes compound semiconductor film growth compatible with methods used for the growth of elemental semiconductors and eliminates many of the difficulties inherent in multitemperature-zone processes.

A key factor in the fabrication of many semiconductor devices is the production of single-crystal material of high purity and quality. Films of Ga-V compounds are normally harder to produce than films of elemental semiconductors. Most of the CVD methods for epitaxy already reported (1, 2) involve at least a two-temperature process: (*a*) at T_1, the formation of volatile Ga compounds by the reaction in hydrogen of metallic Ga or the Ga-V compound itself with a halide or water vapor (3) as a transporting agent; and (*b*) at $T_2 < T_1$, the deposition of the compound on a substrate in an atmosphere containing the Group V constituent. When transporting agents are used to produce high-purity epitaxial films of gallium arsenide (GaAs) on GaAs and a number of other semiconductor substrates, etching may also occur; and the early stages of epitaxial growth probably involve some doping of the growing film with impurities in the substrate or, in heteroepitaxial semiconductor systems, with the major elemental constituents of the substrate. This may result in the production of an interfacial alloyed layer in a system such as GaAs on Ge, for example.

Although the transport technique is amenable to closed-tube methods, many advantages to open-tube processes can be cited; and the latter approach is most often used. However, the nature of the reactions involved in the production of the III-V compounds necessitates that the two temperature zones be carefully controlled for reproducible growth to occur. In addition, depending on the growth technique used, it can be important to keep some of the reactants separate (1) until they reach the deposition zone, so that source materials are not affected.

This paper describes a process which requires only one hot temperature zone for the *in situ* formation and growth of the semiconductor compound directly on the heated substrate. This occurs in an atmosphere essentially free of an etching specie and is sufficient not only for growth on some semiconductors but also for growth on insulating substrates.

In this process, compound semiconductor films are produced by reacting organo-Ga compounds and Group V hydrides. Because of the use of the more volatile organo-Ga compounds, *i.e.* triethylgallium (TEG) and trimethylgallium (TMG), it has been possible to meter appreciable quantities of these room-temperature liquids into the reactor by bubbling a carrier gas through them. They can then be mixed in the reactor with different arsine (AsH_3), phosphine (PH_3), arsine-phosphine (AsH_3-PH_3), or arsine-stibine (AsH_3-SbH_3) concentrations controlled independently by simple flowmeter adjustments. Selenium or sulfur may be added as n-type dopants from tanks containing hydrogen selenide (H_2Se) or hydrogen sulfide (H_2S), respectively, diluted with a carrier gas; and p-type doping is obtained by passing the carrier gas over diethylzinc (DEZ) (4) equilibrated at 0°C in a stainless-steel container.

Experimental

Apparatus.—The apparatus consists principally of a single vertical 60-mm OD quartz tube 38 cm long containing a silicon-carbide-covered carbon pedestal which can be inductively heated; stainless-steel bubblers containing the liquid metal-organic compounds and SbH_3; appropriate flowmeters for monitoring the carrier gas, group V hydride(s), and dopant flows; burn-off area for hydrogen; and a manifold made from ¼-in. stainless steel tubing. Provisions are made for bypassing the quartz reactor and keeping the reactants separate until the gases are equilibrated and ready to be mixed for film formation. A schematic of the apparatus is shown in Fig. 1.

Temperatures, observed on the SiC-coated pedestal, were estimated by comparing the readings of an infrared thermometer with those of an optical pyrometer at pedestal temperatures greater than 750°C, establishing an average emissivity value for the system (0.75), and then extrapolating infrared thermometer signal readings to still lower temperatures. Film thickness was determined either from measurement of an infrared reflectance interference pattern or from angle-lapping and staining multilayer structures.

Materials.—Triethylgallium (TEG) and trimethylgallium (TMG), both air- and water-sensitive liquids, were obtained commercially. The TMG was additionally purified by vacuum-trap distillation until tensiometrically homogeneous fractions were obtained [vapor pressure of TMG at 0°C = 64.5 mm, literature value = 64.5 mm (5)]. The AsH_3 concentrations were nominally 5 or 10% in H_2 and the PH_3, 10% in H_2. SbH_3 was stored under H_2 and equilibrated at −78°C. H_2Se was diluted to 500 ppm in H_2. Diethylzinc (DEZ) was purged with H_2 at −23°C for about 30 min and then stored at 0°C under H_2 until used for doping studies. During doping, the bubbling tube was kept above the liquid.

Ge (111) and GaAs semi-insulating substrates of several orientations were mechanically polished and then chemically polished just before use. Natural faces of flux-grown BeO and ThO_2 were used without polishing after being cleaned with trichloroethylene, water, and methanol rinses. Solvent-cleaned, mechanically polished, essentially scratch-free, basal-plane (0001) Verneuil sapphire (Al_2O_3) and (111), (110), and (100) slices of spinel ($MgAl_2O_4$) cut from Czochralski boules were used as substrates without further treatment.

Procedure.—In the early stages of the investigation, only TEG was commercially available, and it was used in a preliminary study to determine the feasibility of preparing GaAs films by the use of organo-Ga compounds. Thin single-crystal films of GaAs were formed on freshly etched Ge wafers by bubbling H_2 at about 1 liter/min through TEG at about 60°C for 1 hr and decomposing the gases at 700°C on the Ge wafers in an atmosphere containing AsH_3. The crystal character of the overgrowth of GaAs/Ge is shown in Fig. 2, and single crystallinity was confirmed by reflection electron diffraction.

When TMG (bp = 55.6°C at 760 mm) became available, the deposition procedure became more controllable because of its greater volatility as compared with TEG (bp = 143°C at 760 mm). Conditions now considered sufficient for growing good-quality (111) GaAs on appropriately oriented substrates of Ge, GaAs,

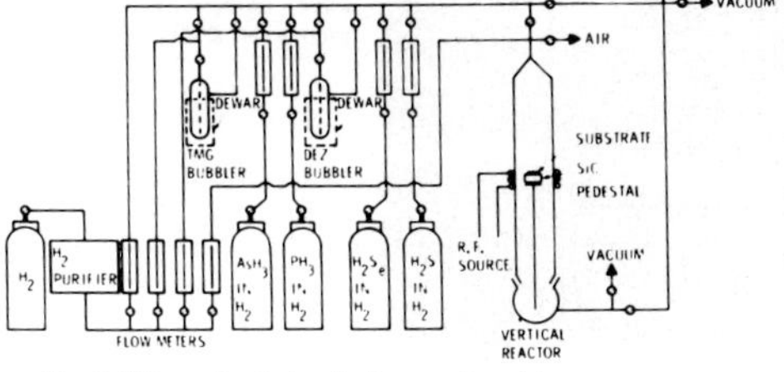

Fig. 1. Schematic of chemical vapor deposition apparatus

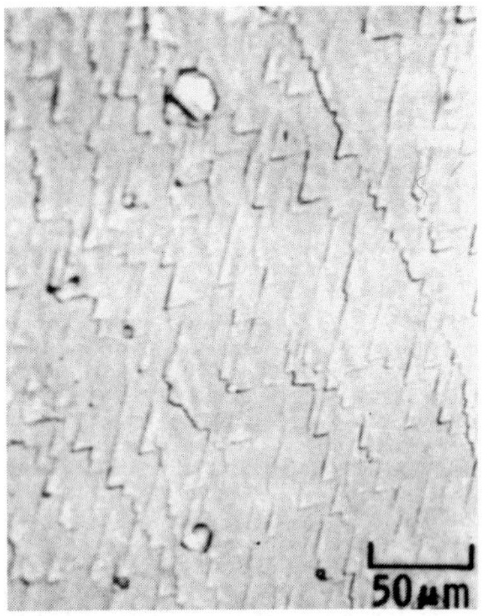

Fig. 2. Surface structure of (111) GaAs growth on (111) Ge (the film was produced from TEG and AsH_3).

and single-crystal insulators incorporate the following typical ranges of concentrations and parameters: TMG 0.2-0.8%; arsine (10%) flow rate about 100-400 ml/min; total H_2 flow rate about 1.5 liters/min; and pedestal temperature 650°-750°C. When the substrate is GaAs, the AsH_3 flow is started independently of the TMG with the pedestal at about 600°C to establish an arsenic atmosphere and help prevent decomposition of the substrate; at the desired deposition temperature, the TMG is introduced to form the GaAs deposit. It was determined for the apparatus in use that better films are produced if the group V hydrides are introduced into the reactor prior to the addition of the TMG for growth on insulating substrates also. Hydride flow is also continued when the deposition is completed and until the temperature has dropped to about 600°C.

The structural nature of the deposit, indicated by the general appearance as viewed in the optical microscope, was determined by x-ray diffraction and/or electron diffraction analysis. The presence and relative compositions of As, P, and Sb in the films were determined with the electron microprobe.

The electrical properties of the films were evaluated from measurements made on Hall samples etched in the GaAs films by standard photolithographic techniques. The carrier concentrations were deduced from the Hall coefficient R_H according to $n = 1/eR_H$, and the Hall mobility was determined from the product $\mu_H = \sigma R_H$, where σ is the electrical conductivity.

Results and Discussion

Using the aforementioned procedures, single-crystal films of GaAs, GaP, and solid solutions of gallium arsenide-phosphide ($GaAs_{1-x}P_x$) and gallium arsenide-antimonide ($GaAs_{1-x}Sb_x$) can be produced on Ge, GaAs, and/or a number of single-crystal insulating substrates.

GaAs *epitaxy.—Film orientation and crystal quality.* As described in a previous publication (6), epitaxial growth of GaAs has been achieved on a number of insulating substrates. The results from that paper are summarized in Table I. Figure 3 shows the surface of a 30-μm film on (0001) Al_2O_3 and the triangular pattern characteristic of (111) growth. The GaAs surface appears rough at thicknesses greater than about 6 μm and displays a rosette pattern, somewhat noticeable in Fig. 3 but more apparent at slightly lower magnifications. Similar growth occurs on (111) $MgAl_2O_4$ and a

Table I. Orientation relationships between GaAs and single-crystal oxides

Substrate plane	Parallel relationships
(0001) Al_2O_3	(111) GaAs ‖ (0001) Al_2O_3
(100) $MgAl_2O_4$	(100) GaAs ‖ (100) $MgAl_2O_4$
(111) $MgAl_2O_4$	(111) GaAs ‖ (111) $MgAl_2O_4$
$(10\bar{1}0)$ BeO	(100) GaAs ‖ $(10\bar{1}0)$ BeO
$(10\bar{1}1)$ BeO	(111) GaAs ‖ $(10\bar{1}1)$ BeO
(0001) BeO	(111) GaAs ‖ (0001) BeO
(100) ThO_2	(100) GaAs ‖ (100) ThO_2

natural $(10\bar{1}1)$ BeO face (Fig. 4). A typical reflection electron diffraction pattern and x-ray Laue pattern for (111) GaAs growth on (0001) Al_2O_3 are shown in Fig. 5. In (a), strong Kikuchi lines are evident and support the single-crystal nature of the overgrowth; in (b), extra spots not due to the substrate can be identified and correlated with the (111) GaAs overgrowth (6).

Simultaneous growth on (0001) Al_2O_3 and on the (111)"A" and (111)"B" faces of GaAs demonstrated that the surface of the film grown on Al_2O_3 resembled the growth on the GaAs "A" face. This suggests that bonding at the Al_2O_3-GaAs interface involves an As bridge, perhaps between metal ions at the substrate surface and the succeeding Ga layer in the film. If so, one might expect different epitaxial relationships to exist between GaAs and Al_2O_3 and between Si and Al_2O_3 (7), in which bonding seemed to be related to a filling-in of metal-ion sites with bonding to the oxygen ions. Preliminary experiments involving GaAs growth on a few other sapphire orientations support the contention that different epitaxial relationships do exist in the different systems, despite the similar cubic-type structure and lattice parameters for Si (5.43A) and GaAs (5.65A).

This contention was further supported in recent studies by the observed growth of (100) GaAs on Czochralski (110) $MgAl_2O_4$,[1] a rather surprising result when compared with the GaAs-spinel relationships reported in Table I. It was also found that the epitaxy is sensitive to the quality of the spinel; for when some Verneuil spinel ($MgO \cdot 3.3Al_2O_3$) was used as a substrate, the intersection of grain boundaries with the crystal surface was readily revealed by the GaAs overgrowth (Fig. 6).

[1] This observation was made during studies being supported in part by the NASA contract No. NAS12-2010.

Fig. 3. The surface structure of a 30-μm GaAs film growth on (0001) Al_2O_3.

Fig. 4. Surface structure of (111) GaAs deposit on natural (1011) face of BeO.

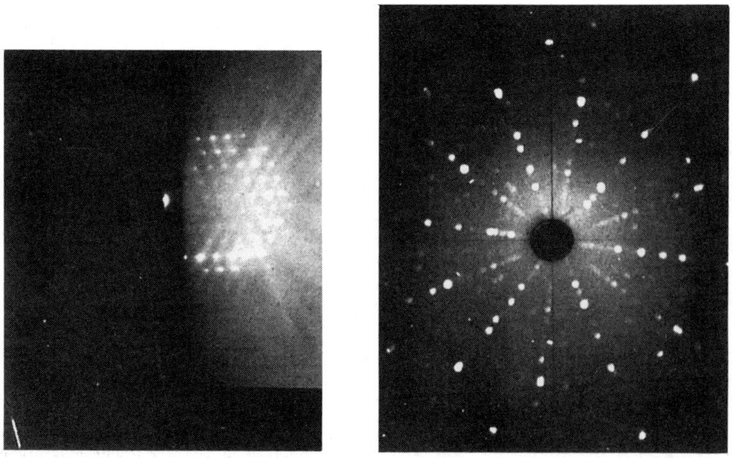

a b

Fig. 5. a—Reflection electron diffraction pattern, and b—x-ray Laue pattern for (111) GaAs growth on (0001) Al_2O_3.

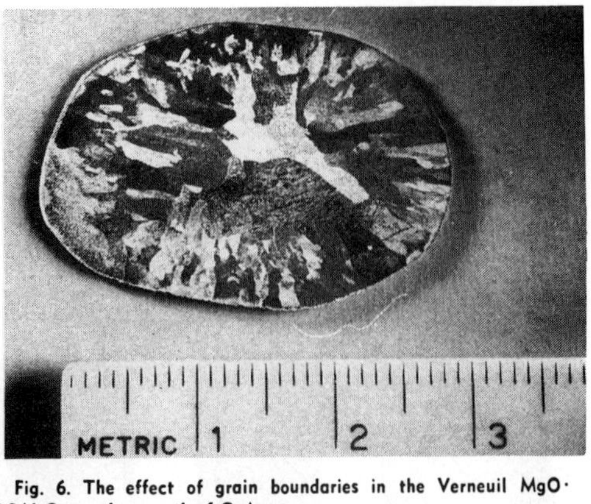

Fig. 6. The effect of grain boundaries in the Verneuil MgO·3.3Al_2O_3 on the growth of GaAs.

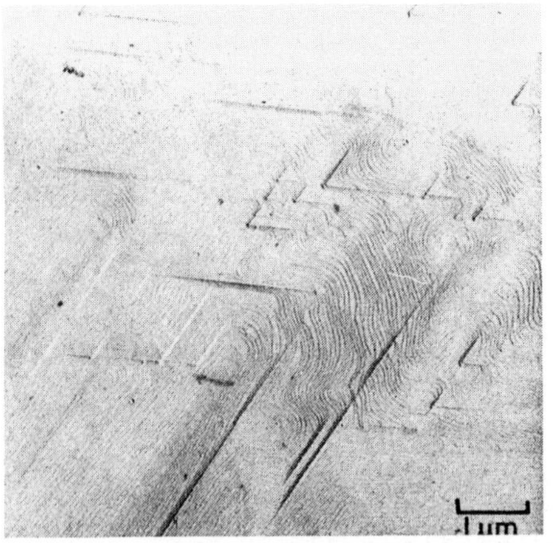

Fig. 7. Replica electron micrograph of (111) GaAs film growth on (0001) Al_2O_3.

As was observed for the silicon growth on (0001) Al_2O_3 (8), a high degree of twinning may exist in (111) GaAs films grown on (0001) Al_2O_3 if the deposition conditions are not optimized. One sample was measured as having a twin density of 7.8%. The technique for twin density measurement has been previously described (8). A replica electron micrograph for a 10-μm film is shown in Fig. 7. An indication of some twinning in the film can be seen. Growth steps in the epitaxial film are also evident. However, the reflection electron diffraction pattern for the film (similar to Fig. 5a) does not support the high twin density value. This correlates with the observation (based on measured charge carrier mobility values) that film quality can improve with film thickness. X-ray techniques provide an average value of twin density for the complete film thickness (8), while reflection electron diffraction basically reveals surface quality. With proper deposition conditions, mirror-smooth GaAs films with no detectable twins (as determined by x-ray evaluation) are being grown on (0001) Al_2O_3 and (111) $MgAl_2O_4$.

Some of the defect structure in films with microtwinning grown on insulators can be revealed by a light polishing-etch such as 1:1:4 hydrogen peroxide-water-sulfuric acid. The triangular pattern shown in Fig. 8a was produced by dipping a mechanically polished 14-μm (111) GaAs film grown on (111) $MgAl_2O_4$ for 10 sec into a freshly prepared 1:1:4 solution. Two minutes of etching (Fig. 8b) (about 2.5 μm removed) revealed a relatively uniform continuation of the defect structure. However, after 5 min of etching, only very small pyramids were evident (Fig. 8c) at the surface of the remaining 7-μm thick film. This also suggests an improvement in film quality with thickness for GaAs grown on $MgAl_2O_4$.

Studies of GaAs grown on BeO have been limited to the natural faces of flux-grown crystals. Attempts to reuse the bare natural faces of the BeO substrates without repolishing have been only partially successful. When GaAs films are etched off with HNO_3-HF mixtures, the substrates seem less amenable to (100) GaAs regrowth but slightly better for (111) GaAs growth on the $(10\bar{1}1)$ face. The $(10\bar{1}0)$ surface is apparently changed significantly by the sequence involving film growth and subsequent removal by the acid mixture.

Effects of deposition parameters on GaAs *film growth.*—At any one temperature, the growth rate of (111) GaAs on Al_2O_3 has been found to be essentially linear with TMG concentration when it is decomposed in an atmosphere containing As and at least a 10-fold excess of AsH_3 over TMG in the gas stream entering the

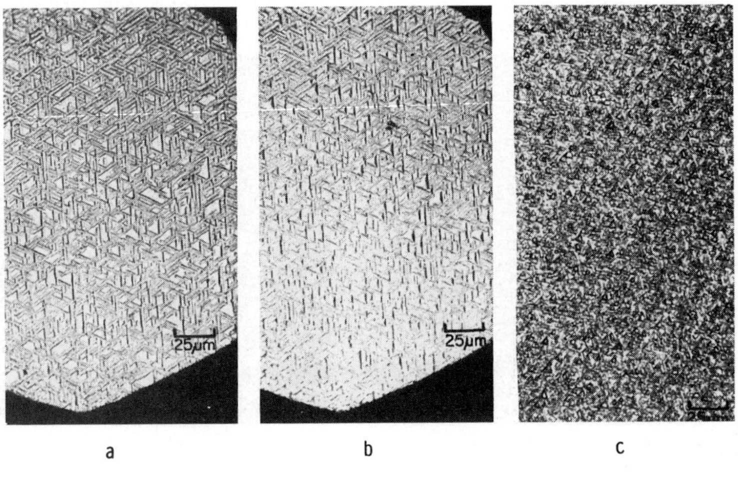

Fig. 8. Structure revealed in a 14-μm (111) GaAs growth on (111) $MgAl_2O_4$ by etching with 1:1:4 hydrogen peroxide-water-sulfuric acid mixture for a total of: a—10 sec, b—2 min, c—5 min (7 μm removed).

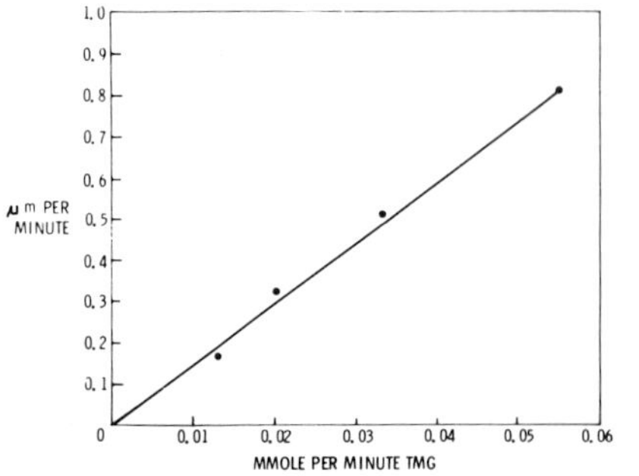

Fig. 9. Growth rate at 725°C of (111) GaAs on (0001) Al_2O_3 as a function of TMG concentration.

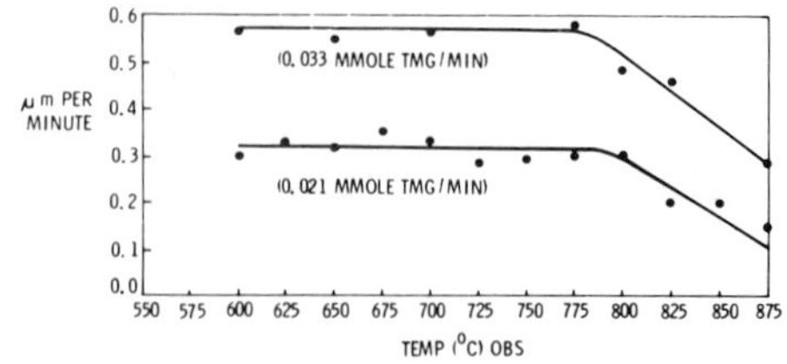

Fig. 10. Effect of substrate temperature on rate of growth of (111) GaAs on (0001) Al_2O_3.

reactor. Typical growth rates at 725°C are depicted in Fig. 9 for different concentrations of TMG carried into the reactor per minute. With higher concentrations and temperatures, considerable turbulence is evidenced near the vicinity of the heated pedestal.

In the temperature range 600° to about 800°C, the growth rate was found to be essentially constant for TMG additions of 0.02 and 0.03 mmole/min but dropped off somewhat at about 825°C (Fig. 10). Films grown on Al_2O_3 at 800° and 825°C were less perfect than those grown at 675°C, as determined by reflection electron diffraction (Fig. 11).

Electrical properties of GaAs *films.*[2]—Hall coefficient measurements were used to examine the electrical properties of the GaAs films. Undoped specimens up to ~5 μm thick produced from one combination of TMG and AsH_3 exhibited high resistivity, about 10^3-10^5 ohm-cm. The addition of H_2Se to the gas stream containing the TMG and AsH_3 produced on pyrolysis n-type films with net carrier concentrations as high as 6.2 x 10^{18} electrons/cm^3, obtained when the H_2Se flow rate was about 100 ml/min. The addition of "excess" H_2Se caused the electron mobility to decrease slightly and changed the appearance of the GaAs deposit. These surface changes are shown in Fig. 12(a-f). The change in crystal character may be due to the formation of another compound such as Ga_2Se_3, As_2Se_3, or an alloy, as the solubility limit of Se in GaAs is exceeded.

The addition of DEZ to the gas stream provided p-type GaAs growths with net carrier concentrations up to 2.8 x 10^{19} holes/cm^3, resistivities of 0.003 ohm-cm,

[2] An up-to-date and more complete description of the electrical properties of GaAs films grown by the TMG-AsH_3 process will appear in a subsequent paper by A. C. Thorsen.

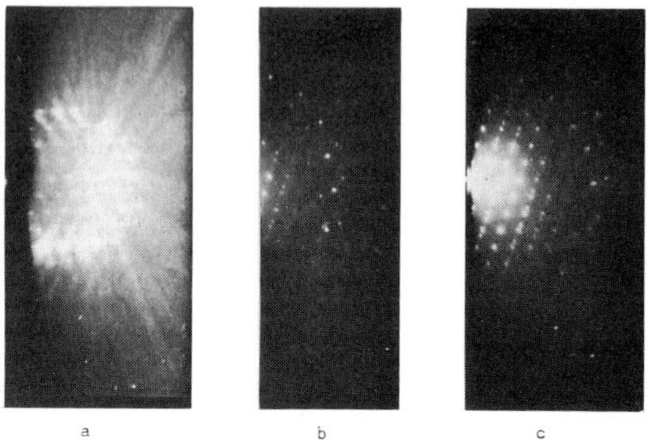

Fig. 11. Reflection electron diffraction photographs of (111) GaAs/(0001) Al_2O_3 films grown at: a—675°C, b—800°C, c—825°C.

and room temperature mobilities of about 75 cm^2/V-sec. The highest doping level was reached when the H_2 flow over the DEZ was about 35 ml/min. Further additions of zinc as DEZ also caused a change in the surface character, as noted in Fig. 13(a-d).

Mobilities of Se-doped GaAs films grown on (0001) Al_2O_3 early in our studies were found to be dependent on film thickness. Films less than about 8 μm thick exhibited average mobilities usually less than 2000 cm^2/V-sec, while films about 8-25 μm thick had average mobility values of about 4000 cm^2/V-sec for carrier concentrations of about 4 x 10^{16} cm^{-3}.

Mobilities of about 5000 cm^2/V-sec at $n = 1 \times 10^{16}$ cm^{-3} have recently been measured for GaAs films not intentionally doped. Experiments are also in progress to compare the properties of the growth of GaAs on GaAs with the films grown on the insulators. The effect

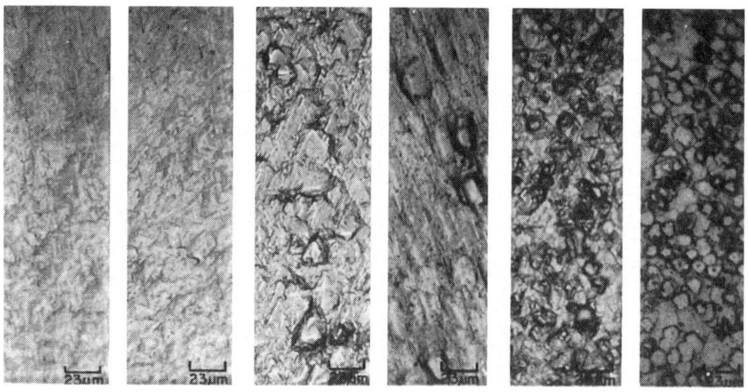

Fig. 12. Effect on appearance of GaAs growth at 725°C on (0001) Al_2O_3 of increases in H_2Se concentration. The doped H_2 flow rates were: a—10 ml/min, b—50 ml/min, c—100 ml/min, d—150 ml/min, e—200 ml/min, f—325 ml/min.

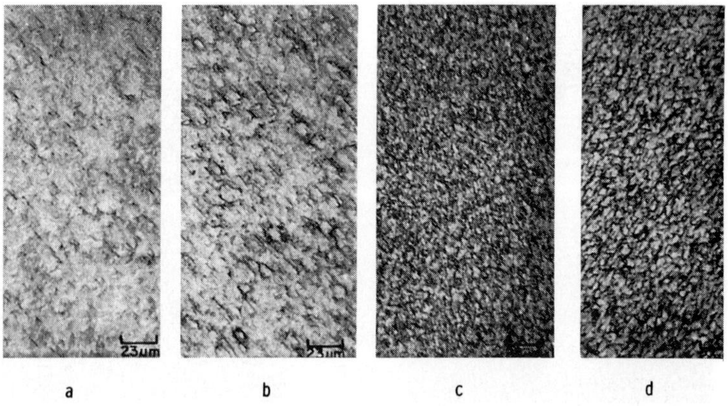

Fig. 13. Effect on appearance of GaAs growth at 725°C on (0001) Al_2O_3 of increases in DEZ concentrations. The H_2 flow rates over DEZ were: a—5 ml/min, b—25 ml/min, c—35 ml/min, d—75 ml/min.

of the purity of the starting materials on film properties is also being studied.

Films of GaAs grown on insulating substrates have been found to possess a much lower degree of residual stress than that found for Si on Al_2O_3 (9, 10) and $MgAl_2O_4$ (11). This is not unexpected, since the mean linear thermal expansion coefficients for GaAs (6.4 x 10^{-6}/°C) (12) and sapphire (⊥ to c-axis, 7.7 x 10^{-6}/°C, between 20°-500°C) (13) are not too far apart at room temperature. Essentially, no bowing could be observed for a 35-μm GaAs film grown on a 10-mil Al_2O_3 substrate. However, a 1-μm film did curl a 5-μm Al_2O_3 platelet concave downward, indicating that the residual stress in the GaAs is compressive. Further studies of the stresses in the films and their effect on electrical properties are in progress.

By varying the amounts and types of dopants introduced into the gas stream during crystal growth, multilayer epitaxial structures have been fabricated on Al_2O_3. A four-layer (p^+, p, n, n^+) 48-μm thick structure was grown on (0001) Al_2O_3, photolithographically processed, and etched into mesas with relatively large p-n junction areas of about 6 x 10^{-4} cm^2. An I-V characteristic of one of these "grown" diodes is shown in Fig. 14. Capacitance-voltage measurements indicated that the junctions were transitionary between graded and abrupt.

GaP and $GaAs_{1-x}P_x$ epitaxy.—Although the emphasis to date has been on the preparation of films of GaAs on insulating substrates, some experiments have been carried out with the TMG-AsH_3 and/or PH_3 reaction to prepare films of GaP and $GaAs_{1-x}P_x$ mixed compounds on GaAs and on insulating substrates.

However, it is apparent that controlling the growth of single-crystal films of GaP on insulators is more difficult than the control of GaAs film growth. Whereas GaAs films only 1 μm thick are single crystal on Al_2O_3, GaP films of the same thickness have to date exhibited only highly preferred orientation on (0001) Al_2O_3 while exhibiting single crystallinity on GaAs. However, the films on Al_2O_3 have improved in quality with additional thickness growth, producing surfaces that were identified as single-crystal (111) orientation by reflection electron diffraction. The electron diffraction pattern for the surface of such a film (7.5 μm thick) grown on (0001) sapphire is shown in Fig. 15. The pattern is sharp, and good structure is indicated.

GaP growth on a thin sapphire platelet caused curling of the platelet in a concave downward direction, which indicated the residual stress in the GaP film to be compressive.

Additions of PH_3 to the AsH_3-TMG mixtures normally used for growing GaAs films will produce thin single-crystal $GaAs_{1-x}P_x$ films on (0001) Al_2O_3. In these preliminary studies, single-crystal films with the compositions $GaAs_{0.9}P_{0.1}$ and $GaAs_{0.4}P_{0.6}$ have been grown on (0001) Al_2O_3 and (111) $MgAl_2O_4$. Additional studies are in progress.

Multilayers of single crystals of GaAs and GaP have also been fabricated on Al_2O_3. Figure 16a shows the multilayer structure revealed by a bevel section through a GaAs/GaP/GaAs/Al_2O_3 film. The order of the surface structure in Fig. 16b indicated a single-crystal com-

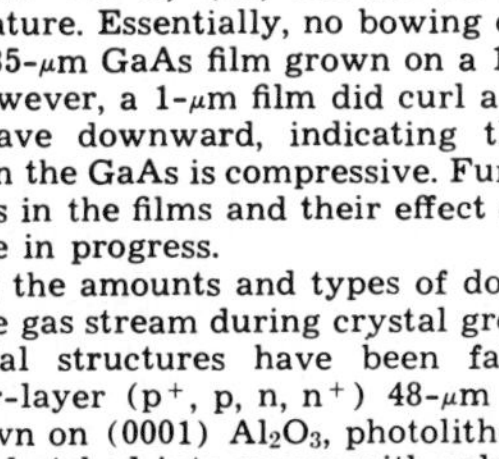

Fig. 14. I-V curve of GaAs/Al_2O_3 (p^+pnn^+) diode

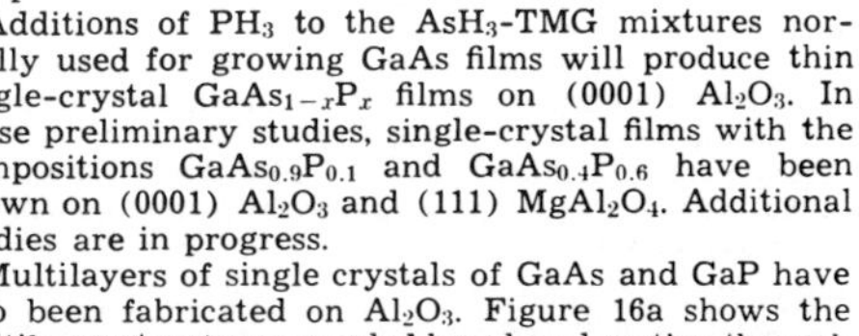

Fig. 15. Reflection electron diffraction evidence for (111) growth of GaP on (0001) Al_2O_3 at 700°C.

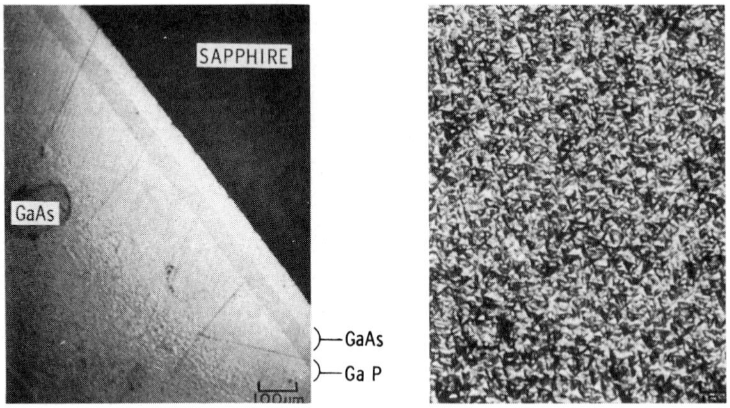

a b

Fig. 16. a—A multilayer GaAs/GaP/GaAs/Al_2O_3 composite as revealed by angle-lapping, b—surface of the composite.

posite. This was confirmed by x-ray diffraction procedures.

$GaAs_{1-x}Sb_x$ *epitaxy*.—A few experiments relating to $GaAs_{1-x}Sb_x$ epitaxy were performed at 725°C on (100) GaAs and (0001) Al_2O_3. Single-crystal films with approximate compositions in the range $GaAs_{0.9}Sb_{0.1}$ to $GaAs_{0.7}Sb_{0.3}$ were obtained when the TMG-AsH_3-SbH_3 ratios were arbitrarily changed by either reducing the arsenic flow or increasing the flow rate of hydrogen bubbling through the liquid SbH_3. Better growth, as determined by reflection electron diffraction, was obtained on (100) GaAs than on (0001) Al_2O_3 at the higher concentrations of Sb. Epitaxial films of $GaAs_{1-x}Sb_x$ can also be achieved by using trimethylantimony in place of SbH_3 (14).

Reaction mechanisms.—The use of the metal-organic for semiconductor film formation was not without concern for the possibility of major carbon contamination. Graham (15) reported that the pyrolysis of TMG at 520°C in an argon carrier gas produced a metallic-looking film containing 8.0% carbon. Plust (16) described the production of Ga of semiconductor purity by photolysis of TEG, but Graham obtained gray-black solids containing metallic Ga using Plust's process. In order to prevent the formation of nonvolatile carbonaceous side-products, two steps were initially taken: (*a*) the use of H_2 as the carrier gas as a means for tying up free radicals that may be assumed to be involved in the mechanism for the pyrolysis of TMG; and (*b*) the use of the Group-V hydride(s) in excess over the stoichiometric amount required to react with a given amount of TMG, as represented, for example, by reaction [1] for the formation of GaAs:

$$(CH_3)_3Ga + AsH_3 \rightleftarrows GaAs + 3CH_4 \qquad [1]$$

The AsH_3 in excess (or other group V hydride) probably reacts with the TMG before it has a chance to pyrolyze, thus avoiding the formation of undesirable products. It also provides an As atmosphere to help prevent the dissociation at elevated temperatures. The relatively low temperatures used for GaAs formation also apparently prevent C from being a major contaminant in the GaAs films. If C were there as a minor contaminant, it would most probably be due to impure starting materials or caused by improper handling in the deposition apparatus.

Harrison *et al.* (18) performed an experiment in which TMG and AsH_3 were mixed at room temperature in 1:1 molecular proportions in the vapor state for 18 hr and then heated to about 200°C. This produced a red film which was postulated to be stoichiometric GaAs. Unfortunately, the experiment was not evaluated sufficiently. If the rate of formation and quantity of methane had been measured, then one would have more confidence in the study of the stoichiometry of reaction [1]. There may have also been a reaction between AsH_3 and a gray film which Harrison reported had formed on the walls of the tube at room temperature. This film may have been a reaction product between TMG and Pyrex, which has been previously observed (19). It was in the belief that reaction [1] was the predominant reaction that studies of reactions between the metal-organics and the hydrides were begun. Knowledge of Harrison's prior investigation at low pressures came to light afterwards.

A few experiments in our laboratories were also performed using $AsCl_3$ and TMG as the reacting materials. Epitaxy was not achieved on the insulators, and this approach was soon discarded. It may be that the reaction is complicated by the formation of HCl, produced by the reduction of $AsCl_3$ by H_2

$$2AsCl_3 + 3H_2 = 1/2As_4 + 6HCl \qquad [2]$$

Further reaction by TMG with HCl could produce in the first stage of the reaction the compound methyl gallium dichloride

$$2(CH_3)_3Ga + 4HCl \rightarrow (CH_3GaCl_2)_2 + 4CH_4 \text{ (20)} \qquad [3]$$

followed by complete dealkylation

$$(MeGaCl_2)_2 + 2HCl \rightarrow 2CH_4 + 2GaCl_3 \qquad [4]$$

HCl could also obstruct epitaxy if the growth rate of the depositing film is less than its etching rate by the HCl.

Summary

The decomposition of alkylgallium compounds (R_3Ga), *e.g.* trimethylgallium or triethylgallium, in the presence of arsine, phosphine, arsine-phosphine, or arsine-stibine has produced single-crystal growth of the corresponding Ga-V compounds on single-crystal insulating substrates as well as on GaAs, GaP, and/or Ge. A reasonable explanation for the formation of the Ga-V compound is expressed by the reaction, *e.g.* for the production of GaAs

$$(CH_3)_3Ga + AsH_3 \xrightarrow[650°\text{-}750°C]{} GaAs + 3CH_4$$

This technique obviates the use of multiple temperature zones for the CVD process, simplifies the procedure considerably, and makes compound semiconductor film growth compatible with the growth of elemental semiconductors, such as Si and Ge. This compatibility has made it possible to fabricate and study, *via,* CVD and appropriate masking techniques, various combinations of single-crystal compound and elemental semiconductor layers on the same insulating substrate. New degrees of freedom and new concepts in device design are now apparent which may make optimum use of the differences in the physical, electrical, and optical properties of different semiconductors.

Acknowledgments

The authors wish to thank F. M. Erdmann for assisting in the growth of the layers; Dr. R. L. Nolder, L. A. Moudy, and E. R. Goldman for electron and x-ray diffraction analyses; Dr. A. C. Thorsen for the electrical measurements; G. W. Johnson, J. L. Healy, and D. Medellin for the angle lapping and some of the photomicrographs; R. W. Stewart for electron microprobe analyses; J. P. Wendt and Dr. B. T. French for the device processing and evaluation of the 4-layer GaAs diode; S. B. Austerman for the BeO crystals; and Dr. R. P. Ruth for his most helpful discussions, encouragement, and direction in the described program.

Manuscript submitted April 14, 1969; revised manuscript received *ca.* Aug. 15, 1969. This was Paper 63 presented at the Boston Meeting, May 5-9, 1968.

Any discussion of this paper will appear in a Discussion Section to be published in the June 1970 JOURNAL.

REFERENCES

1. J. J. Tietjen and J. A. Amick, *This Journal,* **113,** 724 (1966).
2. J. R. Knight, D. Effer, and P. R. Evans, *Solid-State Electron.,* **8,** 178 (1965).
3. M. Michelitsch, W. Kappallo, and G. Hellbardt, *This Journal,* **111**, 1248 (1964).
4. R. W. Conrad and R. W. Haisty, *ibid.,* **113,** 199 (1966).
5. E. Wiberg, T. Johannsen, and O. Stecker, *Z. Anorg. Allgem. Chem.,* **251**, 114 (1943).
6. H. M. Manasevit, *Appl. Phys. Letters,* **12,** 156 (1968).
7. H. M. Manasevit, R. L. Nolder, and L. A. Moudy, *Trans. TMS-AIME,* **242,** 465 (1968).
8. R. L. Nolder, D. J. Klein, and D. H. Forbes, *J. Appl. Phys.,* **36,** 3444 (1965).
9. C. Y. Ang and H. M. Manasevit, *Solid-State Electron.,* **8,** 994 (1965).
10. D. J. Dumin, *J. Appl. Phys.,* **36**, 2700 (1965).
11. P. H. Robinson and D. J. Dumin, *This Journal,* **115,** 75 (1968).
12. M. E. Straumanis, J. P. Krumme, and M. Rubenstein, *ibid.,* **114,** 640 (1967).
13. J. B. Austin, *J. Am. Ceram. Soc.,* **14,** 795 (1931).
14. H. M. Manasevit, Unpublished data.
15. W. A. Graham and A. R. Gatti, A. D. Little, Inc., Cambridge, Mass., Final Report, Contract AF19(604)-4975, Dec. 31, 1960.
16. H. G. Plust, U.S. Pat. 2,898,278, Aug. 4, 1959.
17. N. N. Greenwood and M. Wallbridge, *J. Chem. Soc.,* **1963,** 3912.
18. B. Harrison and E. H. Tompkins, *Inorg. Chem.,* **1,** 951 (1962).
19. H. M. Manasevit, Ph.D. Thesis, "Study of Reactions of Silyl Bases with Selected Lewis Acids," p. 44, Illinois Institute of Technology, Chicago, Ill., June 1959.
20. G. E. Coates, "Organo-Metallic Compounds," 2nd Ed., p. 151, John Wiley & Sons, Inc., New York (1960).

Interaction of Ga and As_2 Molecular Beams with GaAs Surfaces

J. R. Arthur, Jr.
Bell Telephone Laboratories, Incorporated, Murray Hill, New Jersey
(Received 26 January 1968)

Because of the usefulness of vacuum evaporation as a method for preparing metallic films of high purity, there has been considerable interest in the possible use of this technique for obtaining semiconductor films. In the case of compounds such as the III–V semiconductors the situation is complicated by the fact that the group V element generally has a much higher vapor pressure than the group II element. Gunther[1,2] proposed that this problem could be overcome by a "three temperature" technique by which an excess flux of the more volatile component is directed at the substrate in order to compensate for the greater evaporation rate. He argued that the resulting films should be stoichiometric because the vapor pressure of the group V component is greater over the pure element than over the compound. While polycrystalline films of preferred orientation have been described,[3,4] large area single crystal films of Ga compounds have not, to our knowledge, been produced by this technique up to now.[5] *Note added in proof*: J. E. Davey and T. Pankey, J. Appl. Phys. **39**, 1941 (1968), have since reported the growth of large-area GaAs epitaxial films by the "three-temperature" technique.

In this report we will present kinetic evidence from which a more detailed mechanism is obtained for the interaction of gallium and arsenic vapors on a surface. Specifically, measurements of the mean surface lifetime of Ga atoms and the influence of Ga atoms on the sticking probability of As_2 vapor on the (111) surface of GaAs suggest that a temperature dependent surface population of Ga atoms is present above 800°K and that the sticking probability for impinging As_2 molecules depends markedly on the density of this population. In order to grow GaAs it is therefore necessary to supply gallium and arsenic vapors in such a ratio that the rate of collisions between adsorbed Ga and impinging arsenic vapor is equal to the arrival rate of Ga. As further evidence for this mechanism, large area (0.5 cm^2) epitaxial films of GaAs have been grown on GaAs substrates by sublimation of the compound as well as by a three-temperature technique.

A modulated-molecular beam technique[6–8] was used for measuring surface lifetimes and sticking coefficients. Figure 1 shows the detector signal obtained when a pulse of Ga atoms was reflected from a (111) GaAs surface previously cleaned by heating to 925°K. The original Ga pulse was nearly rectangular and was produced by mechanically chopping the beam emitted from a quartz Knudsen cell containing pure Ga. The beam intensity was 1.5×10^{13} atoms/cm^2/sec at the sample which was near the vacuum evaporation rate; consequently the surface atom population was only moderately perturbed. Lower beam intensities produced identical results. When the beam was closed off by the shutter the evaporation rate returned to the vacuum value with an exponential decrease of time constant τ, where τ is the surface lifetime.[9] Figure 2 shows surface lifetime τ for Ga on GaAs (111) and $(\bar{1}\bar{1}\bar{1})$ surfaces vs $1/T$. The results obey

$$\tau = 1.6\times10^{-14}\exp(60\ \text{kcal/mole}/RT)\ \text{on}\ (\bar{1}\bar{1}\bar{1})$$

and

$$\tau = 2.5\times10^{-14}\exp(57\ \text{kcal/mole}/RT)\ \text{on}\ (111).$$

Since there is some scatter in the data which cover only a limited temperature range, the activation energies are accurate to ±4 kcal while the preexponential terms could vary by a factor of five; however, in the accessible temperature range τ was lower by a factor of 2.5 on the (111). Whether this difference is characteristic of the clean (111) surfaces or is the result of traces of impurity is not yet clear. Below 750°K no Ga was reflected; the sticking coefficient was unity.

The sticking coefficient of As_2 on GaAs {111} was determined by observing the reflection of pulses of As_2 produced by vaporization of GaAs contained in another quartz Knudsen cell. (Separate

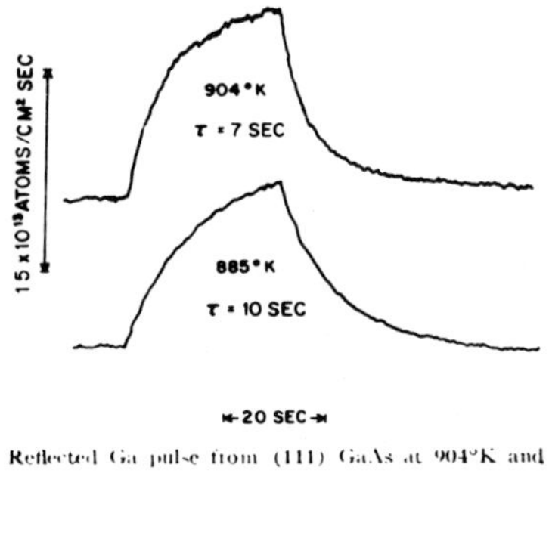

FIG. 1. Reflected Ga pulse from (111) GaAs at 904°K and 885°K.

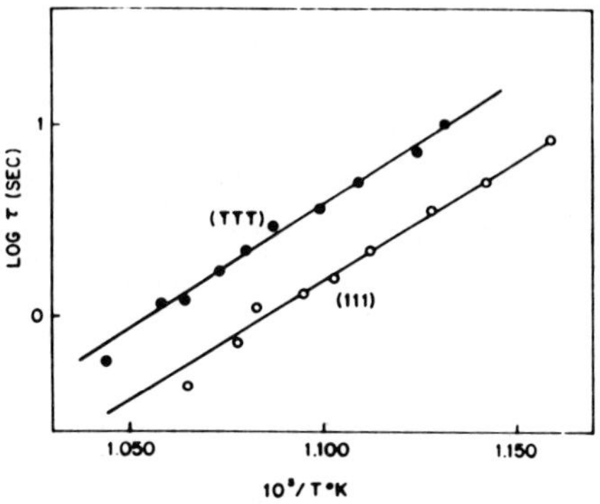

FIG. 2. Surface lifetime τ for Ga on {111} GaAs surfaces.

studies have shown that in the temperature range 1000° to 1400°K predominately As_2 molecules evaporate from GaAs.[10]) For all substrate temperatures the reflected As_2 signal had the same trapezoidal shape as the incident pulse; adsorption of As_2 was indicated either by a small reduction in the height of the reflected pulse or by evolution of arsenic species when the substrate crystal was subsequently flashed to a higher temperature. For both {111} surfaces a measurable reduction in the size of the reflected As_2 signal was observed only under two conditions: (1) when Ga was previously deposited in monolayer quantities at a substrate temperature lower than that necessary for Ga surface migration[11]; (2) when the substrate was heated *above* 775°K. In the first case the magnitude of the reduction depended both on integrated As_2 exposure and initial Ga dosage; we infer that As_2 has a much higher sticking probability on Ga than on GaAs. For monolayer Ga coverage the initial As_2 sticking coefficient was unity. In the second case, the sticking coefficient increased with temperature from ~775°K to ~850°K to an ultimate value of 0.1–0.15. A measurable evaporation flux of Ga was observed in this temperature range, and this flux was reduced when the As_2 beam struck the surface.

The observations can be explained by assuming that a surface population of Ga atoms exist on GaAs above 775°K with which impinging As_2 molecules can react to produce GaAs. If n is the density of adsorbed Ga atoms

$$dn/dt = -(n/\tau) - nk_1F_{As_2} + F_{Ga} + \Gamma, \tag{1}$$

where F_{As_2} and F_{Ga} are the impinging fluxes of As_2 and Ga, k_1 is the rate constant for the reaction between Ga(ads) and As_2, and Γ is the rate of dissociation of GaAs. At steady state

$$n = (F_{Ga}+\Gamma)/[(1/\tau)+k_1F_{As_2}]. \tag{2}$$

The growth rate of a GaAs crystal exposed to Ga and As_2 beams is then

$$nk_1F_{As_2} = (F_{Ga}+\Gamma)/[1+(1/\tau k_1F_{As_2})]. \tag{3}$$

As further evidence for the proposed growth mechanism, epitaxial films of GaAs have been grown on GaAs {111} surfaces in high vacuum ($<10^{-8}$ Torr) both by evaporation of the compound and by coevaporation of Ga and As_2 from separate sources. Reflection electron diffraction patterns indicated that films grown on substrates at 870°K or higher were single-crystal, while films grown at 830°K showed twinning and some streaking of diffraction spots indicating polycrystalline regions. Based on equilibrium vapor pressure data,[10] the As_2:Ga arrival rate ratio varied from 5 to 25 with Ga arrival rates from 2.3×10^{14} to 3.7×10^{15} atoms/cm^2/sec. Despite the large variation in As_2:Ga, the measured film thickness was closely proportional to integrated Ga flux. From Eq. 3, taking $k_1 \sim (7\times10^{14})^{-1}$ cm,[12] $\tau \sim 2$ sec and neglecting

Γ for a typical substrate temperature of 870°K, the growth rate $\simeq F_{Ga}$ for our conditions. The observed growth rate determined from film thickness was within a factor of two of F_{Ga}. The undoped films have been both *n*- and *p*-type, with $\sim 10^{16}$ carriers/cm^3 but with mobilities at 298°K below 1000.

We conclude that adsorbed Ga atoms strongly modify the adsorption rate of As_2 on GaAs, and that this effect provides a *kinetic* mechanism for the growth of stoichiometric GaAs layers from Ga and As_2 vapor. The evidence so far suggests that a similar mechanism holds for the interaction of As_4 and Ga on GaAs, although our data for As_4 are still incomplete. It seems quite likely that a similar mechanism also will hold for the vapor growth of other Ga compounds, e.g., GaSb, GaP, GaN, on which the adsorption rate of the group V element is kinetically slow.

[1] K. G. Gunther, Z. Naturforsch. **13**, 1081 (1958).

[2] K. G. Gunther, in *Compound Semiconductors*, R. K. Willardson and H. L. Goering, Eds. (Reinhold Publishing Corporation, New York, 1962), Vol. I, p. 313.

[3] J. E. Davey and T. Pankey, J. Appl. Phys. **35**, 2203 (1964).

[4] J. E. Davey and T. Pankey, J. Appl. Phys. **37**, 1507 (1966).

[5] P. Hudock, J. Electrochem. Soc. **114**, 64C (1967) describes epitaxial films grown by sublimation; however his growth rates are 10–100 times too large for the source temperature claimed. This suggests that chemical transport of Ga may have been involved. L. G. Lavrent'eva and M. D. Wilisova, Rost Kristallov, Akad. Nauk SSSR, Inst. Kristallogr. **6**, 340 (1965), have reported epitaxial growth by sublimation in sealed ampoules; however under their conditions Ga_2O must have been a major vapor species.

[6] F. L. Hughes and H. Levinstein, Phys. Rev. **113**, 1029 (1959).

[7] M. Kaminsky, Ann. Physik **7**, 53 (1966).

[8] J. R. Arthur, *Twenty-Seventh Conference on Physical Electronics* (Technology Press, Cambridge, Mass. (1967).

[9] I. Langmuir, Phys. Rev. **22**, 357 (1923).

[10] J. R. Arthur, J. Phys. Chem. Solids, **28**, 2257 (1967).

[11] J. R. Arthur, J. Appl. Phys. **37**, 3057 (1966).

[12] nk_1 is the probability of an As_2 molecule striking a Ga atom; we take k_1^{-1} as approximately equal to the number of atoms on a {111} surface.

Molecular Beam Epitaxy of GaAs and InP with Gas Sources for As and P

M. B. Panish*

Bell Laboratories, Murray Hill, New Jersey 07974

ABSTRACT

Arsine and phosphine were decomposed in a high temperature leak-source to provide As_2 and P_2 molecular beams for molecular beam epitaxy of GaAs and InP. Reasonable growth rates (0.5-1.5 μm/hr) were achieved for both semiconductors. The studies demonstrated that with this method, MBE of GaAs can be done with the substrate temperature as high as 700°C. The maximum growth temperature obtained for InP was approximately 600°C. A reasonable increase in leak rate at the source should permit GaAs-MBE at 750°C and InP-MBE at 650°C.

Conventional molecular beam epitaxy of III-V compounds is usually done with a source for the group V element that consists of a condensed phase in an effusion oven (1). Usually the condensed phase is the solid element itself, although many studies have been done in which it is a solution of the group V elements in liquid group III element. Effusion sources utilizing the solid group V elements have several disadvantages. They are rapidly depleted and the surface area of the condensed phase may change. Thus beam flux varies with time, in the nonideal effusion ovens used for MBE. Solid phosphorus may cause beam intensity control problems because the solid red phosphorus source generally consists of an ill-defined mixture of allotropic phases having different vapor pressures (2). When the liquid solution of group V in group III element is used the source is initially the III-V compound in contact with the liquid as the result of preferential loss of group V element at the source temperature. At a given temperature these sources will provide a constant flux of As_2 or P_2 as long as solid III-V compound remains. Such sources are usually exhausted quickly because it is inconvenient and expensive to maintain a large volume of source III-V compound at the high temperatures required. Furthermore, for such sources, the group V element beam intensity cannot be varied independently of the group III element beam intensity.

Several studies (3, 4) have demonstrated that the quality of MBE material, at least for GaAs and $Al_xGa_{1-x}As$, improves with increasing substrate temperature during growth. Furthermore there is an increasing interest in III-V solid solutions containing both As and P. At higher substrate temperatures the efficiency with which the group V element is used decreases rapidly as the result primarily of its rapidly increasing partial pressure over the III-V compound. A source is needed that does not require frequent replenishment. For MBE of the III-V solid solutions containing As and P, a source that provides precise control over the group V element beam intensities is needed.

In this work, AsH_3 and PH_3 were thermally decomposed in a "leak-source" at sufficiently high temperatures for the reaction

$$4MH_3 \xrightarrow{\Delta} M_4 + 6H_2 \qquad [1]$$

to go to completion in a "high pressure" section at approximately 1/2 to 3 atm. An "effusion section" of the source is intended to thermalize the beam to yield a cosine distribution and cause the reaction

$$M_4 \rightarrow 2M_2 \qquad [2]$$

to occur. This gas source for the group V elements does not require replenishment inside the vacuum system. The group V element beam intensity can be precisely controlled simply by exercising control over gas pressures at about 1 atm in a simple gas handling system; and, if necessary, mixed sources can be used to provide constant group V element ratios in the molecular beam.

Experimental

The MBE system used to demonstrate gas-source MBE is a modified vacuum system that was used for early MBE studies in 1970. Because of the necessity to pump rather large volumes of hydrogen, the original ion pumping system was replaced with a 6 in. oil diffusion pumping stack consisting of a 6 in. gate valve, an efficient liquid nitrogen cooled trap, and then the diffusion pump. The lowest pressure the system could achieve was about 5×10^{-9} Torr. The arrangement of the group III and group V element sources is illustrated in Fig. 1. Minimal cryopanneling was provided and the system was clearly not suitable for growth of extremely high purity material (even without oil diffusion pumping). However, it was adequate to permit definition of conditions under which GaAs and InP can be grown with gas source MBE.

The effusion sources for the group III elements were of conventional construction (1) with a pyrolytic boron nitride crucible to contain the group III element and most heated metal parts of molybdenum to preclude

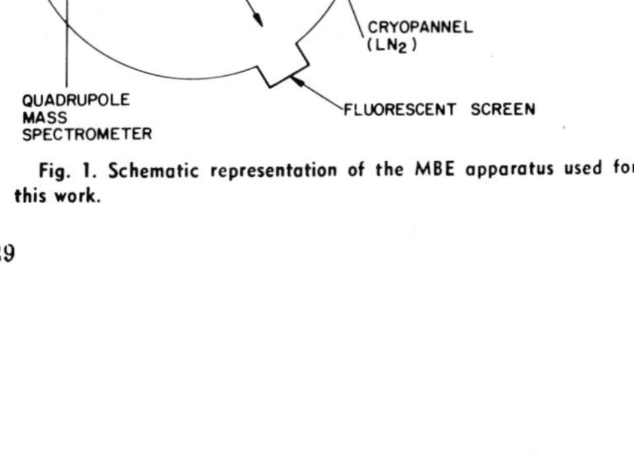

Fig. 1. Schematic representation of the MBE apparatus used for this work.

* Electrochemical Society Active Member.

Key words: semiconductor, arsine, phosphine, crystal growth.

their reaction with H_2. The source for the group V elements (Fig. 2) consisted of an alumina tube with a leaky end seal having a leak rate such that with the pumping stack used, and with the pressure in the gas handling system at about 3 atm, the vacuum system pressure did not exceed $\sim 5 \times 10^{-5}$ Torr during a run. Several centimeters of the end of the alumina tube were heated by a resistance furnace that was maintained at 800°-900°C during a run. As illustrated in Fig. 2, the alumina furnace tube protruded about 2 cm beyond the alumina tube seal to provide an effusion section for the source.

For the studies reported in this paper only one leak-source-furnace combination was used. This source was calibrated for As_2 and P_2 beam flux distribution at the substrate by having the beam impinge on a liquid nitrogen cooled Si wafer masked with a wire grid. The deposited arsenic layer was dense and metallic in appearance, with a surface that mirrored the surface of the Si substrate. Layer thickness was determined with profilometer scans across the masked and unmasked regions of the surface. For the determination of P_2 beam flux distributions, a similar procedure was followed. The only modification to the procedure was that a thin protective layer of As was deposited immediately following the phosphorus deposition. The thickness of the As layer was determined from the previous As runs, and the profilometer thickness measurement for the composite structure then yielded the phosphorus layer thickness.

Epitaxial layers of GaAs were grown on (100) GaAs substrate surfaces that were chemically polished with a Br_2-methanol solution and then briefly etched with a peroxide-H_2SO_4 solution. The InP epitaxial layers were grown on (100) InP substrates that were chemically polished only with a Br_2-methanol solution. During growth the substrate wafers were "glued" to the Mo heating block with indium. The oven orifice of the leak source was 9 cm from the substrate and the group III element source-to-substrate distances were about 12 cm. The group III beam intensities were regulated by monitoring and varying the effusion cell temperature with conventional thermocouple controlled regulators. Nominal effusion cell temperatures ranged from 900° to 1000°C for Ga and 800° to 840°C for In.

For both GaAs and InP epitaxy, the growing crystal surface was monitored by observing the reflection-high energy electron diffraction (RHEED) pattern for electrons diffracted at a glancing angle (1, 5) as illustrated in Fig. 1. In addition, the condition of the crystal surface was monitored visually and the temperature of the wafer surface was monitored with an infrared pyrometer. Calibration for the pyrometer was obtained for GaAs surfaces by observing the Si-Al eutectic transition at 577°C (6) for a partially Al-coated silicon wafer mounted on the heater block with the GaAs wafer. Similarly for InP, the Ge-Al eutectic temperature at 424°C (6) was used for calibration. It was assumed that the calibration corrections were constant over the temperature ranges studied.

Results and Discussion

The leak-effusion source.—The use of AsH_3 and PH_3 as sources for As_2 and P_2 beams requires that the hydrides be thermally decomposed before introduction into the vacuum system. This was done at 800°-900°C with pressures in the range 1/2 to 3 atm on the high pressure side of the leak. Virtually complete decomposition of the hydrides occurred. In the leak-source As_4 or P_4 plus H_2 molecules leak from the high pressure region at about 1 atm into the effusion section of the leak-source heater where the pressure is in the milliTorr range. Within the leak path there should be a transition from hydrodynamic to molecular flow. The leak is essentially a free jet (7), and in the ideal case, would produce a shock wave in the low pressure region. The shock wave is expected to rethermalize the velocity distribution so that the species emitted from tho effusion section would have the cosine distribution expected from an effusive source. Since the walls of the effusion section are at 800°-900°C, decomposition to the binary species (Eq. [2]) is also expected.

The measurements of the beam distribution suggest that for the very simple arrangement of Fig. 2, the jet is only partly rethermalized. In Fig. 3 a typical relative distribution for As actually measured at the substrate location is compared to the intensity curve expected for a cosine distribution from the source. Clearly the beam is much more sharply peaked than the cosine distribution and thus still retains some of the character imposed by hydrodynamic flow. This will be corrected in future experiments. However, the source was adequate for delineating the MBE conditions with small (~ 1 cm²) substrate crystals used in this work.

The actual As_2 flux at the target under various AsH_3 input pressures was determined from the thickness of the As layers on the Si calibration targets. Similar experiments were done with the P_2 beams. However, while the As appeared metallic and fully dense, the thin P layers protected by As were less readily observed. The usual α (white) phosphorus that is found when P_4 vapor condenses is a lattice of P_4 molecules (2). It is unlikely that solid would result from the condensation of P_2 molecules on a cold surface. It is more probable that the condensed phosphorus phase is amorphous with a less open structure and a higher density than the P_4 based α phosphorus. The densities of the various allotropic forms of phosphorus range from 1.83 g/cm^{-3} for white phosphorus to 2.7 g/cm^{-3} for the high pressure induced black crystalline modification. The amorphous black and red, and crystalline red forms have densities from 2.2 to 2.5 g/cm^{-3}. Not knowing the density of the solid it is necessary to resort to our knowledge of the As_2 beam flux to determine that for P_2.

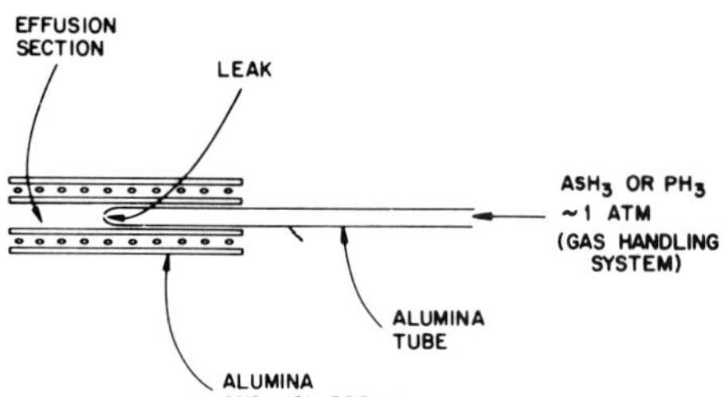

Fig. 2. The leak source

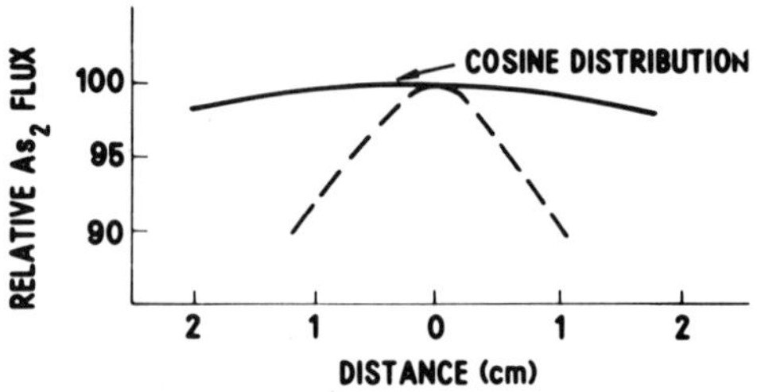

Fig. 3. Approximate relative As_2 flux distribution across the center of the substrate. Pressure on the high pressure side of the source was at about 1 atm. The curve is normalized to unity at the target center. Also illustrated is a cosine distribution.

The leak source under the pressure conditions of this experiment is, in the ideal case, expected to behave like a free jet that is formed by the expansion of a gas through a nozzle into a zero pressure region. For such a source the total flow rate will be linear with pressure and inversely proportional to the half power of the average molecular weight of the gas mixture on the high pressure side (7). In Fig. 4 the dependence of the As_2 beam flux on source input pressure is linear as expected. The dashed curve shows the P_2 flux calculated from the As_2 flux assuming free jet conditions at the leak. The rectangular data points show measured P_2 flux on the assumption that the density of the solid P is 2.7 g/cm^{-3}, the same as the most dense crystalline form. While these ways of arriving at the P_2 flux are certainly very approximate, the agreement in Fig. 4 suggests that the plotted curve is probably correct to within ±25%. That curve is used in the balance of this work.

Gas source MBE of GaAs.—Cho (5) has shown that, depending upon the As_2/Ga flux ratio in the impinging molecular beam, a number of RHEED patterns may be observed during MBE. The easiest to study are those obtained on the (100) surface with the electron beam along the $[\bar{1}\bar{1}0]$ azimuth. Summarizing much previous work, at the start of MBE, surface smoothing accompanied by the appearance of diffraction patterns characteristic of the growth conditions is observed (5, 8). These patterns result from diffraction by several different two-dimensional surface structures for the atoms constituting the crystal surface. These patterns, obtained when the diffracted electron beam strikes a phosphorescent screen, are a series of streaks with characteristic spacing. At relatively high As_2/Ga flux ratios a pattern with streak spacing one-half that of the bulk (1 × 1) crystal structure is observed. This is the one-half order or As-stabilized C (2 × 8) structure (1). With very clean substrates and vacuum systems extremely smooth layers of GaAs have been grown in the As-stabilized regime.

At relatively low As_2/Ga flux ratios a diffraction pattern having three equally spaced streaks between the bulk (1 × 1) streaks is obtained. This is the 1/4 order or Ga-stabilized C (8 × 2) structure. In the Ga-stabilized regime the crystal surface and diffraction pattern gradually degrade as the result of Ga droplet formation on the growing surface. Cho (5, 8) has also observed that in a plot of As_2/Ga flux ratio against $1/T$ the Ga and As stabilized growth regimes are separated by a transition region in which the (1 × 1) or faint transitional diffraction patterns exist. The boundaries of the different regions shifted, depending upon whether the transition was induced by heating or cooling. In this work the Ga and As-stabilized regimes were readily observed. However, they occur without hysteresis and, as shown in Fig. 5, at appreciably higher temperatures.

In experiments with much lower (but unspecified) Ga beam flux, Chang *et al.* (9) observed transitions between the Ga-stabilized, the transitional (3 × 1), and the As-stabilized structures at temperatures intermediate between those reported by Cho (8) and those reported here for As_2/Ga flux ratios in the same range. With comparable Ga beam intensities, but very low As_2/Ga flux ratios that overlap those reported here only at As_2/Ga = 1, the data of Chang *et al.* for the transition from the As-stabilized to the (3 × 1) or 1/3 order transitional structure are at slightly higher temperature. They also report a significant variation of surface transition temperature with absolute beam intensity.

The data of Fig. 5 cover a growth range of 0.45-1.5 μm GaAs/hr, corresponding to an absolute Ga beam flux at the sample ranging from 2.75 to 9.15 × 10^{14} Ga/cm² sec. Transitions from the 1/3 to 1/2 order pattern were gradual, over about a 10° temperature range, without a very precise transition temperature. Transitions to and from the 1/4 order structure were rapid. There seemed to be a region between the 1/3 order and 1/4 order regimes where only the (1 × 1) pattern could be observed. It should be pointed out that with the 5 kV electron gun used in this work the transition (3 × 1) pattern could only be observed under ideal conditions and actually may extend further toward the other regimes. The scatter in the data does not seem to depend upon Ga flux, but is probably related to the As_2 beam nonuniformity. In fact, the slope of the curves appear to become much shallower at As_2/Ga < 1 so that because of the beam nonuniformity shown in Fig. 3 different portions of the crystal surface were in different surface structural regimes. For that reason no attempt was made to study growth for As_2/Ga < 1 in this work.

At the highest As_2/Ga ratio studied, ~10.2, smooth GaAs epitaxy without surface defects was obtained with the substrate temperature as high as 700°C. The transition to nonsmooth (*i.e.*, Ga-droplet coated) surfaces occurred slowly within the transition region and rapidly as soon as the diffraction pattern characteristic of the Ga-stabilized structure appeared. A

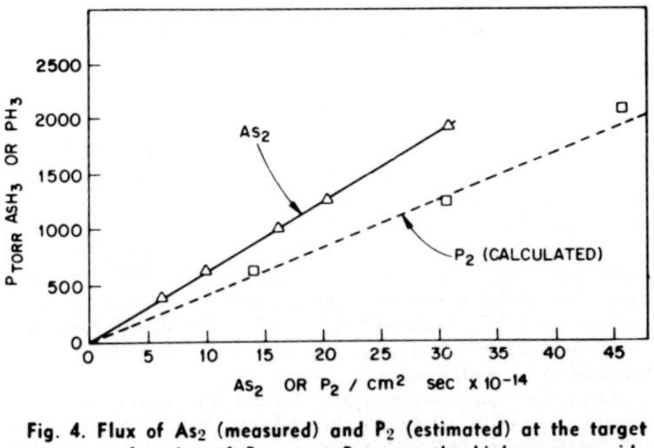

Fig. 4. Flux of As_2 (measured) and P_2 (estimated) at the target center as a function of P_{AsH_4} or P_{PH_3} on the high pressure side of the leak source. The square points were obtained upon the assumption that the density of the deposited phosphorus layer was 2.7 g/cm^{-3}.

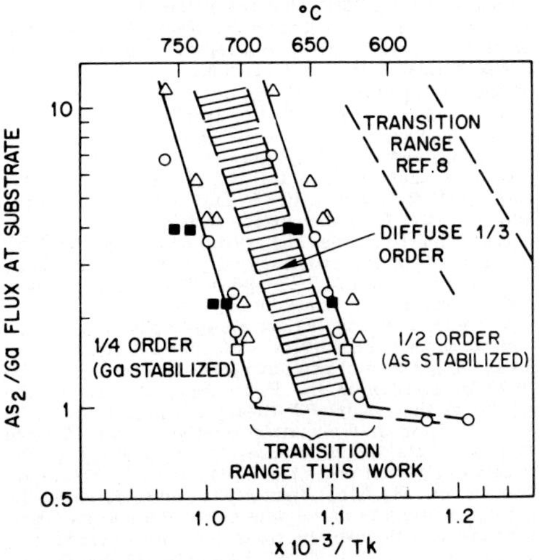

Fig. 5. As_2/Ga molecular beam flux ratio as a function of temperature for transitions between surface structures during MBE of GaAs. The growth rates were: △, 0.45 μm/hr; ○, 0.8 μm/hr; ■, 1.25 μm/hr; and □, 1.5 μm/hr.

clear demarcation from smooth to matte growth was not observed in the transition region. However, the way the experiments were done, changing temperature at a given As_2/Ga flux ratio and then repeating the experiment at different ratios after resmoothing the surface with As-rich growth, made it inconvenient to attempt to observe slow or very subtle surface appearance changes.

Since the apparatus was not designed to give high purity growth, little attempt was made to electrically characterize the grown layers. Several layers were grown on Cr-doped semi-insulating substrates. These samples were deliberately doped with Sn from a separate Sn-containing effusion oven. Hall and several photoluminescence measurements were made. For most of the samples studied ($N_D - N_A$) was in the range 2-4 $\times 10^{17}$ cm^{-3} and Hall mobilities were about 3000 cm^2 V^{-1} sec^{-1} at room temperature. This is about 15% lower than would be expected for the best mobilities for GaAs at that electron concentration. A few samples had mobilities as good as the best reported [*e.g.*, 4200 cm^2 V^{-1} sec^{-1} at $(N_D - N_A) = 1.5 \times 10^{17}$ cm^{-3}]. For these the room temperature photoluminescence peak intensity was as high as that obtained here for equivalently doped liquid epitaxy layers.

Gas source MBE of InP.—Indium phosphide layers were grown on (100) InP surfaces with the same leak source that was used for GaAs growth. During growth RHEED patterns were observed with the electron beam along the $[\bar{1}\bar{1}0]$ azimuth. The 1/2 order C (2×8) pattern could readily be observed on the surface after heating to 550°C with a P_2 flux of $\sim 5 \times 10^{15}$ P_2/cm^2 sec to remove oxide. Opening the shutter to the In oven started growth and the diffraction pattern usually became sharper and completely streaked. The sample surface during growth was visually observed while temperature was increased at a given P_2 and In beam intensity.

Usually a rapid change in gross surface morphology from smooth to matte could be observed with no change in diffraction pattern. The change in the temperature for this smooth-to-matte surface transition as a function of P_2/In flux ratio is given in Fig. 6 for InP growth rates ranging from 0.7 to 1.3 μm/hr (3.75-7.3 $\times 10^{14}$ In/cm^2 sec). With no In beam and a P_2 beam at 7.5 $\times$ 10^{15} P_2 cm^{-2} sec, the smooth-to-matte transition occurred at 600° $\pm$ 10°C. The 1/4 order, C(8×2) pattern could only occasionally be observed when the wafer was rapidly heated to a regime where liquid In was generated on the crystal surface.

In all cases studied the smooth-to-matte transition represented the formation of In droplets on the crystal surface. The surfaces of several InP crystals are shown with phase contrast microscopy in Fig. 7. Figure 7(a) shows the surface of an InP sample heated to 605°C with the P_2 flux at 5 $\times 10^{15}$ P_2 cm^{-2} sec^{-1} for several minutes. Etching of the surface and In droplet formation are clearly visible. The crystal shown in Fig. 7(b) is that used for the experimental point at the molecular beam flux ratio P_2/In = 4.6 in Fig. 6. The run was ended immediately after the smooth-to-matte transition. Figure 7(c) and (d) are micrographs of two locations at opposite ends of the ~1.5 cm wide crystal used for the experimental point at P_2/In = 1.0 in Fig. 6. The 10-20% variation in the P_2/In flux ratio across the crystal as the result of P_2 beam inhomogeneity (Fig. 3) and tilting of the sample relative to the In oven (Fig. 1) yield the differences in morphology at the relatively P_2-rich end [Fig. 7(d)] and the relatively In-rich end, Fig. 7(c). Figures 7(c) and (d) show the great sensitivity of the surface morphology to flux ratio near the smooth-to-matte transition. For several layers grown on the right side of the curve on Fig. 6, surfaces were extremely smooth with some structure barely visible with phase contrast microscopy but at too low a contrast to be photographed. No electrical or optical characterization of the InP layers was done.

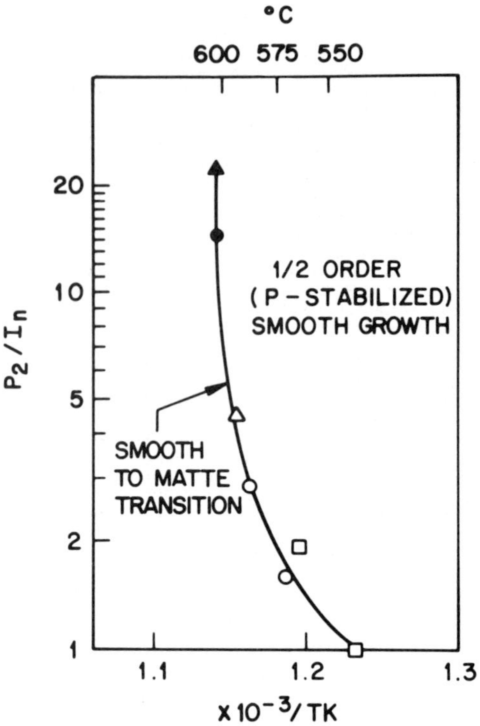

Fig. 6. P_2/In molecular beam flux ratio as a function of temperature for the observed transition from growth of InP with a smooth to growth with a matte surface.

The data of Fig. 6 and the morphological studies represented by Fig. 7 suggest that the limitation represented by the smooth-to-matte transition is simply the more rapid loss of P than In from the crystal lattice at the surface. In other words, the data of Fig. 6 represent the liquidus curve for the In plus P liquid in contact with the InP solid under the P_2 and In flux conditions of the experiment. Since each two impinging In atoms consume one P_2 molecule, the P_2 flux, less half of the In flux, represents the excess flux of P_2 molecules that are equivalent to a partial pressure of P_2 over the InP. The flux F of a vaporizing species can be related to its equilibrium partial pressure P by means of the Langmuir relation

$$F = \frac{P\alpha}{(2\pi mkT)^{1/2}} \quad [3]$$

where α is the accommodation coefficient. If α is taken as constant with T, a plot of log $[(F_{P_2} - 1/2\, F_{In})T^{1/2}]$ against $1/T$ should be equivalent to a plot of log P_{P_2} against $1/T$ and should be linear. The data of Fig. 6 are replotted in Fig. 8. The factor of $T^{1/2}$ is almost constant over the temperature range under consideration and has been omitted. For comparison, the partial pressure of P_2 in equilibrium with the In-P liquidus (10) against $1/T$ is also given in Fig. 8. The two curves appear to be equivalent.

Since the smooth-to-matte transition is actually the liquidus-partial pressure boundary, Fig. 8 represents the maximum InP-MBE growth temperature at any P_2 flux. A leak source with a flux ten times that of the source used in this work is feasible and from Fig. 8 would have an upper InP growth temperature limit of

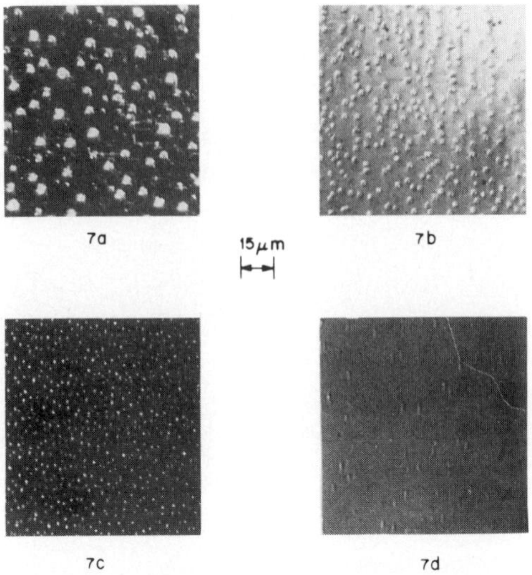

Fig. 7. (a) InP surface after several minutes at 605°C with a P_2 molecular beam flux of 5×10^{15} P_2/cm^2 sec. The smooth-to-matte transition occurred between 600° and 605°C. (b) InP surface after the smooth-to-matte transition during MBE at a P_2/In molecular beam flux ratio of 4.6. (c) and (d) InP surface at two different locations after the smooth-to-matte transition during MBE at a P_2/In flux ratio of 1.0.

650°C at infinitely small growth rate. A small additional P_2 flux with the appropriate In flux would then yield InP growth.

Conclusion

A series of experiments have demonstrated that with an appropriate input device and vacuum system, AsH_3 and PH_3 could be used to generate As_2 and P_2 beams for molecular beam epitaxy of GaAs, InP, and by extension, crystalline solid solutions of GaAs and InP. The leak source devised for this work permitted sufficiently intense beams that GaAs and InP could be grown at temperatures as high as 700°and 600°C, respectively. For InP this is higher than previously reported for MBE of these semiconductors. For GaAs, Gossard and Wiegmann (11) have obtained growth to approximately 750°C by generating an As_2 beam with an auxiliary heater on the end of a solid As source effusion cell. The limitation on the growth temperature of InP, and probably also GaAs by this technique appears only to be the formation of the liquidus as the result of a higher vaporization than flux rate of the group V element at the crystal surface. With modified sources to yield a factor of ten greater flux it is expected that growth at 750°C for GaAs and 650°C for InP could be achieved. Probably more important is the ease of control over beam flux that can be achieved with the gas source. Such a source will be useful for the growth of mixed crystals containing both As and P.

Acknowledgments

The author would like to thank G. Kubiak, J. Robinson, and S. Sumski for their help in building and running the MBE apparatus, and M. Cardillo, A. Y. Cho, and J. C. Bean for their advice and discussions during the course of this work.

Manuscript received May 5, 1980.

Any discusion of this paper will appear in a Discussion Section to be published in the June 1981 JOURNAL. All discussions for the June 1981 Discussion Section should be submitted by Feb. 1, 1981.

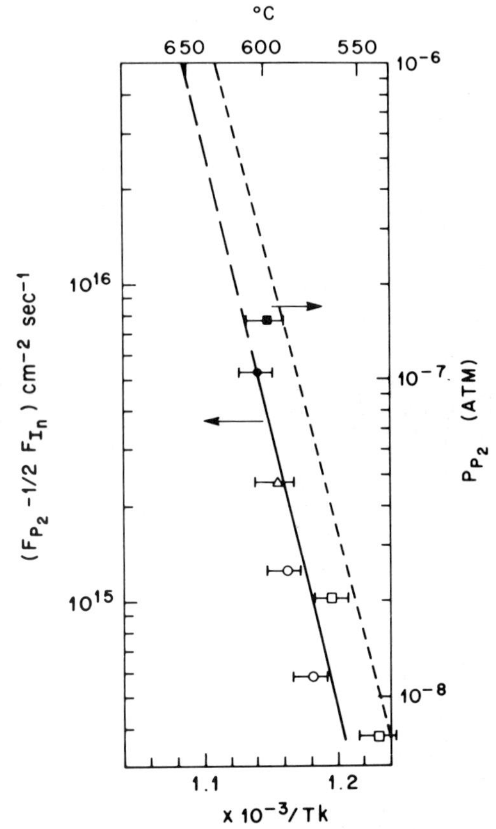

Fig. 8. Excess P_2 flux (F_{P_2} — 1/2 F_{In}) and equilibrium P_2 partial pressure against 1/T at the smooth-to-matte transition during MBE of InP. Except for ■ which is for a P_2 beam only, the experimental points are those of Fig. 6.

Publication costs of this article were assisted by Bell Laboratories.

REFERENCES

1. A. Y. Cho and J. R. Arthur, in "Prog. Solid State Chemistry," Vol. 10, G. Somorjai and J. McCaldin, Editors, p. 157, Pergamon, New York (1975).
2. "Phosphorus: Properties of the Element and Some of Its Compounds," T. D. Farr, Editor, Tennessee Valley Authority, Chemical Engineering Report No. 8, Muscle Shoals, Alabama (1950).
3. H. C. Casey, Jr., A. Y. Cho, and P. A. Barnes, *IEEE J. Quant. Electron.*, **qe-11**, 467 (1975).
4. W. T. Tsang, *Appl. Phys. Lett.*, **34**, 473 (1979).
5. A. Y. Cho, *J. Appl. Phys.*, **47**, 2841 (1976).
6. M. Hansen and K. Anderko, "Constitution of Binary Alloys," McGraw-Hill, New York (1958).
7. J. P. Anderson, in "Molecular Beams and Low Density Gas Dynamics," P. P. Wegener, Editor, p. 1, Marcel Dekker, New York (1974).
8. A. Y. Cho, *J. Vac. Sci. Technol.*, **8**, 531 (1971).
9. L. L. Chang, L. Esaki, W. E. Howard, R. Ludeke, and G. Schul, *ibid.*, **10**, 655 (1973).
10. M. B. Panish, *J. Cryst. Growth*, **27**, 6 (1974).
11. A. C. Gossard and W. Wiegmann, Private communication.

MAN-MADE DIAMONDS

By DRS. F. P. BUNDY, H. T. HALL, H. M. STRONG and R. H. WENTORF, JUN.
Research Laboratory, General Electric Company, Schenectady, New York

IN the 1920's it was quite widely believed that diamond had been made from carbon under conditions of high heat and great pressure. The story was indeed one to capture the imagination. It involved famous chemists, a thoroughly fascinating subject and very striking experimental techniques.

In the recent past, however, informed scientists soberly agree that there has been no certain example of diamond production in the laboratory. More than a century of claims and counterclaims for the synthesis of diamond attest to the fascination of the subject and the extreme difficulty of the experimental techniques. Henri Moissan dissolved sugar charcoal in molten iron and quenched the solution in cold water in order to crystallize the carbon under the great internal pressure supposedly generated by contraction as the mass cooled from the outside. When the metal was dissolved from the solidified melt, there remained traces of transparent material having optical properties similar to those of diamond and giving some carbon dioxide upon combustion. Moissan therefore believed he had made diamond.

In 1880, J. B. Hannay reported he had made diamonds by heating a mixture of hydrocarbons, bone oil and lithium at red heat in sealed wrought-iron tubes. The project was said to be fraught with great difficulty because of exploding tubes; only three out of eighty held. Hannay's identification of his diamonds seemed very conclusive, since it even included a density of 3·5 and a carbon analysis of 97·85 per cent.

Sir Charles Parsons tried for thirty years to synthesize diamonds, including in his experiments many attempts to duplicate the work of Moissan and Hannay. At first Parsons thought he had succeeded; but later, having some doubts, he scrupulously re-investigated all his work on the subject. Parsons's new work clearly demonstrated how he had been misled into regarding as diamond various transparent, singly refracting minerals (spinels) which were very resistant to chemical reagents and would not burn. He finally concluded that neither he nor anyone else had ever succeeded in making diamonds in the laboratory.

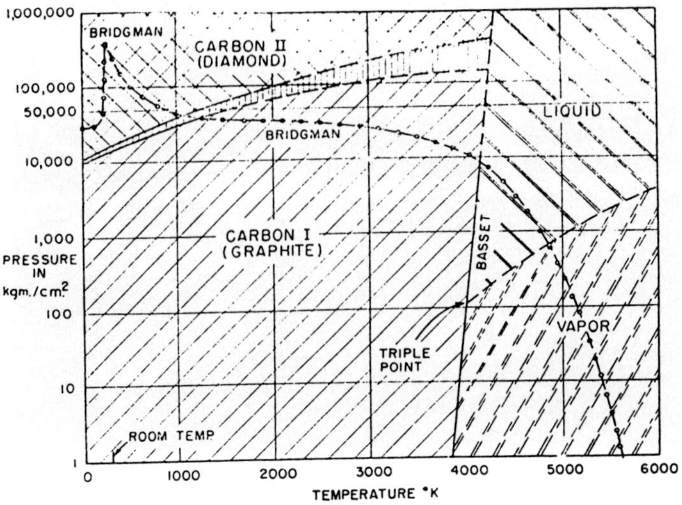

Fig. 1. Phase diagram of carbon

The early claims to diamond synthesis were again reviewed by Prof. N. V. Sidgwick, of Oxford, in 1950, and Henry Eyring, of the University of Utah, in 1952. These authorities conclude that the synthesis of diamond in the laboratory has never been shown to be a success, and that thermodynamic considerations make it seem improbable that diamonds could have been formed under the conditions used in the experiments reported.

For a full account of the arguments the reader is referred to an extensive literature on the subject, a bibliography[1–24] for which is appended.

Suggestions from Thermodynamics

The phase diagram for carbon as now understood is plotted in Fig. 1. Only the boundary between graphite and its vapour at low pressure is accurately established by experimental measurements. The boundaries at higher pressures between graphite, vapour and liquid are based on the work of Basset, and are not fully accepted.

The location of the boundary between the graphite and diamond-stable regions has very little direct experimental evidence at present. The position of the lower temperature part of this boundary was calculated by thermodynamic methods by Rossini and Jessup[25] of the U.S. Bureau of Standards in 1938. The higher temperature part of the boundary shown by broken lines is purely extrapolated from the other part, as the physical data have never been obtained.

The chain-line running across the diagram shows the upper limits of pressure and temperature that are known to have been reached in controlled experiments (this excludes atom bombs) according to the published literature. Prof. P. W. Bridgman, of Harvard University, is the outstanding investigator in this field, working up to more than 400,000 atmospheres at room temperature. He also held temperatures near 3,000° K. at 30,000 kgm./cm.² for very short intervals of time.

The diagram shows that Bridgman has operated well up into the diamond-stable region and has tried many times to synthesize diamonds but without success. He has stated in several of his papers that the reason for his lack of success is that at the relatively low temperatures at which his experiments were carried out the rates of reaction were negligible. He recognized the necessity of going to higher temperatures; but he had not developed apparatus capable of operating at these high pressures and temperatures simultaneously. The maximum conditions he has reported in this direction were 30,000 kgm./cm.² and 2,200°–3,000° K. for periods of one or two seconds.

Bridgman[19] attempted to establish a point on the diamond–graphite equilibrium curve in a series of experiments in which diamonds were heated to about 2,500° K. for a few seconds at pressures which were increased until the diamonds failed to graphitize. This pressure was reached at 30,000 kgm./cm.². He suggested in his paper that this point, 30,000 kgm./cm.² and 2,500° K., might lie near the diamond–graphite equilibrium curve.

In Bridgman's experiment the possibility that pressure reduced the rate of conversion of diamond to graphite cannot be ruled out. If so, the diamonds would fail to graphitize at 30,000 kgm./cm.² in the few seconds at high temperature available. If this be the case, the point 30,000 kgm./cm.² and 2,500° K. is still within the graphite region of stability.

The known evidence about the thermodynamic stability for diamond and graphite led us to believe that diamonds could be formed in the pressure region 30,000–100,000 kgm./cm.² at temperatures somewhere in the range of 1,000°–3,000° K.

Pressure Vessels

Practically all known ultra-high-pressure generators are based on the principle of pushing a piston into a cylinder that encloses the substance to be subjected

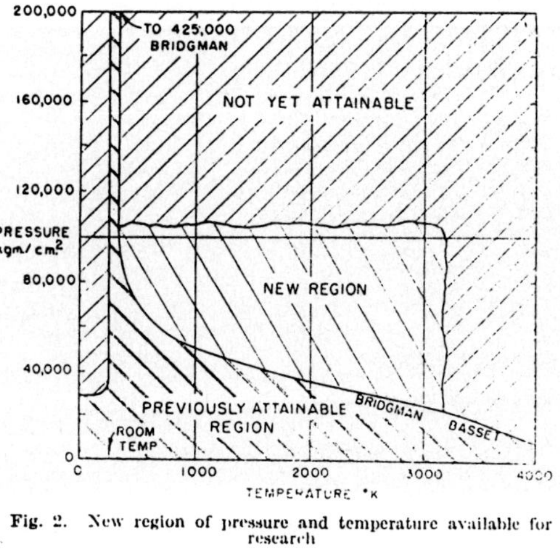

Fig. 2. New region of pressure and temperature available for research

to the pressure. The main factor which limits the maximum pressures that can be reached within vessels is the strength of materials. The strongest steels in the most favourable form and size (piano wire, for example) have ultimate tensile strengths of the order of 14,000–21,000 kgm./cm.^{2}. Sintered carbides, such as 'Carboloy', have compressive strengths of the order of 50,000 kgm./cm.^{2} or more. The pressure required for reasonably rapid synthesis of diamond was thought by our group to be above the compressive strength of 'Carboloy' in the range 50,000–100,000 kgm./cm.^{2}.

Merely making the walls thicker on a pressure vessel contributes very little to its pressure-holding ability after a certain wall thickness is reached. By using multiple support bands on the cylinder part (a technique used years ago in making large gun barrels), and special sealing gasket devices between

(*a*) (*b*)

Fig. 3. Man-made diamonds. (*a*) 1-mm. diamond shown with phonograph needle. (*b*) 0·2–0·5-mm. octahedra

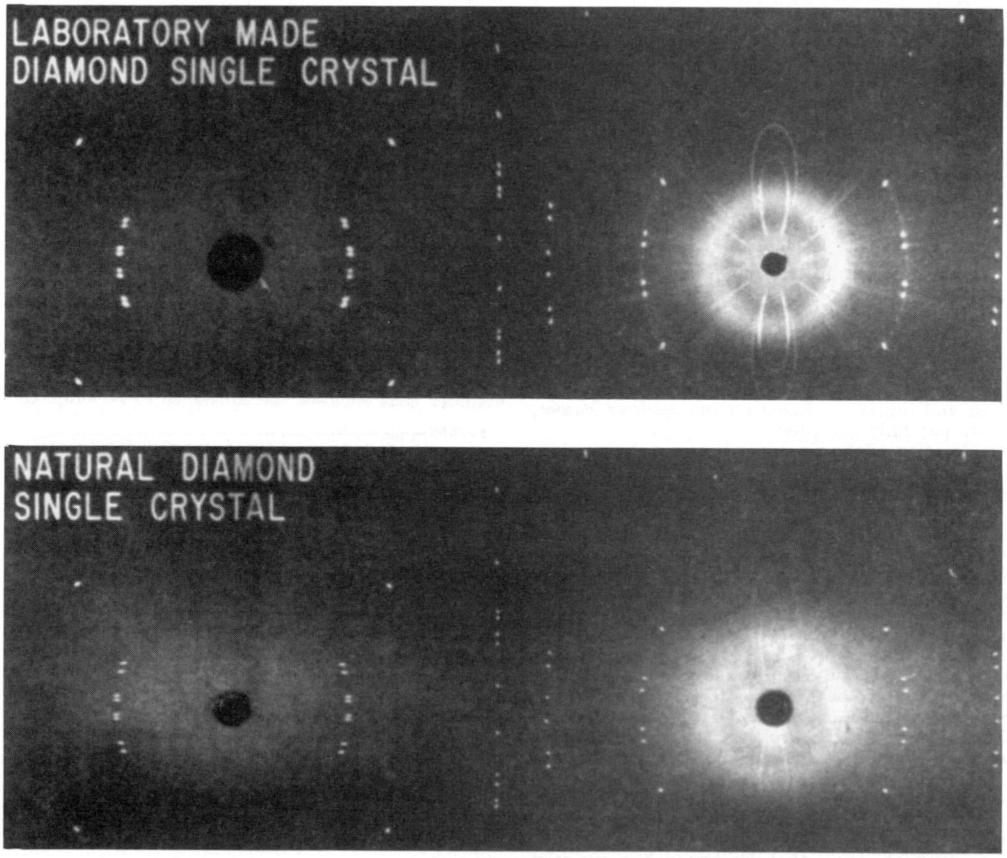

Fig. 4. X-ray diffraction patterns of man-made and natural diamond (powder camera photograph)

the piston and cylinder, Bridgman had developed pressure vessels good for 50,000 kgm./cm.^{2} at room temperature. At high temperatures, materials get weaker and in general the attainable pressures are lower.

By developing some new ways of distributing stress and giving support to critical parts, our research group has succeeded in developing pressure vessels that operate at pressures up to at least 100,000 kgm./cm.^{2} and temperatures in excess of 2,300° K. for hours of continuous operation.

Calibration of Pressures and Temperatures

Pressures of this magnitude are calibrated by making use of four of the electrical resistance transitions observed by P. W. Bridgman[26] in the pressure region up to 80,000 kgm./cm.^{2}. The transitions are bismuth 25,400, thallium 45,000, cæsium 55,000 and barium at 80,000 kgm./cm.^{2}. For pressures greater than 80,000 kgm./cm.^{2}, the melting point of germanium as a function of pressure was used. It was found to decrease linearly with pressure to press loads corresponding to 100,000 kgm./cm.^{2}.

Temperatures inside the pressure cells are measured by use of thermocouples, melting points of materials, change of electrical resistance of wires, Curie points of magnetic materials, thermocolour paints, etc.

Region now Available for Research

In Fig. 2 appears a pressure–temperature diagram, with linear scales on both axes, showing the new region of exploratory research which has been opened up by the development of our new high-pressure and high-temperature apparatus. Note that the newly attainable region covers about as much area as does all the region previously attainable.

Diamond Synthesis

The new region of attainable pressure and temperature extended well into the diamond-stable region as defined in Fig. 1. Under these supposed diamond-stable conditions, processes were discovered which yielded diamonds ranging in size from less than 100 microns to more than 1 mm. along an edge. The various processes have been independently repeated more than one hundred times by a number of workers in this Company. Each time crystals were grown which pass the critical tests for identification with diamond. The present chamber sizes permit the synthesis of up to about ¼ carat of diamond material.

It is not necessary to introduce diamond seeds. Nucleation and growth occur spontaneously and profusely when diamond-stable conditions are reached. In some of the early successful work, diamond seeds were added; but growth occurred independently and apart from the added seed. In a few cases under special conditions, some growth has occurred on the seed crystals.

The man-made diamonds form in many of the different crystal habits found in Nature. These include octahedra, tetrahedra and dodecahedra. Some typical forms are shown in Fig. 3.

Proof that Diamonds were Made

The proof that diamonds were made was based on the following conclusive tests:

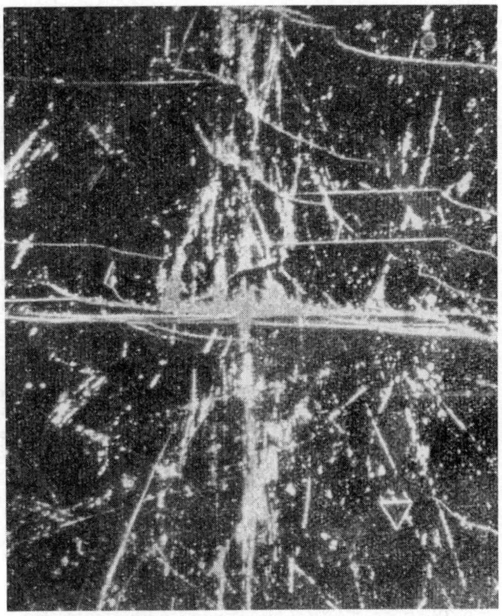

Fig. 5. Scratches made on natural diamond 111 face with man-made diamonds. A large number of scratches appear in a generally vertical direction down through the centre of the picture. The horizontal marks are growth steps on the crystal face. The triangular pit in the lower right-hand corner is also a typical growth mark found on diamond faces

(1) Identity of crystal structure of man-made diamonds to natural diamonds as determined by X-ray diffraction patterns (Fig. 4).

(2) Chemical analysis to show that crystals made were composed of carbon. Those analysed were 86 per cent carbon, 14 per cent inorganic ash identified with the growing media.

(3) Hardness tests. The laboratory-made diamonds were hard enough to scratch the hardest face, the 111 face, of natural diamond (Fig. 5).

(4) Repeatability. The synthesis of diamond has been repeated, entirely independently, by a number of workers in the General Electric Company. The diamonds so made pass the above conclusive tests for diamonds.

In addition, it was shown that the index of refraction for the man-made crystals was within the range 2·40–2·50. Mineral compilations[27] list five isotropic minerals having a refractive index near this range. Natural diamond is one of them and its value is 2·419. The other four are:

	Index of refraction	Mohs' hardness
Franklinite, (Zn,Fe,Mn) O·$(Fe,Mn)_2O_3$	2·36 ±	6
Perovskite, CaO·TiO_2	2·38 ±	5·5
Sphalerite, (Zn,Fe)S	2·428	3·5–4
Eglestonite, Hg_2Cl_2,Hg_2O	2·49 ±	2·3

These four are ruled out as possibilities by the other critical tests.

The result of more than four years effort in this laboratory has been the development of equipment capable of holding pressures and temperatures in the diamond-stable region for hours at a time. Synthesis of diamond has been accomplished more than a hundred times. A number of people have independently repeated the various diamond-making processes successfully. These laboratory-made diamonds can scratch natural diamonds and have a crystal structure identical with natural diamonds.

BIBLIOGRAPHY

Note. References centring about the claims of Hannay and of Moissan, which are the major ones, are dealt with chronologically. Earlier references extending back to 1828 are considered in J. W. Mellor's "Comprehensive Treatise on Inorganic and Theoretical Chemistry", Vol. 5 (Longmans, Green and Co., London, 1924).

[1] Hannay, J. B., *Proc. Roy. Soc.*, **30**, 188 (1880), or *Chem. News*, **41**, 106 (1880).

[2] Story-Maskelyne, N., *The Times*, Feb. 20, 1880, or *Chem. News*, **41**, 97 (1880).

[3] Hannay, J. B., *Proc. Roy. Soc.*, **30**, 450 (1880), or *Nature*, **22**, 255 (1880).

[4] Moissan, H., *C.R. Acad. Sci., Paris*, **118**, 320 (1894), and **123**, 206, 210 (1896).

[5] Hannay, J. B., *Chem. News*, **86**, 173 (1902).

[6] Crookes, W., "Diamonds" (London, 1909).

[7] Ruff, O., *Z. anorg. allgem. Chem.*, **99**, 73 (1917).

[8] Parsons, C. A., *Proc. Roy. Soc.*, **79**, 532 (1907); *J. Inst. Metals*, **20**, 5 (1918); *Phil. Trans.*, A, **220**, 67 (1920).

[9] LeChatelier, H., "Leçons sur le carbone", p. 24 (Paris, 1926).

[10] Desch, C. H., *Nature*, **121**, 799 (1928).

[11] Hershey, J. W. *Trans. Kansas Acad. Sci.*, **31**, 52 (1929), and **40**, 109 (1937); "The Book of Diamonds" (Hearthside Press, 1940).

[12] Bannister, F. A., and Lonsdale, K., *Nature*, **151**, 334 (1943); *Mineral Mag.*, **26**, 309 (1943).

[13] Desch, C. H., *Nature*, **152**, 148 (1943).

[14] Rayleigh, Lord, *Nature*, **152**, 597 (1943).

[15] Travers, M. W., *Nature*, **152**, 726 (1943).

[16] French, J. W., *Nature*, **153**, 112 (1944).

[17] Lonsdale, K., *Nature*, **153**, 669 (1944).

[18] Mellor, D. P., *J. Chem. Phys.*, **15**, 525 (1947); *Research*, **2**, 314 (1949).

[19] Bridgman, P. W., *J. Chem. Phys.*, **15**, 92 (1947).

[20] Rossini, F. D., "Chemical Thermodynamics", 453 (Wiley, 1950).

[21] Sidgwick, N. V., "Chemical Elements and Their Compounds", **1**, 491–3 (Clarendon Press, Oxford, 1950).

[22] Moeller, T., "Inorganic Chemistry", 669 (Wiley, 1952).

[23] Eyring, H., and Cagle, jun., F. W., *Z. Elektrochem.*, **56**, 480 (1952).

[24] Neuhaus, A., *Angew. Chem.*, **66**, 525 (1954).

[25] Rossini, F. D., and Jessup, R. S., *J. Res. Nat. Bur. Stand.*, **21**, 491 (1938).

[26] Bridgman, P. W., *Proc. Amer. Acad. Arts and Sci.*, **81**, 165 (1952).

[27] Palache, Berman and Frondel, "Dana's System of Mineralogy" (J. Wiley, 1951).

Journal of Crystal Growth 76 (1986) 663–672
North-Holland, Amsterdam

PROTEIN SINGLE CRYSTAL GROWTH UNDER MICROGRAVITY

Walter LITTKE and Christina JOHN

Chemisches Laboratorium der Universität Freiburg, D-7800 Freiburg, Fed. Rep. of Germany

Received 5 October 1985; manuscript received in final form 1 April 1986

Crystal growth conditions for proteins under microgravity were investigated with two model compounds (β-galactosidase and lysozyme). The single crystals obtained have been found to be significantly larger than those prepared in the same environment on earth.

Solving the three-dimensional molecular structure of proteins by X-ray diffraction analysis helps to understand their manifold functions (catalysis, transport, supporting functions, immunity, etc.). An essential condition for such structural investigations is the availability of sufficiently large (about 0.5 mm in each dimension) and well shaped single crystals. Especially disadvantageous for such protein crystal growth is sudden multiseed formation: Instead of the desired few large crystals numerous small crystallites are formed which are useless for X-ray analysis. Experiments have shown that this undesirable effect is mainly due to convection which can be almost completely suppressed by crystallization in gels (fig. 1).

Here, however, fragile protein crystals especially those growing as needles break and thereby destroy themselves touching the tight network of the gel (fig. 2).

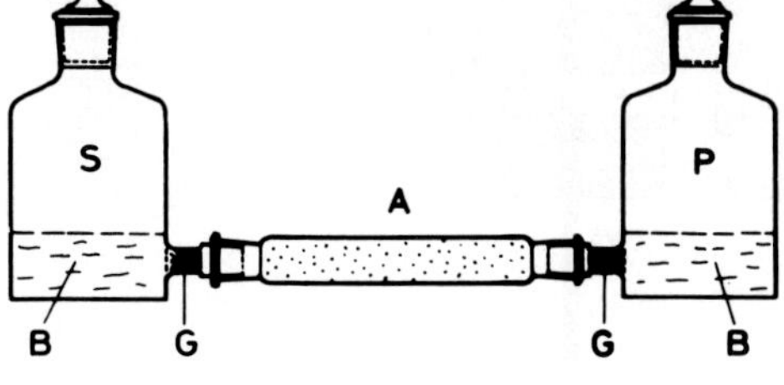

Fig. 1. Equipment for gel crystallization of proteins. P = protein solution in buffer (B); S = salt solution in buffer; G = glass wool plug; A = polyglucane gel or polyacrylamide gel in buffer.

So it seemed sensible to look for conditions under which three solutions of different densities ($\rho_B < \rho_P < \rho_S$), a protein solution (P), a salt solution (S) and a gel-free buffer solution (B) can be simultaneously and slowly combined without any turbulence. Since the middle portion (B) is the lightest, such an experiment cannot be carried out by layering the solutions on top of each other (fig. 3).

All attempts to increase the density (ρ_B) of the middle layer by loading agents (salts, carbohydrates, etc.) led to loss of enzyme activity. Therefore conditions of microgravity where chosen in order to avoid differences in density ($\rho_B \sim \rho_P \sim \rho_S \sim 0$ g cm^{-3}). A schematic representation of the proposed experimental device is given in fig. 4.

Before the experiments, protein solution and salt solution are separated by a sliding divice. The buffer solution is kept in a second system of containers. All containers having been filled free of bubbles are closed to the outside by elastic membranes (M) which allow compensation of pressure. When microgravity is reached, the sliding device is moved without vibration in order to connect the three different containers. Now counter-diffusion of P and S across the buffer solution B takes place. The slowly diffusing salt ions cause the protein molecules to crystallize.

Since thermal changes could occur during this process and even in the absence of gravitational forces lead to undesirable convection, preliminary short-term experiments (6 min microgravity) were

0022-0248/86/$03.50 © Elsevier Science Publishers B.V.
(North-Holland Physics Publishing Division)

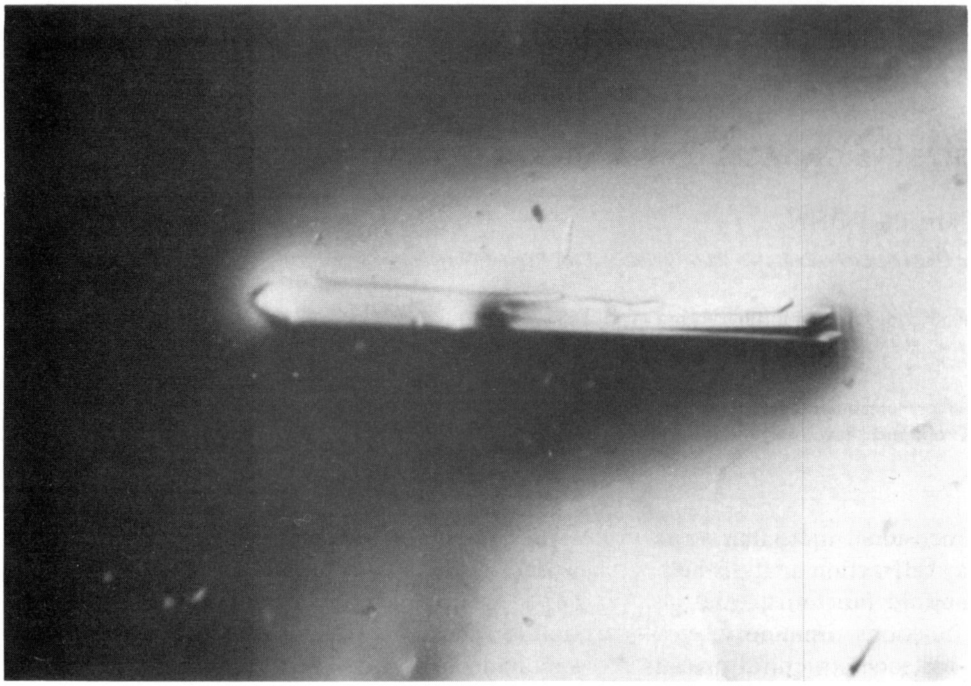

Fig. 2. Damaged single crystal (length 2 mm) of β-galactosidase grown in gel.

carried out using sounding rockets (European TEXUS programs) in order to study the diffusion process by schlieren optics. The high molecular weight protein β-galactosidase and the salt ammonium sulfate both dissolved in 0.033 molar phosphatebuffer, pH = 6.4, were used for testing. The experiments under microgravity showed in contrast to those under terrestrial conditions a strictly laminar diffusion process (figs. 5 and 6).

Convection and turbulence could only be observed when payload began reentering the gravitational sphere of the earth. Besides these observations, a totally unexpected result was obtained: after only 6 min of gravitation-free conditions, several single crystals of β-galactosidase were formed (fig. 7).

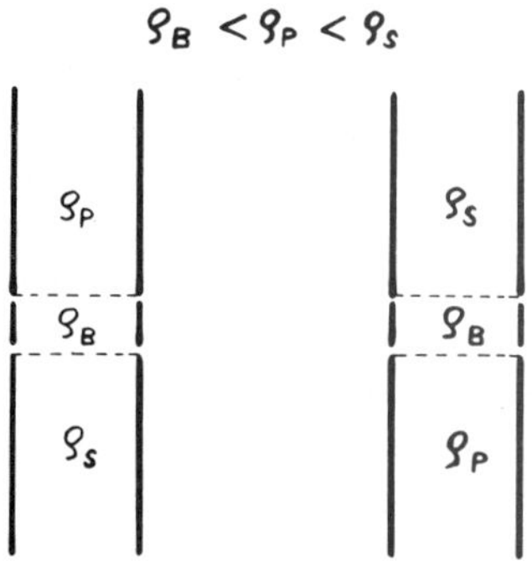

Fig. 3. Layer arrangement of solutions B (buffer), P (protein) and salt (S). ρ = density.

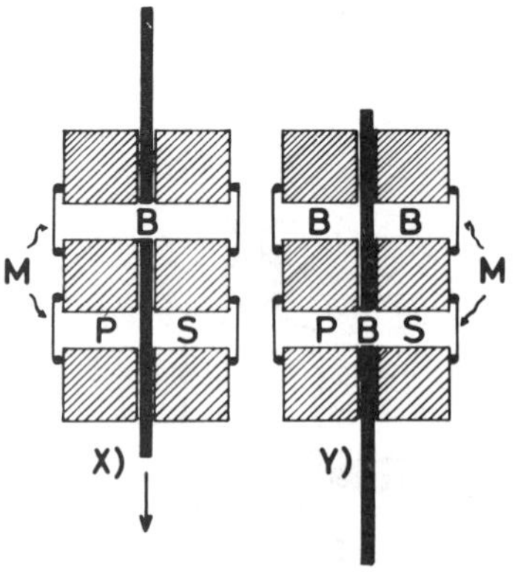

Fig. 4. Device for convection-free protein crystallization in space. X = starting position; Y = end position for initiating diffusion; B = buffer solution; P = protein solution; S = salt solution; M = membranes; black shaded middle section = slide.

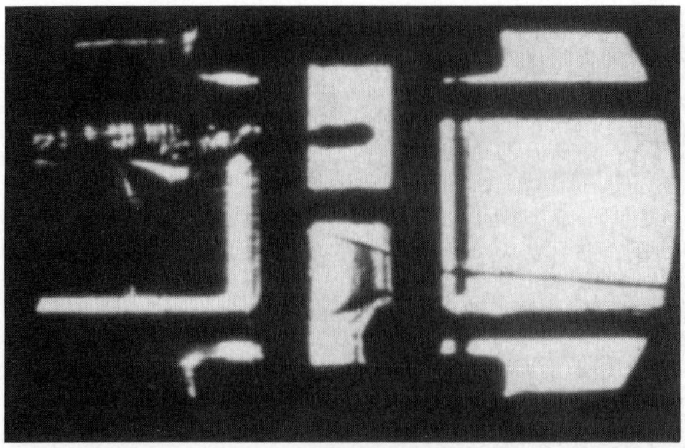

Fig. 5. Diffusion process (to the right protein, in the middle buffer and to the left salt) under terrestrial conditions. High rate of convection.

Most of the material was amorphous. The crystals, examined by microscopy under polarized light (fig. 8), were rod shaped and averaged approximately 100 μm in length. Due to the short time of crystallization, however, the crystals were of inferior quality but still comparable to ones which are obtained under terrestrial conditions in several days.

The strange effect of an increased tendency for crystallization under microgravity may in this case be assigned to existing areas of molecular ordering under the given high protein concentrations (30 mg/cm^3). It is plausible that under conditions free of turbulence such preordered clusters can aggregate more easily into crystalline material whereas strong convections under terrestrial conditions may cause breaking up into smaller size particles

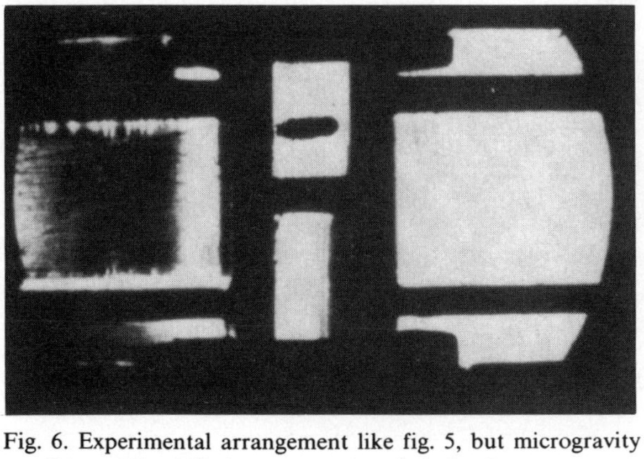

Fig. 6. Experimental arrangement like fig. 5, but microgravity conditions. The diffusion process is strictly laminar.

or even into separate molecules which naturally take longer time for reordering and eventual crystallization [1].

Our assumption could be experimentally verified. Fig. 9 shows the separation of highly purified β-galactosidase in high concentration (gel electrophoresis). The right-hand side band is the marker bromophenolblue, the broad band tetrameric β-galactosidase (G_1). The three left-hand side bands (G_a, G_b, G_c) are higher molecular weight aggregates of β-galactosidase. All proteins represented by the bands show activity towards o-nitrophenyl β-D-galactopyranoside (ONPG). If the bands before fixing are cut out and again submitted to electrophoresis, the same distribution of bands as described before can be observed (fig. 10). This is proof that between native β-galactosidase and higher molecular weight aggregates, an equilibrium exists.

Considerably increased periods of time, advantageous for crystallization experiments were available in the SPACELAB program. Here we used two proteins with widely differing molecular weights in order to mark the extreme limits of future experiments with other proteins which will fall in between the given range of molecular weights:

β-Galactosidase (β-D-galactoside galactohydrolase, EC. 3.2.1.23), molecular weight 465 000 D;

Lysozyme (mucopeptide N-acetylmuramoylhydrolase, EC. 3.2.1.17), molecular weight 14 307 D.

The structure of β-galactosidase, the key enzyme of genetic investigations is, for lack of suitable crystals, still unknown, whereas the structure of lysozyme was solved 19 years ago [2].

In order to gain sufficient material of extreme purity, an essential condition for single crystal growth, we worked out special methods [3,4]. The apparatus used in SPACELAB experiment [1,4] corresponds to the one previously described. With this device, which operates automatically in order to reduce manual operations by scientific astronauts as far as possible, several studies can be carried out in one experiment (fig. 11):

(a) Crystal growth at constant temperatures (20 °C) in a stabilizer.

(b) Crystal growth in an increasing linear temperature gradient (−4 to 20 °C) because the solubility

Fig. 7. Single crystal of β-galactosidase grown in space over a period of 6 min together with amorphous material.

Fig. 8. Examination of two β-galactosidase crystals under polarized light.

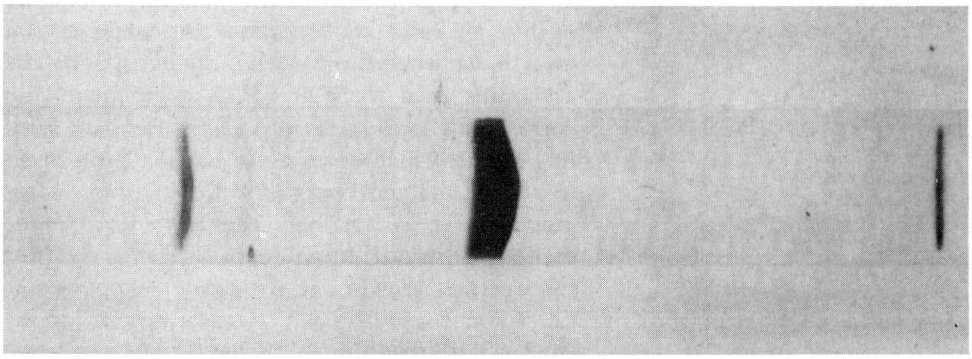

Fig. 9. Electrophoresis of highly concentrated β-galactosidase in polyacrylamide gel.

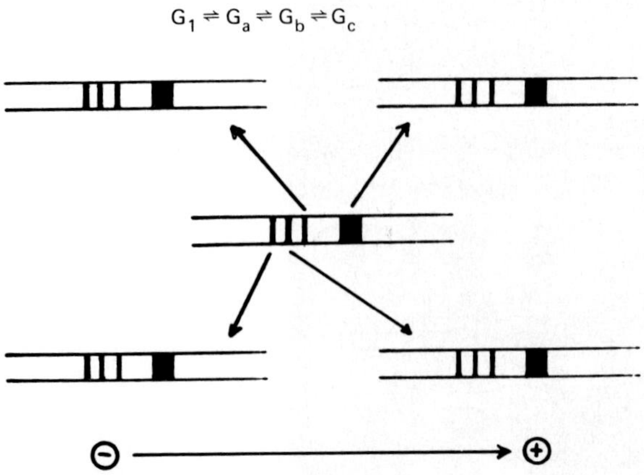

Fig. 10. Equilibrium between native β-galactosidase and higher molecular weight aggregates.

of many proteins decreases in presence of salt with increasing temperature.

(c) Use of differing protein concentrations.

(d) Influence of wide and narrow fronts of diffusion.

Fig. 12 shows one of the two acrylic blocks, each containing four samples for crystallization. To suppress protease activities which may cause protein degradation, the blocks were kept near 0°C in a special Dewar storage container, kept cold by melting ice without any external energy supply and transported as such into the spacecraft where after reaching conditions of microgravity they were removed from the cooling container and placed manually into the apparatus designed for the crystallization experiment (fig. 13). Operating a switch triggered the machinery, set at the different initial temperatures (20°C in the stabilizer, −4°C in the freezer) and started the process of diffusion and crystallization.

After the space mission was terminated (~ 150 h) and the sample containers handed over, the events during space flight were analysed to give the following results:

(a) Protein crystallization takes place in the protein chamber because of the low velocity of diffusion of the protein molecules (compare left-hand side of fig. 14).

(b) Single crystals are significantly larger than those obtained in the same apparatus but under terrestrial conditions. β-galactosidase shows a 27-fold increase and lysozyme a 1000-fold increase in volume. The average length of the β-galactoside needles is 0.6 mm and the average length of the

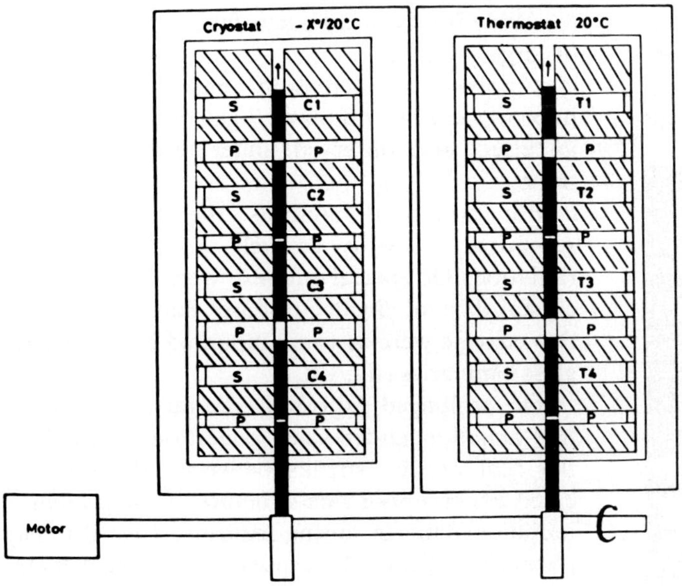

Fig. 11. SPACELAB facility for crystal growth studies of lysozyme and β-galactosidase; X = 4; C1 to C4 and T1 and T2 = containers for β-galactosidase; S = salt containers; T3 and T4 = lysosyme containers; P = buffer containers.

Fig. 12. Plexiglass block with protein/buffer/salt containers for enzyme crystallization.

edges of the lysozyme crystals is 1.2 mm (figs. 15 and 16).
(c) The crystalline material is well shaped and, as microscopic examinations under polarized light show, has the same crystal habit as that grown under terrestrial conditions in the same apparatus.
(d) Whereas β-galactoside needles are almost totally found free floating in the mother liquor, about

Fig. 13. Protein crystal growth facility (freezer and stabilizer).

90% of the lysozyme crystals are attached to the wall. The free floating lysozyme crystals (10%) are of significantly better habit than those grown an the wall.
(e) Wide fronts of diffusion favour the formation of large crystals.
(f) Applying an increasing temperature gradient improves crystallization of β-galactosidase. This is an effect also observed under terrestrial conditions.

For structural analysis the crystals were submitted to X-ray as well as to synchrotron radiation. Of special interest were the unknown crystal data of β-galactosidase. Single crystals of this enzyme were as usual mounted in thin-walled glass capillaries (fig. 17).

On prolonged exposure (several hours) to Cu Kα radiation under usual conditions (1.5418 Å), the film results (streaks between reflexes) indicated either a poor fine structure of the protein or radiation damage during exposure (fig. 18). This phenomenon could be explained using high energy irradiation (1.283 Å) and correspondingly shorter exposure times (some minutes). Then the single

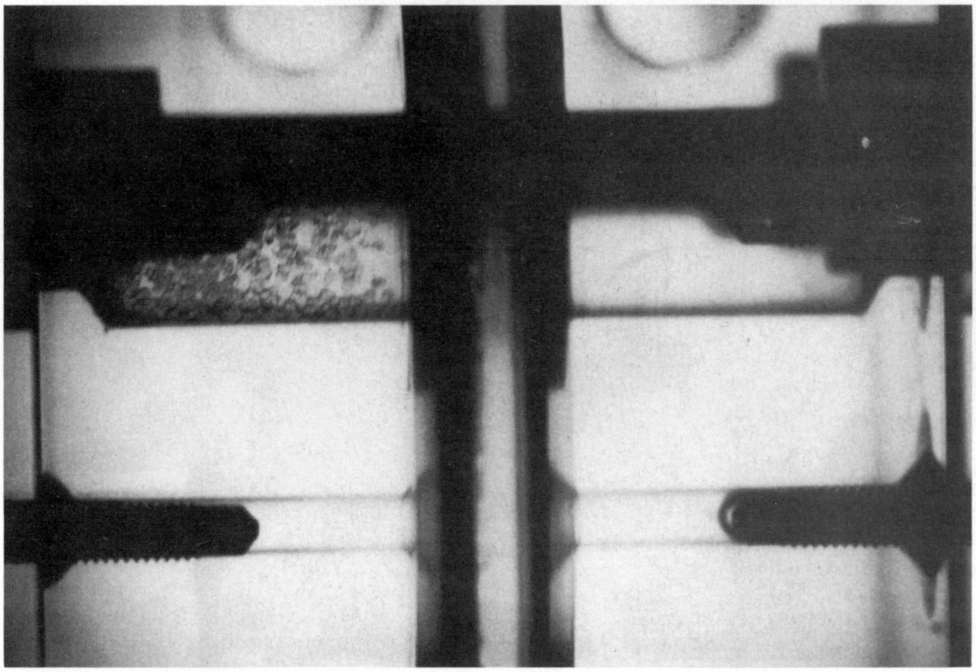

Fig. 14. Protein chamber with large single crystals of lysozyme (left-hand side) and salt chamber (right-hand side). Edge length of crystals: ca. 1.2 mm.

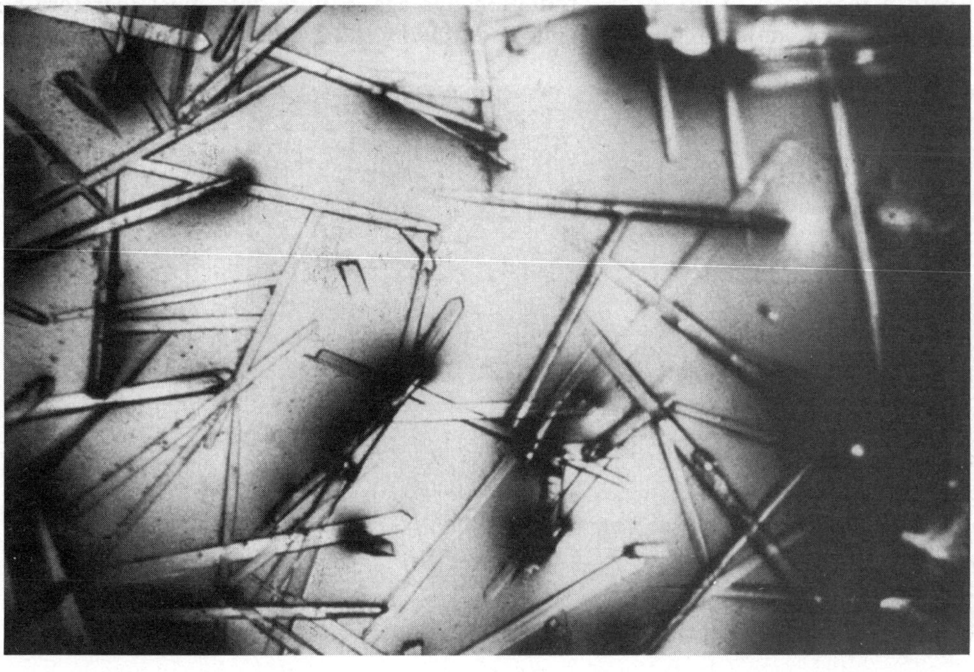

Fig. 15. Single crystals of β-galactosidase produced in SPACELAB. Crystal length: ca. 0.6 mm.

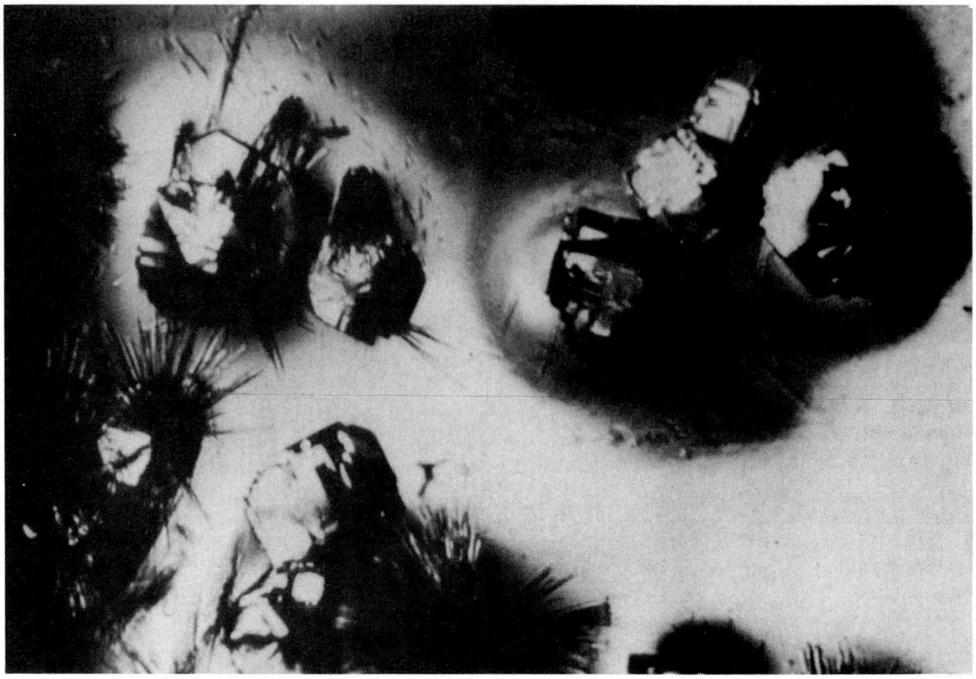

Fig. 16. Crystals of lysozyme produced in SPACELAB. Average edge length of crystals: 1. 2 mm.

crystals remained of good quality and gave distinct reflexes (fig. 19) with a resolution of up to 4.2 Å, demonstrating that diffuse reflexes obtained with Cu Kα radiation were probably due to radiation damage. Future data must therefore be collected only by using synchrotron radiation. The

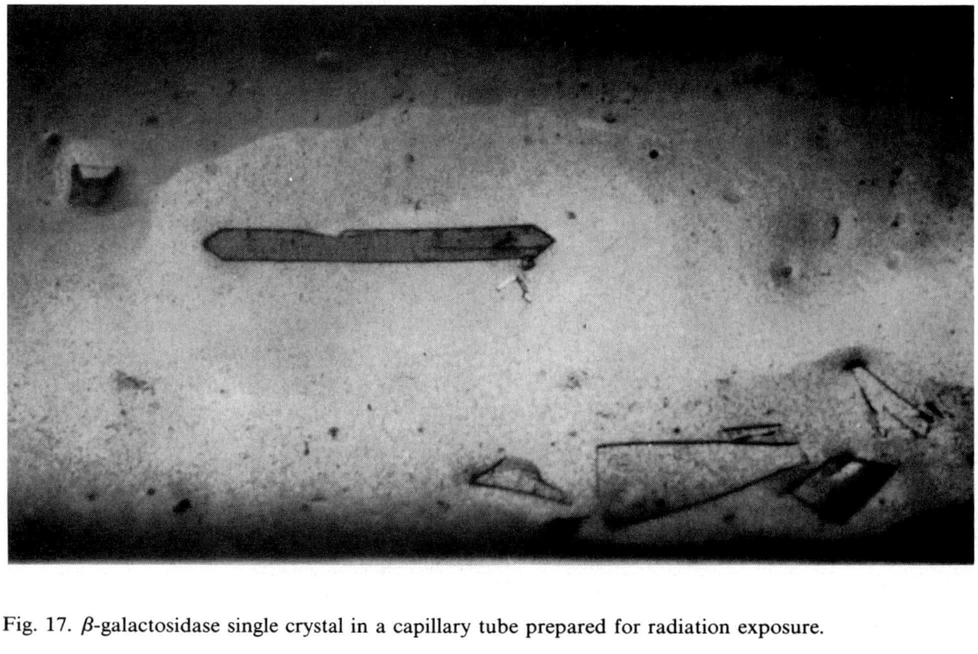

Fig. 17. β-galactosidase single crystal in a capillary tube prepared for radiation exposure.

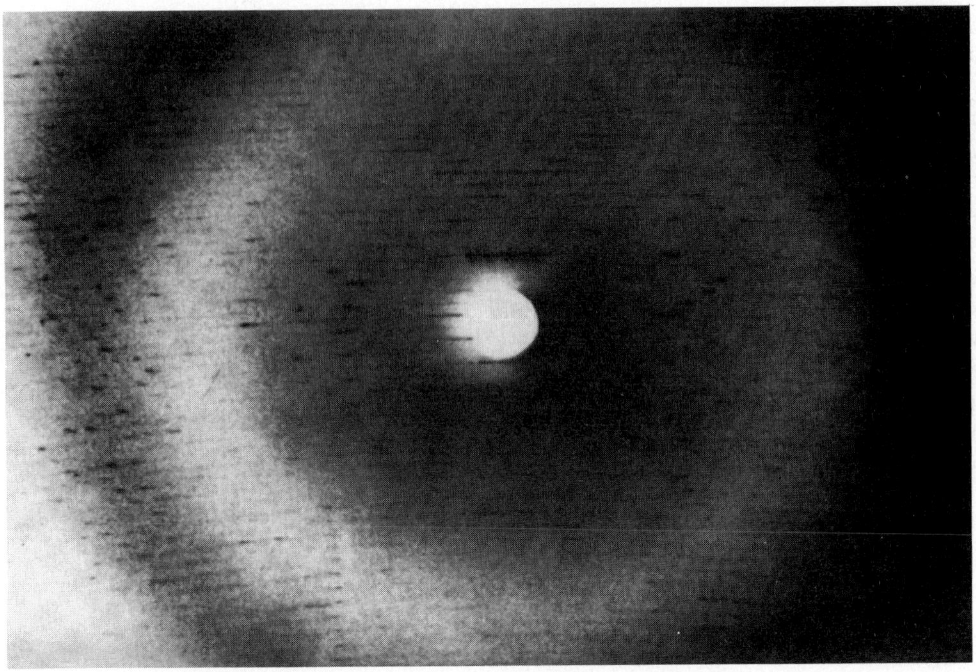

Fig. 18. X-ray (1.5418 Å) photograph of β-galactosidase. Radiation damage.

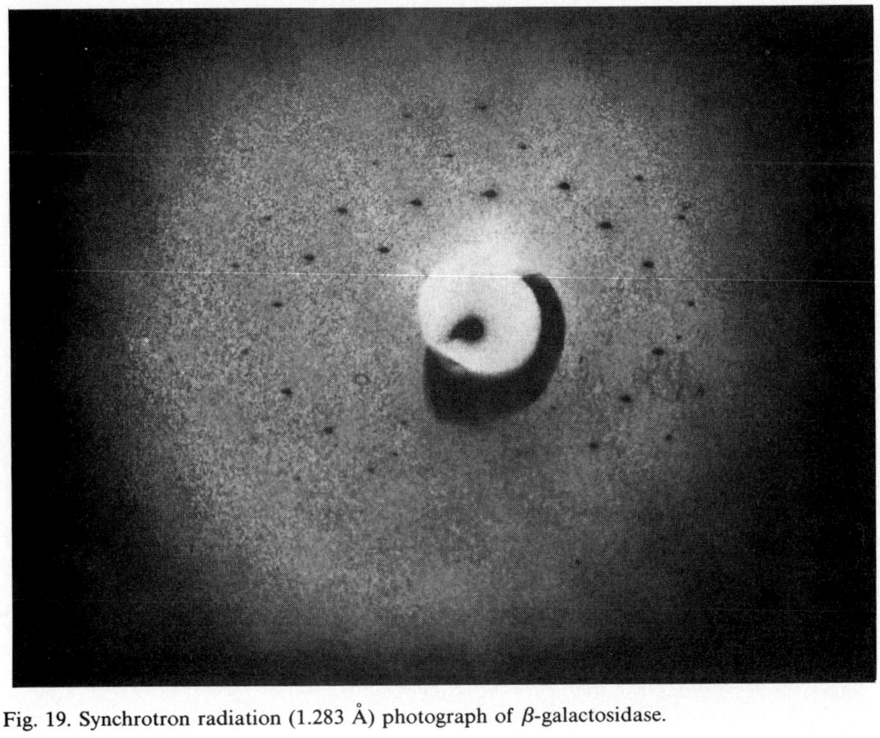

Fig. 19. Synchrotron radiation (1.283 Å) photograph of β-galactosidase.

terrestially grown crystals were not large enough for radiation investigations. Therefore comparison between space-grown and earth-grown crystals was not possible. Crystal data for β-galactosidase (unit cell, symmetry, space group, density, asymmetric unit, number of asymmetric units, etc.) was determined. The results will be published elsewhere.

By organic synthesis a competitive inhibitor carrying a heavy atom could be prepared. The enzyme shall be crystallized in the presence of this compound. We expect that investigation of the enzyme–inhibitor complex will tell us something about distances between active sites and their spacial arrangement within the enzyme molecule.

We thank the Bundesministerium für Forschung und Technologie, Bonn, for financial support and DESY, Hamburg, for synchrotron measurement.

References

[1] W. Littke and Chr. John, Z. Flugwiss. Weltraumforsch. 6 (1982) 325.

[2] C.C.F. Blake, L.N. Johnson, G.A. Mair, A.C.T North, D.C. Phillips and V.R. Sarma, Proc. Roy. Soc. (London) B167 (1967) 378.

[3] W. Littke, Jahresbericht zu 01 QV 626 BMFT, Bonn (1977).

[4] W. Littke, 17th Aerospace Sciences Meeting, New Orleans, 1979, AIAA paper 79-0311.

A PRISMATIC SUBSTRUCTURE FORMED DURING SOLIDIFICATION OF METALS[1]

By J. W. Rutter[2] and B. Chalmers[3]

ABSTRACT

Single crystals of tin grown from the melt under a wide range of conditions are shown to exhibit a fibrous structure which manifests itself as parallel ridges ("corrugations") on the free surface of the specimen and as a hexagonal network ("hexagonal cells") on the growing solid–liquid interface. The center of each cell projects into the liquid. Segregation of impurities is shown to occur during solidification in a manner intimately related to the structure. The structure is suppressed by growth at low speeds or under a steep temperature gradient. The size and regularity of the elements of the structure depend upon speed of growth, temperature gradient, and impurity content. A theory is advanced which accounts for the origin and observed properties of the structure. This theory shows that the structure consists essentially of a particular distribution of impurities resulting from nonequilibrium solidification.

INTRODUCTION

This research was undertaken as part of a study of solidification of metals at the Department of Metallurgy, University of Toronto. Its purpose was to investigate a particular substructure known to occur in metal crystals grown from the melt. The results of two other pieces of research, forming part of the solidification study, have been reported previously. One concerns another substructure known as "striations" (9), which occurs in crystals grown from the melt; the other concerns dendritic growth (11).

The structure to be described here consists of parallel elements of rodlike form, having the appearance shown in Fig. 1 when viewed from a direction perpendicular to their axis. They form in a direction approximately parallel to the direction of growth. The cross section of each element is approximately hexagonal, as shown in Fig. 2. This structure was observed as early as 1934 by Buerger (1), who referred to it as a "lineage structure". His experimental information was not sufficient to allow a satisfactory explanation of its existence to be given. The most recent work concerning this phenomenon is that of Pond and Kessler (7) reported in 1951. These workers recognized only thermal effects and, as a result, their experiments were incomplete. They failed to give a satisfactory explanation of the existence and observed properties of the structure. A criticism of their paper will be published elsewhere (4).

In contrast to the work of Pond and Kessler, the present work consists of an investigation of the phenomenon in terms of thermal, constitutional, and crystallographic conditions. This broader approach to the problem has made it possible to develop a theory which accounts for the observed facts.

[1] *Manuscript received July 15, 1952.*
Contribution from the Department of Metallurgical Engineering, University of Toronto, Toronto, Ontario.

[2] *Graduate Student, Department of Metallurgical Engineering, University of Toronto.*
[3] *Professor of Physical Metallurgy, Department of Metallurgical Engineering, University of Toronto.*

MATERIALS AND METHODS

The principal material used in this research was "Chempur" tin, supplied by Messrs. Johnson, Matthey and Company, of London, England. The purity of this material is stated to be 99.986%, with the major detectable impurities lead, bismuth, iron, antimony, and copper.

Specimens were produced by growth from the melt, using the technique described by Chalmers (2). This technique allows growth of specimens consisting of a controlled number of crystals, each with a predetermined crystallographic orientation. This is accomplished by growing specimens from "seed" crystals of known orientation. Growth is carried out in a horizontal graphite container or "boat". This has the important advantage of yielding a specimen with one surface which solidifies out of contact with the container. The heat required to melt the tin is supplied by a small nichrome-wound furnace mounted on a trolley and placed around the boat. Removal of the furnace at a controlled rate allows solidification to proceed at the desired speed. The rate of movement of the interface separating solid and liquid, that is, the speed of solidification, depends upon the rate at which the latent heat of fusion can be conducted away from the interface into the solid. The speed of solidification is not, in general, equal to the speed of movement of the furnace. With this method of growth, heat flow in the specimen is approximately linear. The technique has been used for many metals, with modifications according to the temperature, atmosphere, and boat material required in each case. A complete description of this technique has recently been given by Chalmers (3).

In order to record the speed of growth of a specimen, the surface of the liquid was disturbed at regular intervals during growth, causing a ripple to be frozen in at the position occupied by the top of the solid–liquid interface at that time (9).

The solid–liquid interface was exposed for subsequent observation by rapidly pouring the liquid out of the boat at the desired stage of growth (11). This was accomplished either by tilting the boat or by removing a graphite stop to allow the liquid to run out.

Determinations of crystallographic orientation were made by means of back reflection Laue X-ray diffraction photographs. These were analyzed by the method due to Greninger (6).

Modifications of the general techniques noted above, and also other special techniques, were used in this research. They will be described in connection with the observations which they yielded.

EXPERIMENTAL OBSERVATIONS

Introduction

For the sake of convenience, a definition of speeds of growth from the melt follows:

Designation	*Speed Range*
Slow	Less than 1 mm. per min.
Intermediate	1 mm. per min. to 13 mm. per min., approximately
Fast	Greater than 13 mm. per min., approximately

These limiting speeds mark changes in the structure found in specimens grown by the method described previously. However, these structural changes depend upon factors other than speed. Therefore, the definition is restricted to specimens grown under conditions closely similar to those usually used in this research. Modification of the limiting speeds given above will be dealt with subsequently.

The top, free surface of unetched crystals of tin grown in the intermediate speed range shows a "corrugated" appearance at low magnification (Fig. 1). The corrugations (as they will be called hereafter) are actually ridges running along the surface of the specimen. They are not visible on the sides of the specimen which solidified in contact with the graphite boat. Examination of the interface exposed by decanting the liquid metal during growth in the intermediate speed range reveals a network of cells, roughly hexagonal in shape, as shown in Figs. 2, 3, and 4. Using oblique lighting, it was found that the center of each cell projects into the liquid metal with respect to the boundary of the cell. This observation was confirmed by making a light scratch on the decanted interface of a specimen with a glass rod which had been drawn to a fine point. Examination with a microscope showed that, where the scratch was not too deep, it existed only in the center of each cell crossed, and it was therefore concluded that the boundaries are depressed with respect to the centers of the cells.

The question arises whether the structures described above are surface or volume phenomena. In order to answer this question, a tin crystal was cut chemically with ferric chloride etching solution. The etching reagent was applied locally to the specimen by means of a fine nylon thread which was driven around two pulleys, through a tray of etching solution, and over the specimen. Pressure of the thread on the specimen was very light, so that it only served to convey the fresh etching solution to the cut being made and to get rid of the reaction products. This method of cutting leaves a strain-free surface. Fig. 5 is a photomicrograph of the surface obtained by cutting a tin crystal in this manner, approximately perpendicular to the specimen axis. It shows that the cellular structure persists in the interior of the crystal. Fig. 6 was obtained from the surface exposed by cutting electrolytically a silver crystal which showed the corrugation structure. These photomicrographs show that the cellular structure persists in the interior of the crystal and is, therefore, a volume phenomenon. It is concluded that the corrugations and cells are two views of one structure consisting of parallel elements of prismatic form, each having a cross section which is approximately hexagonal.

FIG. 13. (Upper left) Decanted interface of tin crystal showing enlarged cells which appear at fast speeds of growth. Speed of growth 12 mm. per min. Magnification 75×. Bright field illumination.

FIG. 14. (Upper right) Branching of corrugations on free surface of tin bicrystal. Magnification 75×. Bright field illumination.

FIG. 15. (Center) Autoradiograph of lead crystal containing antimony. Magnification 4×. Copied from original by transmitted light.

FIG. 16. (Lower left) Decanted interface of tin crystal, showing suppression of the cellular structure by a steep temperature gradient. Temperature gradient in liquid during growth was 75 C.° per cm. Speed of growth 2.8 mm. per min. Magnification 75×. Bright field illumination.

FIG. 17. (Lower right) Area adjacent to Fig. 16. Disappearance of the cells was caused by the steep temperature gradient present.

Corrugation and Cell Size

Several specimens were produced in which the [110] direction was parallel to the specimen axis and the (001) plane parallel to the top, free surface. Conditions of growth were the same for each except for the modifications imposed by withdrawing the furnace at a different rate in order to obtain a different speed of growth for each specimen. Measurements of the spacing between corrugations were made on these samples by using a microscope with a travelling stage. It was found that the spacing is a function of the speed of growth, becoming smaller as the speed is increased. This relation is shown in Fig. 18. Each point plotted represents the average of approximately 15 measurements made on one specimen.

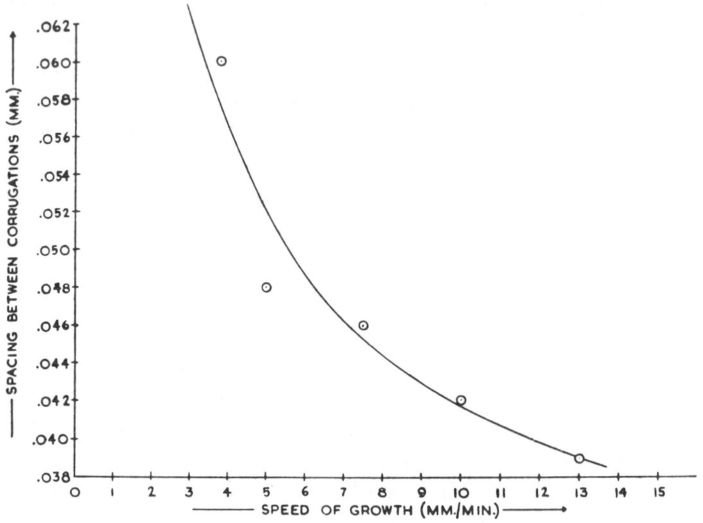

FIG. 18. Corrugation spacing vs. speed of growth.

A decanted interface was obtained on each crystal of this series. From photomicrographs of these interfaces, the average cell diameter was measured. It was found to correspond, within experimental error, to the measurements of corrugation spacing as a function of speed of growth given in Fig. 18.

As shown by Figs. 2, 3, and 4, the cells in any one specimen may vary considerably in size. The corresponding corrugation spacing behaves in the same way. It must, therefore, be noted that the measurements above give only the average dimensions. The regularity of size and shape of the cells which is evident at speeds of about 5 mm. per min. is lost, to some extent, at higher and lower speeds.

No measurements were made of the extent to which the centers of the cells project into the liquid with respect to the cell boundaries. However, for the intermediate speed range, it is estimated that this extent, on the decanted interface is of the order of one-tenth of the cell diameter. It was observed that the average height of the cell centers increases as the speed of growth increases in this speed range. It should be noted that if the cell boundaries take the form of very narrow grooves during growth, then part of the liquid which they contain will be retained by surface tension when decantation is carried out. Therefore, the depth of the cell boundaries observed on a decanted interface may not be the same as that which was in existence during growth of the crystal.

Direction of Formation of Corrugations

Several crystals were grown in which the (001) plane was parallel to the free surface of the specimen and the [110] direction made an angle ϕ with the specimen axis. In each case, the speed of growth was varied along the length of the specimen. Measurements of corrugation direction were made on these specimens with a microscope fitted with a rotating stage which was calibrated in tenths of a

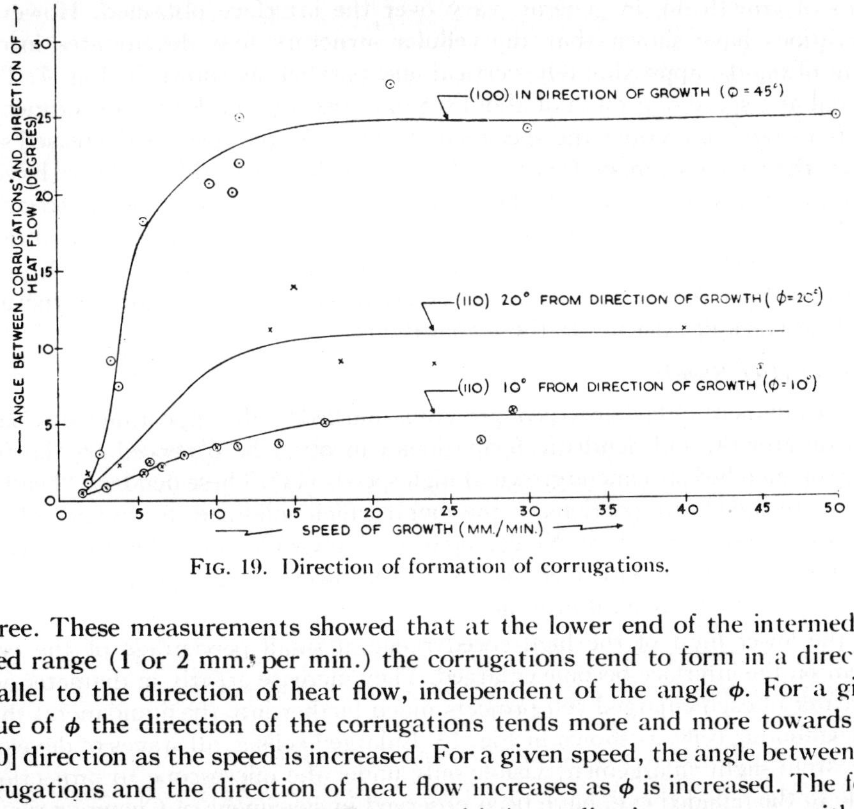

FIG. 19. Direction of formation of corrugations.

degree. These measurements showed that at the lower end of the intermediate speed range (1 or 2 mm. per min.) the corrugations tend to form in a direction parallel to the direction of heat flow, independent of the angle ϕ. For a given value of ϕ the direction of the corrugations tends more and more towards the [110] direction as the speed is increased. For a given speed, the angle between the corrugations and the direction of heat flow increases as ϕ is increased. The form of this relationship is shown in Fig. 19 and is in qualitative agreement with the same relation for striations studied by Teghtsoonian and Chalmers (9). The lack of quantitative agreement must be due to a difference in experimental conditions other than speed of growth since it has been observed that corrugations and striations never cross, but always run in the same direction in the same regions of the specimen.

Bounding Planes of the Structural Elements

From the photomicrographs (Figs. 2, 3, and 4) of decanted interfaces, which are cross-sectional views of the corrugation structure, it is clear that the boundary planes of the elements do not run in any preferred crystallographic directions. The hexagonal boundary lines appear to be randomly oriented.

Growth at Slow Speeds

As the speed of growth approaches the lower limit of the intermediate range, the corrugation spacing and cell size become relatively large and do so quite rapidly, as indicated in Fig. 18. The corrugations then cease to be visible and the surface of the specimen appears smooth, on their scale of size. Observations on the decanted interface are difficult under these limiting conditions because of the narrow range in which the structure changes and the fact that precise knowledge of the speed of growth when decanting took place is not readily obtainable. Conditions of growth do, in general, vary over the interface obtained. However, observations have shown that the cellular structure first degenerates into a system of bands, approximately vertical and parallel, as shown in Fig. 7. This occurred at a speed of growth of about 0.5 mm. per min. under the experimental conditions used to produce the specimen of Fig. 7. As the speed is decreased still further, these bands vanish, leaving only a few widely-spaced boundaries having the appearance shown in Fig. 8. These boundaries can be identified as striation boundaries (9), and are visible in Fig. 7 also. It is concluded that the conditions of growth which occur when the furnace is withdrawn at a rate which gives growth at slow speeds will not support the existence of the corrugation structure. The striations still exist under these conditions.

Growth at High Speeds

The attainment of fast speeds of growth is marked by the appearance of visible dendritic growth, and dendritic formations can often be observed on the free surface of unetched specimens grown at high speeds (11). These dendrite "heads", as they are called, are portions of the metal which solidified in advance of the general solid-liquid interface. No corrugations are visible in the dendrite "head" itself, but they are present over the rest of the surface, which was produced by advancement of the general interface.

At the lower limit of the high speed range, a small percentage of the cells present on the interface become enlarged. They increase greatly in diameter and the center of each enlarged cell projects much farther into the liquid metal than the neighboring cells, as shown in Fig. 13. Enlarged cells in all stages of development, from slight enlargement visible only under the microscope to projections visible to the unaided eye, have been observed in specimens of Chempur tin. It is concluded that the cellular structure which occurs in the intermediate speed range becomes unstable under the conditions of growth brought about by removing the furnace at a rapid rate, without forced cooling of the specimen, to secure a high speed of growth. Observations indicate that these enlarged cells may be the beginnings of dendrite stalks (11). Again, it should be borne in mind that the speed at which enlarged cells first appear depends upon the details of the experiment. Working with lead of 99.999% purity, Weinberg and Chalmers (11) found that dendrites can only grow into a supercooled liquid. Their specimens were grown by the method used in this research.

Incubation of Corrugations

Striations and corrugations are both present in the seed crystals which are normally used, and these continue into the crystal grown from the seed. However, it is possible to produce specimens grown at any desired speed which contain an area that is free from striations (9). By using a seed which is narrower than the crystal being grown, an area ("*A*" in Fig. 20) is produced where the crystal widens and in which new striations must nucleate, since those present in the seed do not continue into this area although the orientation of the seed crystal is maintained. A considerable incubation period is found for the striations so that they may not be present for a distance of a centimeter or more from the graphite insert. However, the corrugations were found to be in existence as close to the insert as observations could be made. Owing to the curvature of the surface caused by surface tension, close examination was not possible at less than 1 or 2 mm. from the insert.

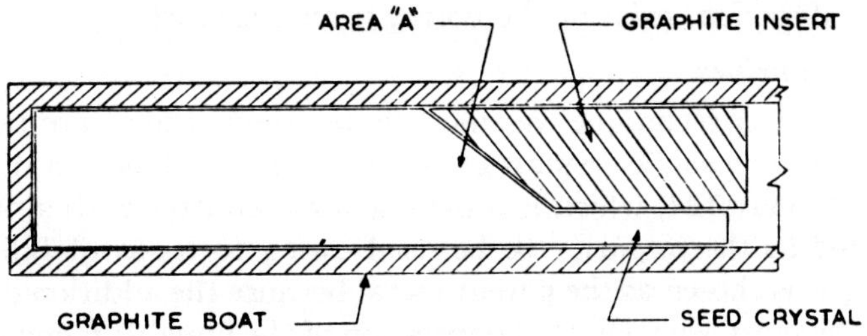

FIG. 20. Position of striation-free area.

It is possible to grow a bicrystal (two-grain specimen) in which the boundary between the crystals runs in a direction different from that of the striations and corrugations. Thus, in one grain of a bicrystal, an area can be produced which is free from striations owing to their long incubation period, by causing the boundary to run in a direction similar to that of the edge of the graphite insert mentioned above. The corrugations and striations form independently in the two parts of the bicrystal and do not cross the crystal boundary. Fig. 14 is a photomicrograph taken on the boundary of such a bicrystal. It is seen that the corrugations do not require an incubation period and, in fact, fill in the region where new corrugations are required by branching. One corrugation appears to run continuously beside the boundary, and branching from it occurs when its distance from the existing corrugations becomes somewhat larger than normal for the speed of growth. The appearance at the boundary on the decanted interface of cells which are larger than normal is in accord with this observation.

It is of interest to note that the crystal boundary does, in general, follow the cell boundaries from the top to the bottom of the specimen. There are exceptions to this, and cases are often found where a crystal boundary cuts across a cell on the interface of a specimen. It is possible that this may be due to movement of the crystal boundary subsequent to solidification.

Orientation Differences

To determine whether orientation differences exist in the corrugation structure, X-ray back reflection Laue photographs were made from the top surface and the decanted interface of a number of specimens, including both striated and non-striated areas. Good angular resolution was obtained by using a fine pinhole made from a length of glass thermometer tubing. The piece used was 45 mm. in length, with a bore of elliptical cross section measuring 0.22 × 0.11 mm. A specimen-to-film distance of 8 cm. was used, and this gave an X-ray spot which covered about 60 cells on the interface of a specimen, or 5 to 10 corrugations on the free surface. Individual orientation differences, between neighboring elements of a structure of the size of the corrugations, could not be measured with this arrangement.

The Laue photographs obtained showed spots which had a fine structure different from that obtained for striations (9). In photographs obtained from striated areas, the normal structure given by striations was present also. Detailed analysis of the spots indicated that orientation differences of up to 15 min. of arc, and random in direction, exist in the corrugation structure.

Segregation of Impurities

A radioactive tracer technique was used to determine the disposition of small amounts of impurity in single crystals grown by the method used in this research. Radioactive antimony 124, which is a beta–gamma emitter with a 60-day half-life, was selected as the impurity to be used owing to its availability; lead of purity 99.999% was chosen as the parent metal because the addition of antimony to lead causes the most usual effect of depression of the liquidus temperature. The corrugation and cell structure described for tin occurs also in the case of lead of 99.999% purity. A specimen was grown using this lead with $\frac{1}{10}$th% by weight of the radioactive antimony added to it. It was desired to make an autoradiograph of the free surface of the specimen. For this purpose, the surface must be very clean. To produce the required surface on lead, which oxidizes rapidly at its melting point compared to tin, a special technique of growth was used (10).

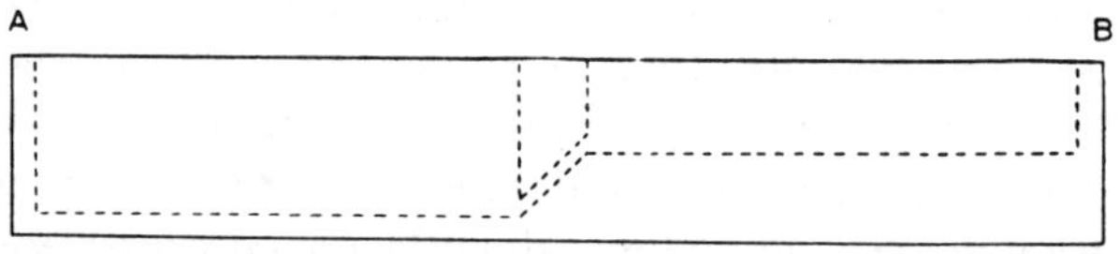

FIG. 21. Graphite boat of special design, used to obtain specimens which had a clean, oxide-free surface.

To obtain a clean, oxide-free surface, the specimen was grown under a nitrogen atmosphere in a special graphite boat. This boat was made in two levels, connected by a narrow hole, as shown in Fig. 21. It was placed in a Pyrex tube through which a small flow of nitrogen gas was maintained and the moving furnace was placed around the tube. The unalloyed metals were located initially in the upper half of the boat and melted from end *B* (Fig. 21) towards the hole. Melting of the metal adjacent to the hole allowed the liquid filling the upper half of the boat to run into the lower level, leaving the oxide in the upper half and giving a melt which had a very clean surface. A Geiger counter showed later that some of the radioactive antimony remained in the upper half of the boat. As a result, it is probable that the antimony content in the specimen was only about 0.05%. The specimen was solidified, without seeding, from the hole towards end *A* of the boat at a speed which ranged from 0 to 10 mm. per min., approximately. It was found to consist of one large crystal with a few smaller ones at the end which solidified last.

The specimen was placed on a Kodak nuclear track plate (N.T.B. type) with the top, free surface in contact with the emulsion, for an exposure of 28 hr. A portion of the autoradiograph thus obtained is reproduced in Fig. 15; it shows clearly segregation of the radioactive antimony into lines running at a small angle to the specimen axis. The spacing and direction of these lines were found to be the same as the spacing and direction of the corrugations visible on the specimen.

After the specimen was annealed for 23 hr. at 300°C. in a nitrogen atmosphere, another autoradiograph was made from the free surface; this showed that the lines of radioactive antimony had disappeared during the annealing.

It was concluded from these observations that segregation of small amounts of impurity occurs during freezing and that this segregation is intimately related to the corrugation structure, since it occurs with the same spacing and direction.

The autoradiograph also revealed a variation of average antimony content along the axis of the specimen. Average blackening of the plate was greater at the end of the specimen which solidified last, becoming progressively less as the end which solidified first was approached. This showed that the average antimony content of the solid increased progressively along the specimen as solidification proceeded. This distribution was relatively unaffected by annealing for 23 hr. at 300°C.

"Banding", which is a segregation of impurities into layers transverse to the direction of solidification, is also visible in Fig. 15. This effect has been reported previously for polonium in bismuth and for gold in silver (8).

Visible Effects of Impurity Addition

Using Chempur tin as the starting material, two series of specimens were prepared with increasing impurity content in each. Lead was added as impurity in one series, and antimony in the other. Added lead lowers the liquidus temperature of tin, while antimony raises it. Thermal conditions, specimen and apparatus geometry, and crystallographic orientation were the same during growth for each specimen. The speed of growth was 3.7 ± 0.5 mm. per min. when decantation was carried out in each case.

The structure is very sensitive to impurities. Figs. 9, 10, and 11 show that, in both cases, the addition of impurity caused an increase in average cell size and a decrease in cell regularity. An increase in impurity content caused a marked increase in the length of the projections formed on the growing interface.

When Chempur tin was used, the solid–liquid interface appeared clearly defined to the unaided eye during growth of the specimen. Addition of lead or antimony to the extent of 0.1% or more caused the interface to become much less well-defined on the surface of the growing specimen. Agitation of the melt showed that a thin layer of liquid existed on the surface to a distance of about 1 mm. behind the average position of the interface below the surface. Since the top surface is a particular case of cell boundaries, this observation indicates a marked difference in solidification temperature between the cell boundaries and cell centers. This is in accord with the observation of segregation of impurities shown by autoradiography, because the temperature at which solidification can begin in a metal depends upon its composition.

Effect of Temperature Gradient

To determine the effect which the temperature gradient present along the specimen axis during growth has upon the cellular structure, several specimens of Chempur tin were grown from a seed crystal which was water-cooled at one end. The seed crystal was fused to a tin block cast around a copper coil which carried the cooling water. The temperature gradient present at the time of de-

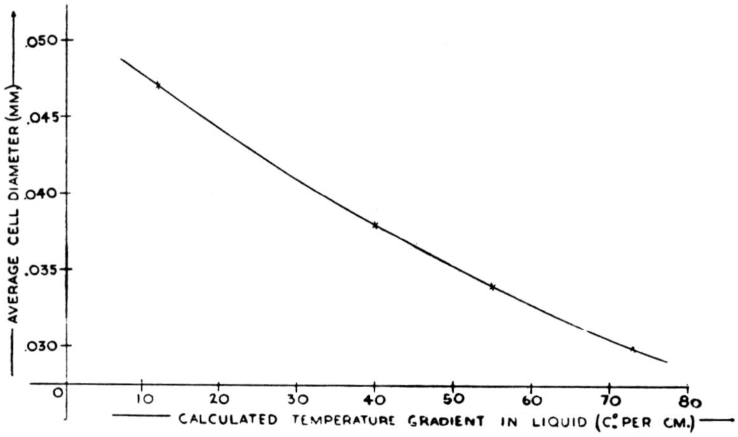

FIG. 22. Cell diameter vs. temperature gradient in liquid, for speed of growth of 5 mm. per min.

canting was varied by altering the position, along the boat, at which decantation was carried out. The average temperature gradient in the solid was known from the temperature of the cooling water and that of the solid–liquid interface. From this, the temperature gradient in the liquid was calculated, approximately.

It was found that the cell size decreases as the temperature gradient is increased, as shown in Fig. 22. For a given speed of growth, a critical temperature gradient is reached at which the cellular structure breaks down, as shown by Figs. 16 and 17, in the manner described for slow speeds of growth. It is concluded that the structure can be suppressed by a sufficiently steep temperature gradient. For example, a temperature gradient in the liquid adjacent to the interface of about 75 C.° per cm. is just sufficient to suppress the structure in a specimen of Chempur tin when the speed of growth is 2.8 mm. per min.

Observations on the corrugations showed that the temperature gradient does not affect their direction of growth.

The speed of growth of a specimen from the melt is determined by the rate at which the latent heat can be conducted away from the solid–liquid interface into the solid. This rate of removal of heat is controlled by the difference between the temperature gradients in the liquid and in the solid adjacent to the interface. The usual method of obtaining a high growth rate is to increase the speed of movement of the furnace, with no provision for cooling the solid end of the specimen. This method was used in the experiments relating cell size and corrugation spacing to speed of growth, described previously. Since the interface temperature, which is the highest temperature in the solid, must remain nearly constant and no forced cooling is used, the temperature gradient in the solid must be relatively unaffected by speed of movement of the furnace. The lowest temperature in the liquid is fixed, since it is the interface temperature, and, as a result, the temperature gradient in the liquid is affected relatively to a much greater extent. A high speed of furnace movement produces a small temperature gradient in the liquid by moving the hottest point away from the interface. It will be seen, therefore, that an increase in speed brought about by this method is accompanied by a decrease in the temperature gradient in the liquid.

The question arises whether cell and corrugation size are controlled by speed of growth, by temperature gradient, or by both. Suppose that temperature gradient in the liquid were the only factor controlling cell size. Since an increase in speed of growth causes a decrease in the temperature gradient in the liquid, it would be concluded from Fig. 18 that a decrease in the temperature gradient in the liquid produces a decrease in cell size. However, the results described in this section show clearly that an increase in temperature gradient in the liquid causes a decrease in cell size. Since these two statements are contradictory, the original hypothesis that the temperature gradient in the liquid is the only factor controlling cell size must be incorrect. It is therefore concluded that an increase in speed of growth causes a decrease in cell size.

Summary of Observations

(1) Under the conditions established during growth from the melt in the intermediate and fast speed ranges, the solid–liquid interface and the free surface of a specimen are not plane or uniformly curved over distances greater than about 0.05 mm. It is concluded that a smooth interface is unstable under these conditions.

(2) This instability leads to the production of a fibrous structure in the crystal. The structure manifests itself as parallel ridges (corrugations) on the top, free surface of the specimen and as cells, roughly hexagonal in shape, on the growing solid–liquid interface. The center of each cell projects into the liquid with respect to the cell boundary.

(3) Added to lead as an impurity, radioactive antimony segregates during solidification of the lead in the intermediate speed range. The antimony appears as lines which have the same spacing and direction as the corrugations present in the specimen. In addition to this effect, there is also a progressive increase in average impurity content from the part of the specimen which solidified first to

the part which solidified last, as well as segregation into bands transverse to the direction of growth.

(4) In the case of Chempur tin, the cell diameter and corrugation spacing are of the order of 0.05 mm. This size is decreased by an increase in growth rate and by an increase in temperature gradient in the liquid metal; it is increased by an increase in impurity content.

(5) The regularity of the corrugation and cell structure is influenced by speed of growth, temperature gradient, and impurity content. The cells are most regular in size and shape when growth is carried out at speeds near the middle of the intermediate range; this regularity is lost to some extent with increase or decrease in speed. An increase in impurity content causes a decrease in cell regularity. An increase in temperature gradient along the specimen axis causes an increase in cell regularity, except as noted in (9) below.

(6) The bounding planes of the structure are randomly oriented with respect to the crystallographic axes of the specimen.

(7) Under conditions of growth at the lower limit of the fast speed range, established by moving the furnace at a suitable rate without forced cooling of the specimen, a small percentage of the cells present on the interface become greatly enlarged in comparison to their neighbors. A further increase in speed produces visible dendritic growth.

(8) Under the conditions in existence during growth at the lower limit of the intermediate speed range, the corrugations cease to be visible and the hexagonal cell structure degenerates into a system of bands, approximately vertical and parallel. These bands vanish with further reduction in speed of growth and the solid–liquid interface then appears smooth. The striations are still present after the corrugations and cells have disappeared completely.

(9) The structure of corrugations and cells can be suppressed by the use of a sufficiently steep temperature gradient along the specimen axis.

(10) No observable incubation period is required for initiation of the structure in an area into which it is not propagated.

(11) Orientation differences, random in nature and up to approximately 15 min. of arc, exist in the structure.

(12) The direction of formation of the structure depends upon the crystallographic orientation of the specimen and the speed of growth. The preferred direction of growth in tin is [110]. It is approached more closely as the speed of growth is increased. The direction of formation is not influenced by the temperature gradient present.

(13) The structure has been observed in specimens of tin, lead, zinc, aluminum, nickel, silver, and copper.

THEORY OF CORRUGATION AND CELL FORMATION

It must be emphasized that the metal used in this research was not completely pure; it is, of course, impossible to remove all the impurity from a sample of metal. However, the impurities were usually present to such an extent as to be soluble in the solid parent metal. It is therefore necessary to consider what can occur during solidification of metal of such composition that it forms a single phase, at least just after solidification.

Equilibrium Solidification

Solidification under equilibrium conditions is represented by the equilibrium diagram. It will be assumed that the solid is a single phase, continuous with the pure metal. Under this assumption, the equilibrium diagram can take either one of two alternative forms, as shown in Figs. 23 and 24. The binary equilibrium diagram will be used here for simplicity because the principles which it represents apply also to systems having more than two constituents.

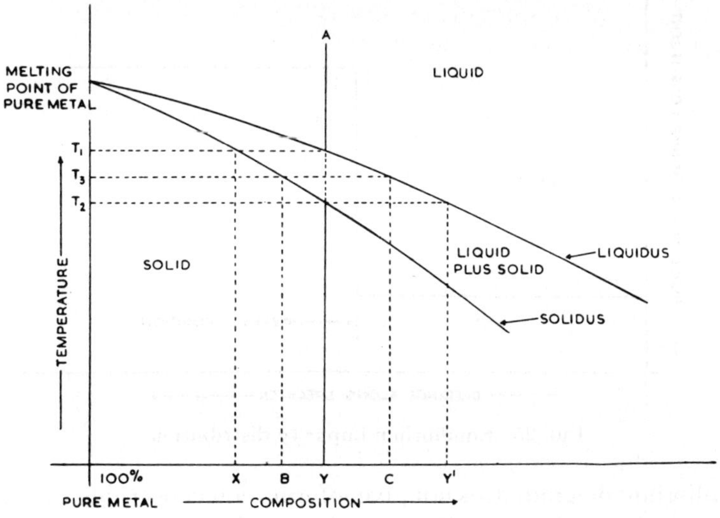

FIG. 23.

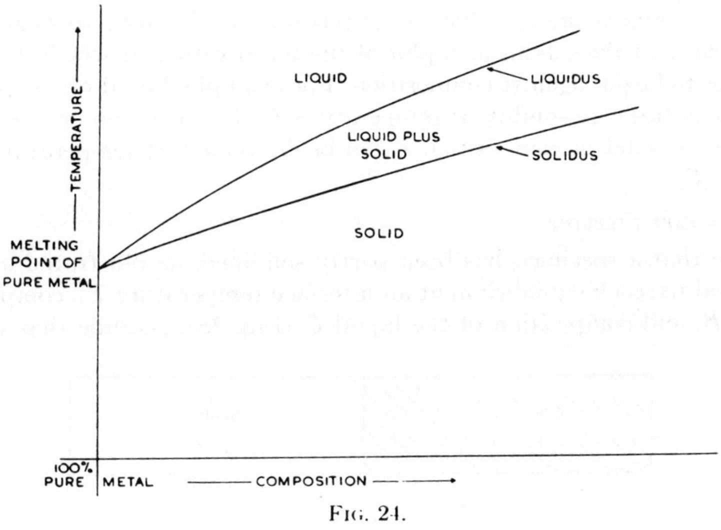

FIG. 24.

As shown by the equilibrium diagram, at any stage in the process of equilibrium solidification, the solid present is all of one uniform composition and is in equilibrium with liquid which is all of another uniform composition. This situation is illustrated by Fig. 25, which indicates the distribution of the minor constituent along the axis of a specimen that is being solidified from one end under equilibrium conditions. The uniformity of composition must be maintained by the process of diffusion. Since diffusion is a relatively slow process, particularly in the solid state, specimens produced by the method used in this research do not solidify under equilibrium conditions, especially at intermediate and fast speeds of growth.

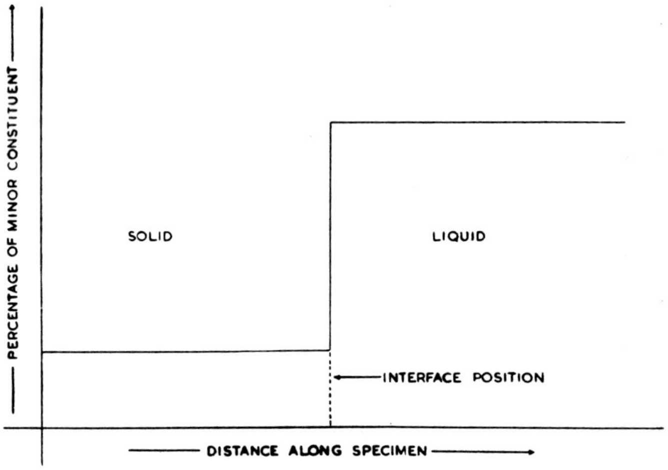

FIG. 25. Equilibrium impurity distribution.

The equilibrium diagram does not give information concerning nonequilibrium freezing, but it does tell what will happen if an indefinite period of time is available for the process to occur. Accordingly, the liquidus may be regarded as a plot of the temperature at which it is possible for freezing to begin, against composition, and the solidus as a plot of the temperature at which it is possible for melting to begin, against composition. For example, liquid of composition Y (Fig. 23) can begin to solidify at temperature T_1, if nucleation occurs in it, and not above T_1; solid of composition Y can begin to melt at temperature T_2, and not below T_2.

Nonequilibrium Freezing

Suppose that a specimen has been partly solidified, as illustrated in Fig. 26, and allowed to reach equilibrium at an interface temperature T_3, composition of the solid B, and composition of the liquid C (Fig. 23). Assume that the solid

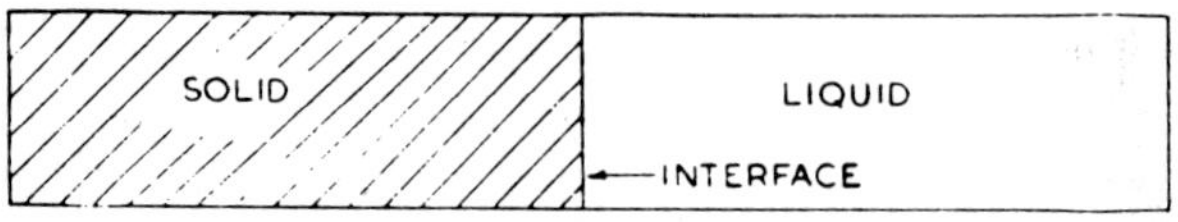

FIG. 26.

liquid interface is a plane surface, perpendicular to the axis of the specimen. If now the temperature gradients are modified to allow extraction of latent heat from the interface into the solid, solidification will start from an equilibrium condition.

The first solid which forms must be of composition B; if the composition were to the right of B in the diagram, the solid would melt. As solidification proceeds, the composition of liquid and solid must move to the right in the equilibrium diagram to reach the final over-all composition of Y. However, time is not allowed during nonequilibrium freezing for the diffusion of impurity, which is necessary to maintain uniform composition throughout the solid and throughout the liquid, to occur. The impurity concentration change must originate at the interface where freezing is taking place and, as a result, the concentration of impurity in the liquid must increase in the neighborhood of the solid–liquid interface. The impurity distribution in the liquid will then take the form shown in Fig. 27.

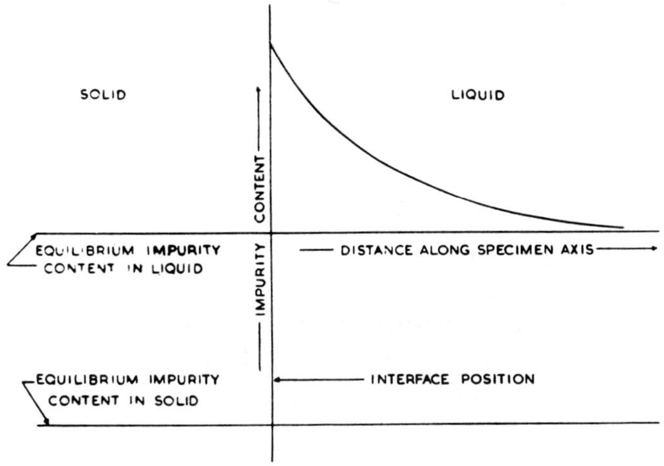

FIG. 27. Impurity distribution in liquid along a line perpendicular to the interface under nonequilibrium conditions.

Since the impurity concentration in the liquid adjacent to the interface is increased, the temperature at the interface must fall, or the impurity content must decrease again, before solidification can proceed. This is because the temperature at which it is possible to obtain solidification decreases as impurity content increases. Under nonequilibrium conditions, diffusion is slow, but temperature changes are relatively rapid. Therefore, starting from equilibrium, an increase in impurity content in the neighborhood of the interface will be accompanied by a decrease in interface temperature as solidification under nonequilibrium conditions proceeds. The curve of Fig. 27 can then be interpreted as in Fig. 28, where the temperature at which freezing can begin in the liquid is plotted as a function of distance from the interface.

If the temperature distribution in the liquid is as shown by the straight line in Fig. 28, then it is seen that each element of the liquid between the interface and a parallel surface at distance X from it is at a temperature below that at which it is possible for solidification to begin. That is, each element of this volume is below its equilibrium liquidus temperature, and is therefore in an unstable condition since it would begin to solidify if nucleation were to occur in it. Part of this layer can solidify without extraction of heat from it.

Since this layer of liquid is below its equilibrium liquidus temperature, it is supercooled. However, the supercooling is, in this case, caused primarily by the composition changes which have occurred in the liquid, rather than by thermal changes such as might be brought about by rapid cooling of the melt (11). Supercooling caused by composition changes will be referred to here as "constitutional supercooling".

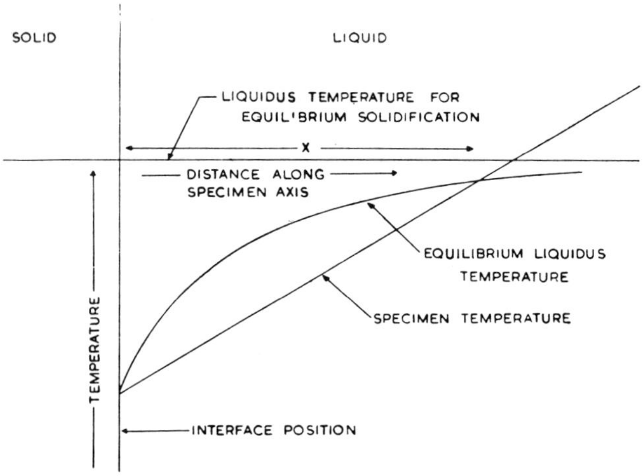

FIG. 28. Variation of equilibrium liquidus temperature and of specimen temperature with distance from interface during growth.

Consider a small element of volume, fixed at some distance in the liquid ahead of the original interface position. As the advancing solid–liquid interface approaches it, the impurity concentration in this volume element must increase and, therefore, more impurity must enter it than leaves it while the interface is approaching. As a result, the impurity content vs. distance curve must be as shown in Fig. 27 to cause this necessary increase. Since the equilibrium liquidus temperature is approximately a linear function of composition, in general, over the range under consideration, the equilibrium liquidus temperature vs. distance curve must have the form shown in Fig. 28.

Suppose that the possible spontaneous solidification without heat extraction which can occur in the unstable layer of liquid is initiated by the solid crystal present. Part of the liquid will then solidify, forming a small projection on the plane interface as shown in Fig. 29. Assume that the projection is stable, and grows at the same rate as the adjacent interface. The temperature at the surface of the projection is open to question; suppose that the entire interface, including the projection, is an isothermal. If this is the case, lateral heat flow will occur into the projection from the adjacent liquid, reducing the amount of latent heat which can be conducted through the projection and suppressing its growth. Therefore, if the projection is stable, the interface cannot be an isothermal.

If the tip of the projection, *B*, and the point *A* on the plane interface (Fig. 29) are growing at the same rate and temperature, then the distribution of impurity in the liquid adjacent to each will be the same, as shown in Fig. 29. As a result, a concentration gradient will exist between point *B* and a neighboring point, *C*, in the liquid, and diffusion of impurities will take place from *B* towards *C*, reducing the concentration at *B* and increasing it at *C*. The liquid adjacent to the tip of the projection will be depleted by this diffusion of impurities and, therefore, solidification will be able to take place at a higher temperature there. The liquid

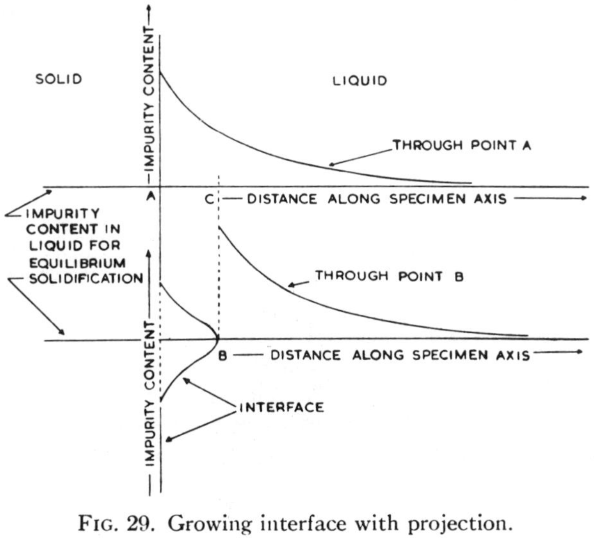

FIG. 29. Growing interface with projection.

adjacent to *A* will be enriched in impurities and thus solidification must take place at a lower temperature in that region. As a result of this diffusion, point *B* can continue to grow at the same rate as point *A*, although the temperature at *B* is higher than at *A*. It is clear that as a projection forms on a plane interface, diffusion of impurities will enable its tip to grow at a higher temperature and will force the adjacent plane interface to grow at a lower temperature. The resulting interface, therefore, cannot be an isothermal unless the conductivity of the solid or liquid is infinite.

The effect of a higher temperature at the tip of the projection on the thermal conditions is illustrated in Fig. 30, where temperature is plotted as a function of distance along the specimen axis. In Fig. 30, the temperature vs. distance curves are drawn as straight lines. This would be the case for linear heat flow were it not for the specific heat which is evolved owing to the fall in temperature of all parts of the material during growth. This causes the slope of the temperature vs. distance curves to increase continuously from the hot (liquid) end to the cold (solid) end of the specimen if the heat flow is linear. However, the temperature must be uniform across the specimen at large distances from the interface both in the solid (T_c) and in the liquid (T_H) and, therefore, the relative positions of the curves shown in Fig. 30 will not be affected. It is seen that the temperature along a line parallel to the direction of heat flow through the tip of the projection, B, is higher at all points near the interface than at corresponding points on a similar line through A. Therefore, lateral heat flow must occur from the projection to the neighboring solid and liquid. Because of this lateral heat flow, more latent heat can be removed at the projection than at the neighboring interface. This promotes growth of the projection while suppressing growth of the interface adjacent to it.

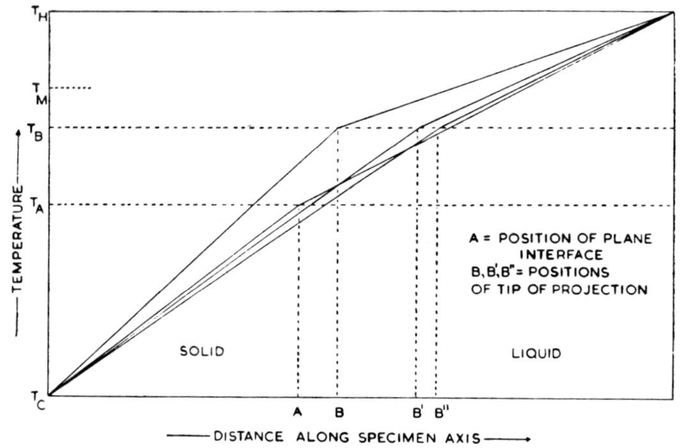

FIG. 30. Temperature distribution along specimen through plane interface and through projection.

The above considerations show that if a projection is formed on a plane, growing interface, both diffusion and thermal conditions are established which favor growth of the projection relative to the interface adjacent to it. It is therefore concluded that such a projection will be stable and will persist as long as the conditions of growth necessary for its initial formation are maintained.

There is a limit to the extent to which a projection can advance into the liquid and still maintain favorable heat flow conditions. The temperature, T_B, at B cannot rise above the solidification temperature, T_M, of the pure metal and the lowering of the temperature, T_A, of the interface adjacent to the projection will be limited by the amount of impurity which can build up there in view of the process of diffusion into the main body of liquid. If conditions such as those shown in Fig. 30 for the point B' are reached, lateral heat flow into the base of the projection will begin and this will have attained large proportions if the point B'' is reached by the tip of the projection. This unfavorable heat flow would suppress growth of the projection and, as a result, a projection can advance only to a limited extent into the liquid with respect to the interface adjacent to it.

Growth of a projection in a direction parallel to the interface is hindered by the accumulation of impurity accompanying it. There is no possibility of diffusion of impurity comparable to that which can take place at the tip of the projection.

It will be seen that the alternative possible form of the equilibrium diagram, shown in Fig. 24, does not basically alter the arguments presented above. In this case, diffusion of impurity would occur towards a projection, resulting in the same thermal conditions and a similar, though reversed, diffusion pattern.

The diffusion of impurities parallel to the interface from a projection and the lateral heat flow produced both cause a local reduction in the extent of the zone of liquid which is below its equilibrium liquidus temperature and also in the number of degrees by which it is below that temperature. These effects reduce the probability of spontaneous initiation of solidification in the zone of liquid around the projection, or suppress growth of another projection if it does start in that region. However, at some distance from the projection, conditions at the interface will be practically unaffected by its presence. The influence of the projection will extend to the circumference of a circle, the size of which is governed by the rate of diffusion of impurities in the liquid and the thermal diffusivity of the liquid and solid. Outside this circle, the conditions which gave rise to the first projection still exist. Therefore, a number of projections, each with its own "circle of influence", will form on an initially plane interface if the unstable constitutionally supercooled zone of liquid is established during nonequilibrium freezing. It is, therefore, concluded that the solid–liquid interface should consist of an array of projections when growth under such nonequilibrium conditions takes place.

Summary of Theory

(1) Accumulation of impurities in the liquid adjacent to a growing solid–liquid interface occurs during nonequilibrium freezing.

(2) This accumulation of impurities results in the formation, adjacent to the growing interface, of a layer of liquid which is below its equilibrium liquidus temperature and is, therefore, in an unstable state. It is necessary that the equilibrium liquidus temperature vs. distance curve and the temperature vs. distance curve in the liquid should intersect as shown in Fig. 28 to produce this effect of constitutional supercooling.

(3) A spontaneous solidification, without heat extraction, is initiated in this unstable zone at the solid–liquid interface by the large crystal present, resulting in formation of a small projection on an initially plane or uniformly curved interface.

(4) Diffusion of impurity from the liquid at the tip of the projection to the surrounding liquid occurs. This allows solidification at the tip of the projection to proceed at a higher temperature than at the plane interface and forces solidification to occur in the region around the base of the projection at a lower temperature than at the plane interface.

(5) This rise in temperature at the tip of the projection produces the favorable thermal condition of lateral heat flow from the projection to the surrounding

liquid and solid, promoting growth of the projection. This favorable thermal condition is maintained only if the projection does not extend into the liquid beyond a certain amount, provided that the temperature increases away from the interface into the liquid.

(6) The factors noted above should result in formation of an array of projections on an initially smooth solid–liquid interface during nonequilibrium solidification.

DISCUSSION

The theory which has been presented shows that, if certain conditions are met during solidification, a smooth solid–liquid interface is unstable and that this instability should result in the production of an array of projections on the growing interface. This accounts qualitatively for the presence of the cellular structure observed on the decanted interface. The diffusion of impurities away from the tips of the projections must result, according to the theory, in a difference of impurity content between the center and the boundary of each element of the structure. Such segregation was found by using the radioactive tracer technique, as described previously. If the equilibrium diagram is as shown in Fig. 23, the cell boundaries should be enriched in impurities, while in the case of Fig. 24 the cell boundaries should be depleted in impurities. The fact that the impurities are dispersed by annealing shows that they must have taken up their position during freezing, in agreement with the theory. It is clear, both theoretically and experimentally, that the structure consists essentially of a particular distribution of the impurities contained in the specimen. The features of this structure, as observed experimentally, will now be discussed in relation to the theory.

The decrease in volume of the metal on solidification causes a lowering of the liquid level in the boat as solidification proceeds. As a result, some of the liquid contained in those vertical cell boundaries which terminate at the top, free surface of the specimen will run out before it can solidify, producing the ridges which are here called corrugations.

The formation of the first few cells on an interface which is initially plane will occur at random, resulting from chance initiation of spontaneous solidification in the zone of unstable liquid. This randomness must decrease as the number of projections increases and the possible sites become occupied, but the initial complete formation will be comparatively random. The projections which survive this initial period will continue to grow as long as growth conditions are not changed, and it is to be expected that some lateral growth of each projection will occur if growth conditions are not the same on all sides of it. If the "circles of influence" of two projections overlap, then growth will be slower on the neighboring faces than on the outside faces, resulting in translation of the axes of the projections parallel to the interface and away from each other. The projections will therefore tend to adjust themselves in such a way that their circles of influence fit together in the most advantageous way; they can best do this by forming a close-packed array. This will result in hexagonal boundary lines between elements of the structure, and accounts for the shape of the cells observed on a decanted interface.

The size of the cells will be controlled by the following factors which are properties of the material of the specimen:

(*a*) The probability of spontaneous solidification occurring at the interface when the liquid adjacent to it is below its equilibrium liquidus temperature by a given amount.

(*b*) The coefficient of volume diffusion of the impurities in the liquid metal.

(*c*) The thermal diffusivities of the liquid and solid metal.
It appears very difficult to estimate the cell size which will result from simultaneous operation of these factors. No attempt to do so will be made here.

The effect of various conditions of growth on cell size may be deduced qualitatively:

(*a*) If the temperature gradients in the liquid and solid are steep, a high proportion of the latent heat liberated at each projection will be conducted into the solid in a direction parallel to the specimen axis, and a relatively small proportion will be conducted parallel to the interface. This will cause a reduction in the "circle of influence" of each projection and, therefore, a reduction in cell size should occur as the temperature gradient along the specimen axis is increased. This has been shown experimentally to be the case.

(*b*) When the speed of growth is high, little time is allowed for diffusion ot impurities parallel to the interface. The "circle of influence" of a projection is, therefore, reduced as the speed of growth is increased and the cell size must reduce accordingly, as is observed experimentally.

(*c*) If the total impurity content in a specimen is increased, the length of the projection will be increased because the width of the unstable zone of liquid has been increased. These longer projections may be expected to exert an influence over a large area on the interface. The cell size should, therefore, increase as the impurity content is increased, as was observed.

Some irregularity of the structure is to be expected on the basis of chance initiation of spontaneous solidification in the unstable zone of liquid. However, by means of lateral growth, the projections should tend to form a very regular structure. For this to occur, there must be the possibility of establishing very uniform thermal and diffusion conditions at the growing interface. At speeds of growth well within the intermediate speed range, the cellular structure shows no asymmetry. That is, the cells do not tend to be elongated in any particular direction. But at speeds of about 0.5 mm. per min., asymmetry does occur in a very pronounced manner, as shown by Fig. 7. The appearance of the vertical lines shown there can be accounted for by convection set up in the liquid. It is therefore probable that the lack of regularity observed in the cell structure as these slow speeds are approached is due to the effects of convection. The process of convection is a relatively slow one and, therefore, it only has a noticeable effect at speeds near the lower end of the intermediate range, where it has time to operate and where the extent of the projections is not large enough to break up possible convection paths. At speeds approaching the fast range, little time is available for diffusion parallel to the interface. It seems likely that this is the cause of cell irregularity at these speeds.

The bounding planes of the elements of the structure will be determined initially by the positions on the interface in which the projections first form. Since this is governed by random initiation of spontaneous solidification in the unstable zone of liquid, the bounding planes should show no preferred orientation except that imposed by subsequent adjustment of the projections into a close-packed arrangement. This is in agreement with the observations.

As noted previously, the achievement of a high growth rate by rapid removal of the furnace, without forced cooling of the solid, is brought about largely by a reduction in the temperature gradient in the liquid. Since it is the rise in temperature from the interface to the hot end of the boat which controls the extent to which the projection can grow ahead of the average position of the interface, a condition will be reached on lowering of the temperature gradient in the liquid such that they may grow practically to an unlimited extent. Under these conditions, one projection may grow ahead of its neighbors. If this occurs, greater diffusion of impurity will be possible, and it will continue to grow ahead into the liquid, since the restraining influence of the temperature gradient is not present. As the projection moves into regions free from the influence of neighboring projections, conditions will be established along it similar to those existing at a plane, growing solid–liquid interface, and growth perpendicular to the axis of the extended projection will become possible. It will then increase in width. This accounts for the appearance on the interface of enlarged cells at high speeds of growth. Finally, secondary projections may form on the extended one when it has advanced to a region uninfluenced by conditions at the interface from which it grew. This may account for the production of dendrites at high speeds of growth. It should be noted, however, that the formation of enlarged cells, and perhaps dendrites, is a result of heat flow and diffusion conditions established in the liquid, and not directly of the speed of growth (11).

It will be seen from Fig. 28 that when the temperature vs. distance curve is tangent at the interface to the curve relating equilibrium liquidus temperature to distance, then there exists in the liquid no region which is below its equilibrium liquidus temperature. When this condition is attained, no projections can form and a smooth interface will be stable. If the speed of growth is slow, more time is available for diffusion of impurities into the main body of the liquid and, therefore, the slope of the equilibrium liquidus temperature vs. distance curve will be relatively small. This results in reduction of the unstable zone of liquid as the speed of growth is reduced and finally in its disappearance, for a fixed temperature gradient in the liquid. This accounts for the disappearance of the corrugation structure at low speeds of growth. It is clear that an increase in the temperature gradient in the liquid will reduce the extent of the unstable zone, and therefore a sufficiently steep temperature gradient will suppress the structure for a given speed of growth. This is in accord with the observations.

The experimentally observed absence of any appreciable incubation period for formation of the corrugation structure is predicted by the theory. As soon as any area comparable with the size of a cell is formed into which the existing structure is not propagated, then is established the condition of a plane interface, with, adjacent to it, a zone of liquid which is below its equilibrium liquidus temperature. A new element of the structure may then form, or branching of the existing corrugations may occur as is usually observed.

If solidification occurs at a given fixed rate, the impurity concentration near the interface of the specimen should reach a certain value, determined by equality of the rate of accumulation of impurity caused by movement of the interface and the rate of diffusion of the impurity into the main body of liquid. However, when the impurity content at the extreme hot end of the boat is affected by diffusion of impurities from the interface, the concentration will rise there. This will affect the concentration gradient along the specimen, resulting in an increase in the average impurity content at the interface and an accompanying decrease in average interface temperature. The solid formed will then be less pure than before. Therefore, there should be a gradual increase in impurity content along the specimen after the impurity concentration at the hot end of the liquid is affected. This accounts for the observed increase in average impurity content along the specimen towards the end which solidified last. The effect which has been called "banding" is not accounted for by the theory presented here.

The existence of orientation differences in the corrugation structure seems to bear no direct relationship to the mechanism of their formation. It is possible that the projections formed on the interface may be very thin near the tip and, therefore, mechanically very weak near the solidification temperature. Such a thin tip would not be detected by the decantation technique. Mechanical disturbances would bend such thin sections, producing small, random orientation differences of the type noted in X-ray photographs made from specimens having a corrugation structure. The existence of such orientation differences is, therefore, not inconsistent with the theory.

Existing information is insufficient to explain the direction of formation of the corrugations. The effect appears to be one of preferential deposition from liquid to solid on certain crystallographic planes, in a manner similar to that which causes development of crystallographically defined faces on crystals grown from solution or from the vapor phase. This effect is not inconsistent with the theory presented here; it modifies the direction of the axis of a projection forming on the interface.

The theory developed is in no way restricted in application to one metal. It demands only that a small quantity of impurity be present in the metal used. The occurrence of the structure in many metals, therefore, is in agreement with the theory.

It has been shown that the observed properties of the substructure are in qualitative agreement with those predicted by the theory. It appears impossible, at present, to derive quantitative values. However, it is possible to obtain an estimate of the coefficient of volume diffusion of impurities in the liquid metal.

According to Frenkel (5), the diffusion coefficients of widely different dissolved substances in the liquid state differ from each other by a factor of 10 at most:

they are much less temperature-sensitive than diffusion coefficients for the solid state; and there is only a relatively slight variation from one solvent to another. Therefore, the exact nature of the impurities present in a specimen should have little effect as far as diffusion is concerned, and for the purpose of estimating the diffusion coefficient it is reasonable to assume that the only impurity present is lead.

When the specimen temperature vs. distance curve becomes tangent at the solid–liquid interface to the equilibrium liquidus temperature vs. distance curve (Fig. 28), the cellular structure is suppressed. This critical temperature gradient can be transformed into a concentration gradient with the aid of the equilibrium diagram. It was observed that a temperature gradient of approximately 75 C.° per centimeter was just sufficient to cause suppression of the structure at a speed of growth of 2.8 mm. per minute in a specimen of Chempur tin. The lead–tin equilibrium diagram shows a drop in the liquidus temperature of about 1.8 C.° per 1% increase in lead content near the tin end. The majority of the impurities present in Chempur tin give approximately this change in liquidus temperature with composition. Taking the specimen density as 7.3 gm. per cm.^{3}, the concentration gradient at the interface is:

$$\frac{dc}{dx} = \frac{75}{1.8} \times 0.073 \text{ gm. per cm.}^3 \text{ per cm.}$$

The rate of movement of impurity down this concentration gradient per unit area of interface is then:

$$\frac{dQ}{dt} = D\frac{dc}{dx} = \frac{D \times 75 \times 0.073}{1.8} \text{ gm. per cm.}^2 \text{ per sec.} \quad [1]$$

where Q = quantity of material,
t = time,
D = coefficient of diffusion,
c = concentration,
x = distance from interface.

This rate of movement of impurity down the concentration gradient can be estimated in another way. Fig. 12 shows a portion of the decanted interface of a specimen of Chempur tin which contained 0.3 weight per cent of lead. This specimen was grown in the usual manner at a speed comparable to that used for the specimen which was grown under a steep temperature gradient as noted above. The appearance of a second phase at the cell boundaries, as shown by Fig. 12, gives an indication of the impurity content in the liquid near the interface. An average impurity content at the interface of one-half the solubility limit of lead in solid tin at the melting point seems a reasonable estimate. This value is about five times the average impurity content of the specimen as a whole. For tin containing 0.014% lead (the purity of Chempur tin), this increase of five times gives a concentration at the interface of:

$$5 \times 7.3 \times 0.00014 \text{ gm. per cm.}^3$$

Judging from the equilibrium diagram, about 70% of the impurity present in an element of liquid is rejected into the remaining liquid when the element freezes. Hence, the quantity of material which is diffused into the liquid may be estimated for the specimen grown at a speed of 2.8 mm. per min. as follows:

Volume swept out per second by moving interface

$$= \frac{2.8}{60} \times \frac{1}{10} \text{ cm.}^3 \text{ per sec. per cm.}^2 \text{ of interface.}$$

Amount of impurity diffused into liquid per second

$$= 0.7 \times \frac{2.8}{600} \times 7.3 \times 0.00014 \times 5 \text{ gm. per cm.}^2 \text{ per sec.} \quad [2]$$

Equations [1] and [2] give the diffusion coefficient as 5.5×10^{-6} cm.^{2} per sec., or about 0.5 cm.^{2} per day. According to Frenkel, the diffusion coefficients of gold in molten lead and tin at 500°C. are equal respectively to 3.19 and 4.65 cm.^{2} per day. Agreement between these values and that calculated above is considered satisfactory in view of the approximations made in the calculation.

Although the calculation is only an estimate, it does verify that the rate of diffusion of impurities in the liquid metal is that required by the theory. It is clear that the structure formed is essentially a particular distribution of the impurities present in the metal used.

ACKNOWLEDGMENTS

The authors are indebted to Dr. C. Barnes of the Department of Physics, University of Toronto, for many helpful discussions during the course of this work. They wish to thank Dr. W. C. Winegard, Mr. W. R. Thomas, and Mr. R. S. Davis for assistance with the radioactive tracer work. The authors gratefully acknowledge the financial assistance of the School of Engineering Research, University of Toronto.

REFERENCES

1. Buerger, M. J. Z. Krist. 89: 242. 1934.
2. Chalmers, B. Proc. Roy. Soc. (London) A, 175: 100. 1940.
3. Chalmers, B. In course of publication.
4. Chalmers, B. and Rutter, J. W. Discussion of the work of Pond and Kessler (Reference 7) for Trans. Am. Inst. Mining Met. Engrs.
5. Frenkel, J. Kinetic theory of liquids. Oxford University Press, London. 1946. p. 201.
6. Greninger, A. B. Trans. Am. Inst. Mining Met. Engrs. 117: 61. 1935.
7. Pond, R. B. and Kessler, S. W. J. Metals, 3: 1156. 1951.
8. Stewart, M. T., Thomas, R., Wauchope, K., Winegard, W. C., and Chalmers, B. Phys. Rev. 83: 657. 1951.
9. Teghtsoonian, E. and Chalmers, B. Can. J. Phys. 29: 370. 1951.
10. Thomas, W. R. Unpublished work. Department of Metallurgy, University of Toronto. 1951.
11. Weinberg, F. and Chalmers, B. Can. J. Phys. 29: 382. 1951.

Journal of Applied Physics

Volume 30, Number 4 April, 1959

Growth of Silicon Crystals Free from Dislocations*

WILLIAM C. DASH
General Electric Research Laboratory, Schenectady, New York
(Received August 29, 1958)

The dislocations which occur in silicon crystals grown by the Czochralski method with and without a crucible are studied by etching and copper decoration techniques. A representative crystal with about 500 dislocations per cm^2 is examined in detail to provide general information about their distribution. Sources of dislocations which are important at particular stages of growth are isolated and means found to minimize or eliminate them. The sources include generation by thermal shock from surface damage or residual dislocations in the seed; poor epitaxy at the seed; plastic generation in the bulk of the crystal; effects of segregation of impurities. Plastic generation is the only source found in the bulk of a crystal. "Spontaneous" formation of dislocations from excess vacancies is not found. Impurity segregation causes some generation at the tip end of crystals. For certain crystallographic directions it is possible to eliminate residual dislocations and thenceforth grow a dislocation free crystal. This is interpreted in terms of climb. In a super-saturation of vacancies, an edge dislocation can be forced completely out of a crystal; a screw will remain straight or may be distorted into a coaxial helix. By growth along ⟨100⟩ or ⟨111⟩ axes under conditions which favor a vacancy supersaturation, screw as well as edge and mixed dislocations can propagate to the surface and be eliminated. The observations are consistent with this interpretation. When the dislocations are eliminated, the growing crystal can withstand large temperature fluctuations without further generation of dislocations. A procedure is outlined for the growth of dislocation free silicon crystals. Germanium crystals free of dislocations have been grown by a direct application of the method. It is believed that the conclusions reached during the course of this investigation may be applied to the development of methods for growing dislocation free crystals of other substances.

I. INTRODUCTION

SILICON has a number of properties which permit simple and reliable investigations of the origin of dislocations. Single crystals of high purity can be grown. The points of emergence of dislocations through the surface can be detected by etch pits formed on any crystallographic plane.[1] Specimens can be prepared and handled conveniently at room temperature without disturbing the internal structure.[2] Decoration of screw, edge, or mixed dislocations by precipitated copper makes possible their direct observation in the bulk by use of an infrared image tube.[1,3,4]

In a recent note,[5] the writer reported that silicon crystals free from dislocations have been grown from the melt. It is the purpose of the present article to discuss the origin of dislocations in silicon and to describe a procedure by which dislocation-free crystals can be grown.

II. EXPERIMENTAL PROCEDURE

The observations to be presented were made using zone-refined silicon[6] with resistivity of 50Ω-cm or greater as starting material. The crystals were grown by the Czochralski technique from a quartz crucible or from a silicon "pedestal".[5] These methods are described briefly in the following.

A schematic diagram of the quartz crucible and graphite resistance heater is shown in Fig. 1. Each chamber contains argon at atmospheric pressure. A seed is lowered into the melt to initiate growth, then

* An abbreviated version of this article has appeared in the report of a conference on the growth of crystals at Cooperstown, New York, in August, 1958: *Growth and Perfection of Crystals*, edited by Doremus *et al.* (John Wiley and Sons, Inc., New York, 1958), p. 361.

[1] W. C. Dash, J. Appl. Phys. **27**, 1193 (1956).

[2] W. C. Dash, J. Appl. Phys. **29**, 228, (1958).

[3] W. C. Dash, *Dislocations and Mechanical Properties of Crystals* (John Wiley and Sons, Inc., New York, 1957), p. 57.

[4] X-ray methods recently reported by A. R. Lang, J. Appl. Phys. **29**, 597 (1958); J. B. Newkirk, Phys. Rev. **110**, 1465 (1958); and Bormann, Hartmann, and Irmler, Z. Naturforsch. **13a**, 423 (1958), corroborate the decoration and etch pit techniques for identifying dislocations in silicon.

[5] W. C. Dash, J. Appl. Phys. **29**, 736 (1958).

[6] E. A. Taft and F. H. Horn, J. Electrochem. Soc. **105**, 81 (1958).

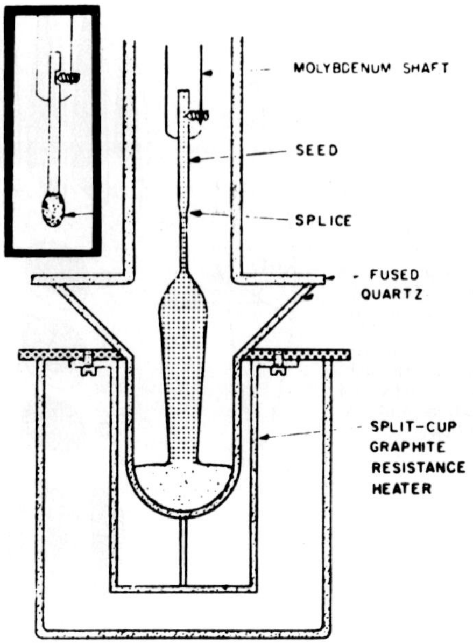

FIG. 1. Schematic diagram of quartz crucible furnace The lower chamber is insulated with quartz wool. Both upper and lower chambers contain an argon atmosphere. The arrow in the inset indicates a "meltback" made from the lower end of a bar of silicon suspended in the furnace.

withdrawn at a rate of about 2 millimeters per minute with rotation at about 10 rpm. The approximate temperature gradient under typical growth conditions was determined by inserting a thermocouple into a hole in a partially grown specimen, lowering this assembly into the melt as a seed, and measuring the temperature as it was withdrawn. The gradient thus determined was about 125°C per cm. It was found to be linear for about 4 centimeters over which the diameter was approximately constant. Figure 2 shows a typical crystal weighing about 20 grams.

The "pedestal" method was devised to avoid oxygen contamination[7,8] and at the same time achieve the high perfection attainable with the Czochralski technique. In this method the melt is an inductively heated mound held on top of a solid silicon support by surface tension and electromagnetic levitation. The support is sectored to inhibit electromagnetic coupling to the pedestal. A seed is inserted and the growing crystal is withdrawn at a rate which may vary from 3 cm per minute at the start to 3 or 4 mm per minute during the major part of its growth. Studies of the 9 μ absorption at room temperature in pedestal-grown crystals have shown that oxygen could not be detected. Although the oxygen content of floating-zone crystals is also low, they generally have too many dislocations to permit detailed studies. For the purposes of the present investigation, the pedestal crystals are of interest because the growth conditions differ considerably from those maintained in withdrawal from a crucible. Despite this, the considerations which apply to the growth of dislocation-free crystals by either method are shown to be closely related.

"Meltbacks," illustrated in the inset in Fig. 1, have also been utilized in some experiments. To make a meltback the lower end of a bar is melted by radiation from the walls of the furnace. Surface tension holds the drop of molten silicon, generally about $\frac{1}{2}$ gram, which is then recrystallized by lowering the temperature. The oxygen content in the meltback is found to be below

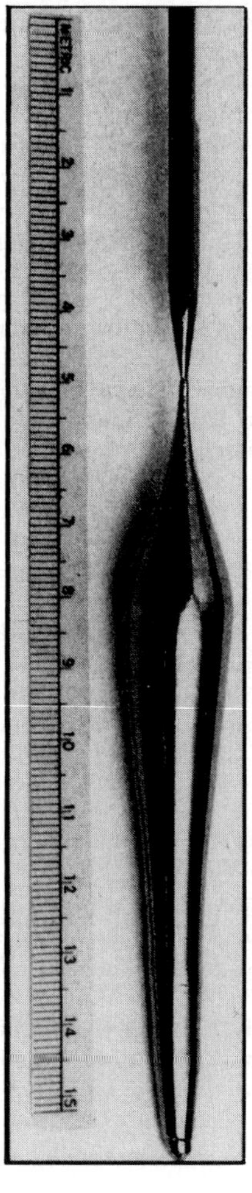

FIG. 2. Typical single crystal grown from quartz crucible.

[7] Kaiser, Keck, and Lange, Phys. Rev. **101**, 1264 (1956) have reported that the oxygen content of silicon withdrawn from quartz can be determined by infrared absorption of 9 μ. The concentration is generally around 10^{18} cm^{-3}.

[8] R. A. Logan and A. J. Peters [J. Appl. Phys. **28**, 1419 (1957)] have reported that in some cases the presence of oxygen may lead to errors in the identification of dislocations by etch pits. They found, however, that in these specimens identification by copper decoration was not affected.

the limit detectable by 9 μ absorption. An additional feature is that some residual impurities are concentrated in the bottom tip, permitting examination under more favorable conditions.

In order to obtain an estimate of the number and distribution of dislocations in a crystal, it is etched in a mixture consisting of 50% HF solution, 70% HNO_3 solution and glacial acetic acid in the ratio of 1:3:10 by volume. [This mixture is hereafter referred to as (1:3:10); two other mixtures, with volume concentrations (1:3:0) and (1:3:6) are used for special purposes to be described.] The time required to form identifiable pits is one to two hours; pits several hundred microns deep are formed by etching overnight.

The crystal is then cut into parallel-sided slabs, lapped smooth and chemically polished in (1:3:0) solution. A water solution of copper nitrate with copper equivalent to about 10^{-6} to 10^{-5} atom percent of the silicon is spread in droplets over one side of each slab and evaporated to dryness. They are then put into a hydrogen atmosphere in a quartz tube and heated at about 950°C for 30 minutes and quenched by dropping onto a quartz plate. Rapid cooling is necessary to prevent formation of large precipitate particles which result in poorly defined dislocation lines. The contact with the quartz plate makes possible cooling below the temperature of luminosity of slabs weighing as much as ten grams in a few seconds with no apparent change in the number or distribution of dislocations. Faster quenching, for example by contact with a copper plate, results in too light a decoration for convenient examination.

Following decoration, the slabs are optically polished on the flat sides and viewed with a microscope and infrared image converter as described in reference 1.

Over a hundred silicon crystals have been examined either by etching or by both etching and decoration. The discussion will be limited to specimens which contain a maximum of 10^3 dislocations per cm², because the arrays in less perfect crystals are complicated and difficult to analyze. Two of the specimens contained one and two twins, respectively. These crystals were selected for study because twins form crystallographic barriers to glide, thereby making it possible to separate motion and multiplication from other origins of dislocations.

III. DETAILED EXAMINATION OF A CRYSTAL WITH ABOUT 10^3 DISLOCATIONS PER Cm²

A specimen which was decorated and examined throughout most of its volume contained a single (111) twin boundary about half-way along its length, as shown schematically in Fig. 3(a). The twin was nucleated at the point marked A, possibly by a speck floating on the surface of the melt, after which it grew completely across the crystal. Except for the twin, this specimen is typical of crucible-grown crystals of moderate perfection.

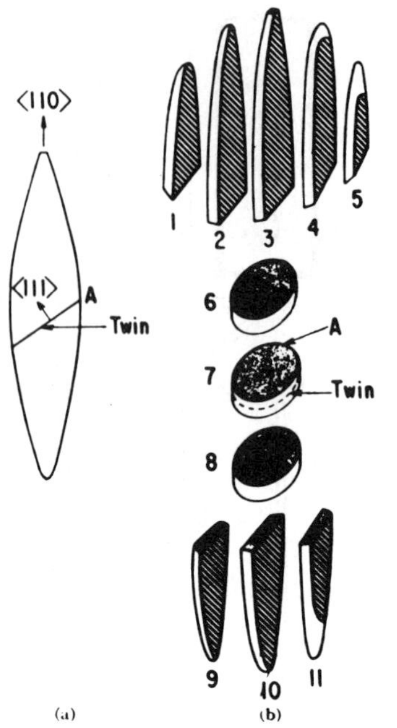

FIG. 3. Schematic diagram of ⟨110⟩ crystal with a {111} twin plane which changed the axial orientation to approximately ⟨113⟩. The specimen was cut up into the indicated sections for decoration and examination.

Figure 3(b) illustrates how the crystal was cut for examination of the decorated dislocations. In what is to follow only slices 3, 6, 7, and 8 and a portion of slice 10 are illustrated, since these show all the important features. Saw cuts and polishing account for a removal of about one mm of material from between the slices; this must be taken into account in tracing the lines from one slice to another.

Figure 4 shows dislocations in slices 3 and 10, viewed in a [1$\bar{1}$0] direction. (The following comments apply specifically to slice 3; the lower part of the figure corresponding to slice 10 is discussed later.) Although the dislocations present here are too numerous for extensive analysis, some interesting observations have been made. In the center the density of dislocations is relatively low: they are present mainly in the form of long lines. Many are over a centimeter in length and run parallel to each other and to the [110] axis. This is a close-packed crystallographic direction in the diamond structure. It is also the preferred orientation for both screw and "60°" dislocations during plastic deformation at temperatures around 900°C.[1,3]

In addition to the long [110] dislocations, many loops are observed near the seed end and near the outer edges of the slab. Isolated loops can be seen on edge lying in the (111) and (111) planes. Others, presumably in (111) and (1$\bar{1}\bar{1}$) planes, appear to be parallel to the plane of the sample because of the large depth of focus. It is very likely that these loops result from a light plastic deformation produced by thermal stresses, because they resemble the noncrystallographic loops

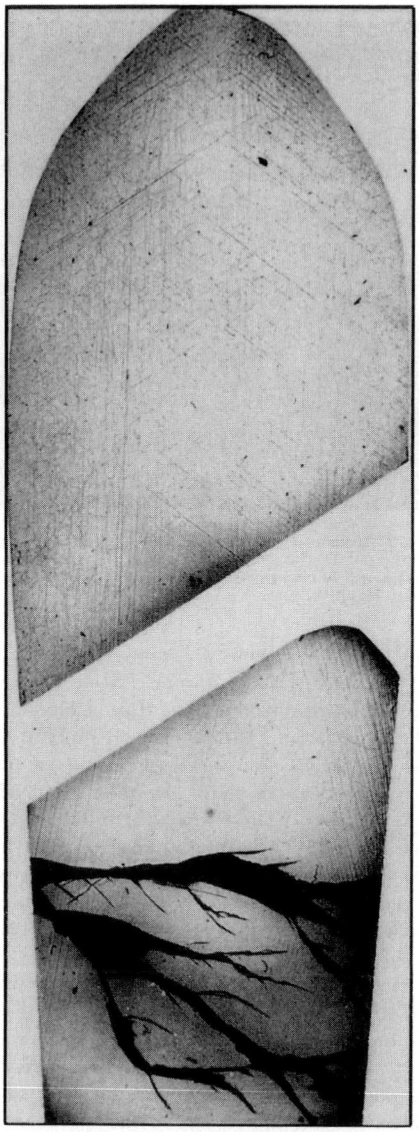

FIG. 4. Upper part shows decorated dislocations in slice 3 of the specimen in Fig. 3. Many long lines lie accurately parallel to the ⟨110⟩ axis. Lower part shows dislocations in slice 10, with axial orientation approximately ⟨113⟩. The sample was broken in handling after decoration, then pieced together, resulting in the jagged dark areas. Most of the dislocations in the lower specimen diverge from the axis and are soon eliminated. Some of the dislocations appear to terminate; the ends of these were curved and consequently were cut off in preparing the specimen. Maximum width is 1.3 cm. The dark specks in this photograph and others are caused by lint and dust which were difficult to eliminate entirely.

found in crystals slowly deformed at temperatures considerably higher than 900°C.[3]

Figure 5 is a photograph of slice 6 cut parallel to the twin. Dislocations which are essentially parallel to the crystal axis appear as lines of equal length parallel to the long axis of the elliptical section. A number of loops on (111) glide planes can be seen; their "pinning" dislocations extend out of the plane of the loops. From this figure the dislocation density is estimated to be of the order of 500 cm^{-2}.

Figure 6 is a photograph of slice 7 containing the twin. The most striking observation is the large number of long straight lines, mostly [011] and [101] directions. As nearly as can be determined, these lie at the position of the twin. (The twin is not independently identifiable by decoration except where dislocations lie at or very near to it.) In most cases it is found that the lines terminate at the periphery at one end, leave the twin in the interior and pass through either the upper or lower surface. A few have been found to lie parallel to the twinning plane over their whole lengths, with both ends emerging at the periphery.

Figure 7 is a photograph at a higher magnification of the region at (*D*4), illustrating the intersection of several lines from above the twin with the twinning plane. The arrows indicate two points of intersection. It is probable that many of the ⟨110⟩ lines in the twinning plane are partial dislocations. This would account for the apparent immobility of these dislocations.

A possible mechanism for the formation of some of these lines is suggested by the loop lying on a $(1\bar{1}1)$

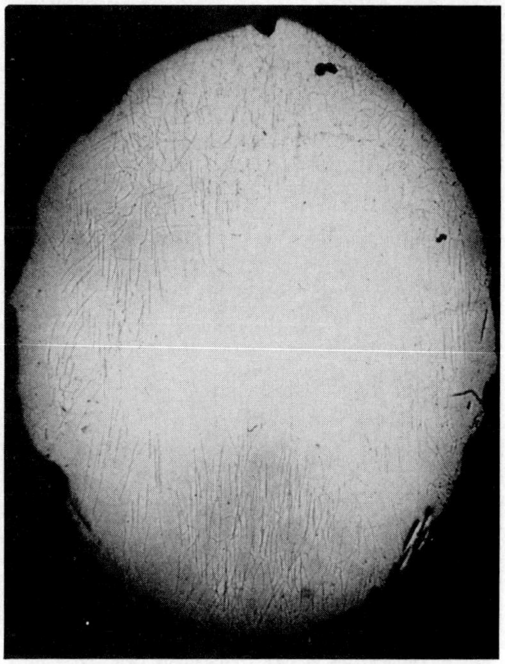

FIG. 5. Dislocations in slice 6 parallel to {111}. There are approximately 500 dislocations per cm^2. Minimum diameter is 1.3 cm.

plane at the center of the section in Fig. 6. The loop appears to be expanding on the glide plane as a result of local stresses. Part of it, indicated by the arrow, lies in the twinning plane as nearly as can be determined and extends in a [110] direction. Further motion of this part of the loop is not possible because the glide plane ends abruptly at the intersection with the twin. If the stress were applied for a sufficiently long time, the line at the twin would extend to the edge of the section at the right.

Several "pileups" of dislocations, which are a series of lines of similar orientation on the same glide plane held apart by mutual repulsion, are clearly visible at (A3) in Fig. 6, and in the stereoscopic view in Fig. 8. Many other such groups are not quite so easily distinguishable but can be detected from etch pits at the surface as shown in Fig. 9. Each group of these dislocations probably originated at a single source some distance above the twin.

At (C5) in Fig. 6 there are hexagonal networks in the twinning plane. These are seen in higher magnification in Fig. 10. They appear to have formed from the interaction of moving dislocations from two different sources in planes parallel to the twin. Hexagonal networks of this nature are conspicuous by their rarity in the silicon crystals studied.

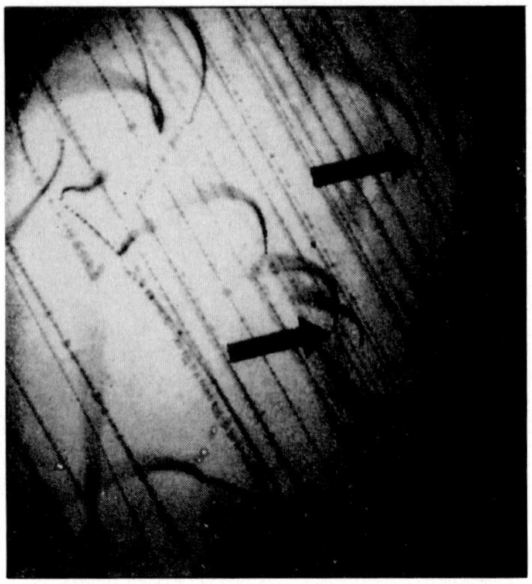

FIG. 7. Enlarged view of region near $D4$ in Fig. 8. The arrows indicate the points where dislocationsfro m above enter the twin plane and abruptly change direction to [011]. Arrow length corresponds to about 0.2 mm.

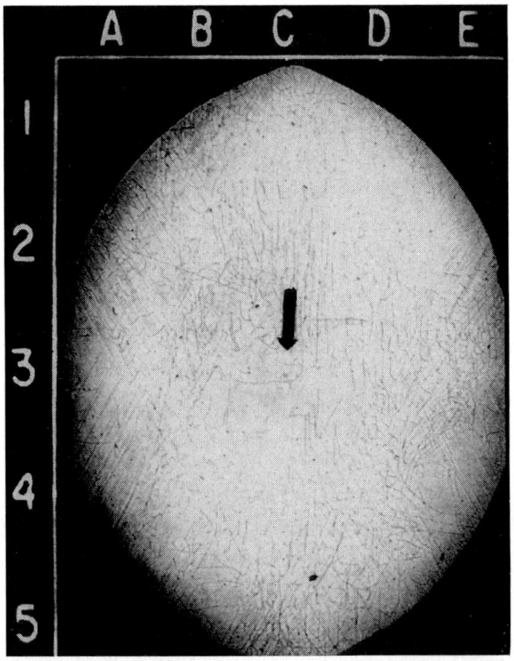

FIG. 6. Dislocations in slice 7 containing twin. Long rows of parallel lines lie in ⟨110⟩ directions at or very near twin plane. Arrow points to a loop forming a [110] line at twin plane. Minimum diameter is 1.25 cm.

Many of the dislocations which intersect the twinning plane from above pass on through. Some have rather abrupt changes in direction as at (C3) in Fig. 6; others have little deviation. Abrupt changes probably occur because the intersection with the twin is a pinning point the parts above and below move independently under local stresses. Those which get through to slice 8 are seen in Fig. 11. The total number is about half as great as that in slice 6. It is probable that this large decrease is due to the fact that the twin serves as a barrier to propagation of the dislocations by deformation.

An observation of considerable importance can be made from slices 3 and 10 in Fig. 4 representing the regions above and below the twin, respectively. (Slice 10 was broken in handling and had to be pieced together. Cracks are responsible for the large dark areas.) The marked tendency of the dislocations to follow the growth axis in the upper part of the specimen is not evident in the lower part. Examination of slices 9, 10, and 11 indicated that most of the dislocations grew toward the surface of the crystal, resulting in a continuously decreasing concentration except for a small amount of plastic generation. This is not a result of a change of growth conditions, but rather of crystallography, since the lower part of slice 3 and upper part of slice 11 grew at the same time. Moreover, the shape of the solid-liquid interface, identified by diffuse groups of copper specks faintly visible in Fig. 4, is everywhere convex toward the melt and does not change noticeably in going through the twin plane. This observation gives

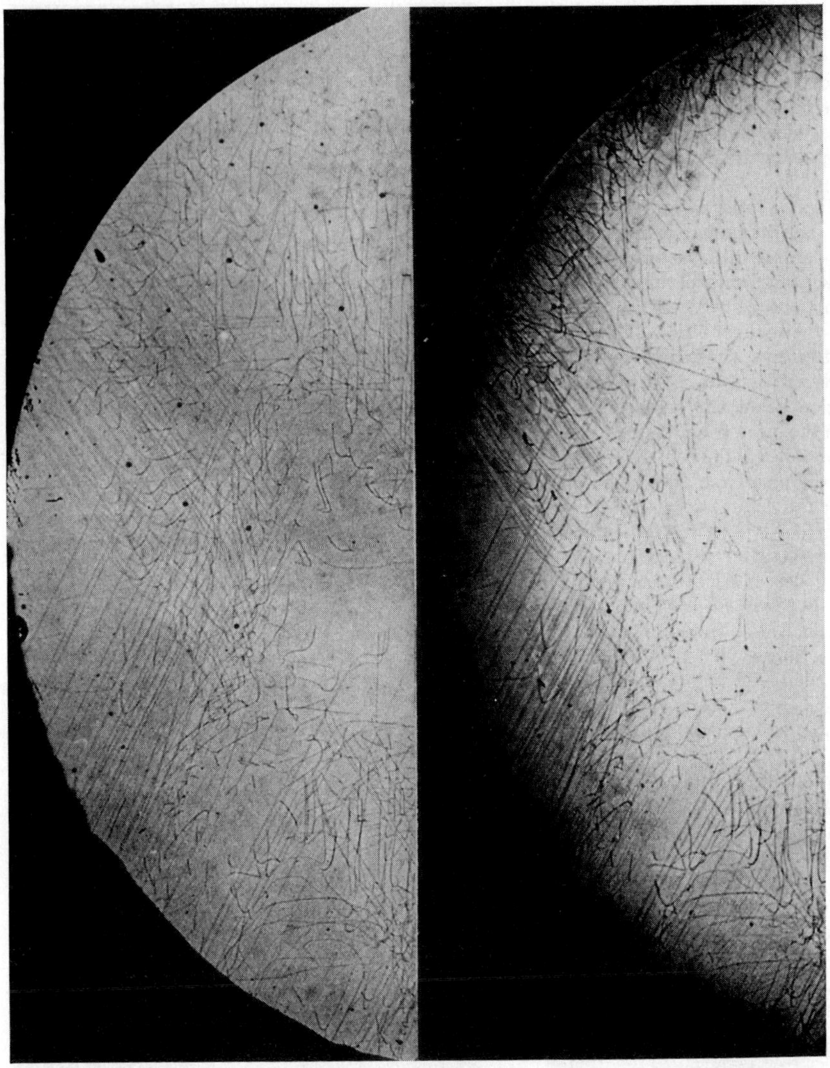

FIG. 8. Stereoscopic view of a portion of slice 7 containing twin. Several groups of "pileups" are clearly visible.

a clue to a mechanism for the elimination of dislocations. This is discussed more fully in a later section.

The specks of copper precipitate mentioned above are commonly observed in regions remote from dislocations. They are more evident in the specimen in Fig. 16. They are usually grouped with a periodicity corresponding to the amount of growth in a single revolution of the crystal. The nuclei at which they form may be aggregates of oxygen or other impurities or possibly vacancy clusters. The size of the specks is very sensitive to the rate of cooling after decoration relatively slow cooling gives rise to large specks, and vice versa. These specks are discussed further in the following in relation to pedestal-grown crystals.

IV. SOURCES OF DISLOCATIONS DURING GROWTH OF A CRYSTAL

A. Generation of Dislocations in the Seeding Process

There appear to be four sources which introduce dislocations into the crystal at the inception of growth on a seed. These are listed and described in the following.

1. *Propagation by growth of the dislocations which emerge from the seed at the solid-liquid interface.*
2. *Multiplication by thermal shock of the dislocations in the seed and propagation by growth of those which emerge at the solid-liquid interface.*
3. *Generation from surface damage.* –Deformation

studies reported in references 1 and 3 indicated that groups of dislocation loops frequently entered from the surface where there was no evidence of a grown-in dislocation to serve as a source. A characteristic of arrays of this type is irregularity of spacing and overlapping of consecutive loops, as seen in Figs. 3 and 4 of reference 3. This differs markedly from the coherence and regularity of spacing of loops observed to originate from a Frank-Read source (Figs. 5 and 6 of reference 3). Recently we discovered that the surface arrays originate from vestiges of surface damage introduced in preparing the specimens for the deformation experiments.

The effect can be demonstrated by using the meltback method to simulate the thermal conditions which occur in a seed. A dislocation-free crystal was lightly scratched with a tungsten carbide scriber at a point several mm from one end. The region below the scribe mark was then melted as shown in the inset in Fig. 1, then allowed to freeze. Upon decoration, it was found that incoherent dislocation loops had expanded from the region of the scratch into the bulk of the crystal (Fig. 12). There is little doubt that these loops were formed when the crystal was heated in the meltback furnace rather than when it was scratched or decorated with copper. If the specimen is etched in (1:3:6) for about 15 minutes after scribing, the damaged material is preferentially removed; the loops do not form when it is heated. The lines in Fig. 12 have the shape characteristic of deformation well above the decoration temperature.[3] It is believed that dislocations are generated in the region very near the scratch, and that they expand into the bulk at high temperature under the influence of thermal stresses. This experiment demonstrates the necessity of careful etching and handling of the seed.

4. Imperfections formed by poor epitaxy.—Dislocations can form at the seed or in other parts of the crystal during growth without multiplication of those already present. This occurs when liquid comes in contact with a solid surface which is contaminated or at too low a temperature to permit perfect epitaxy. The effect is easily demonstrated with a meltback. Surface tension draws the liquid up the bar as the size of the drop increases. When the drop is allowed to freeze before the entire tip is melted through, the result is as shown in Fig. 13. The position of the original surface of the bar is indicated by the arrows.

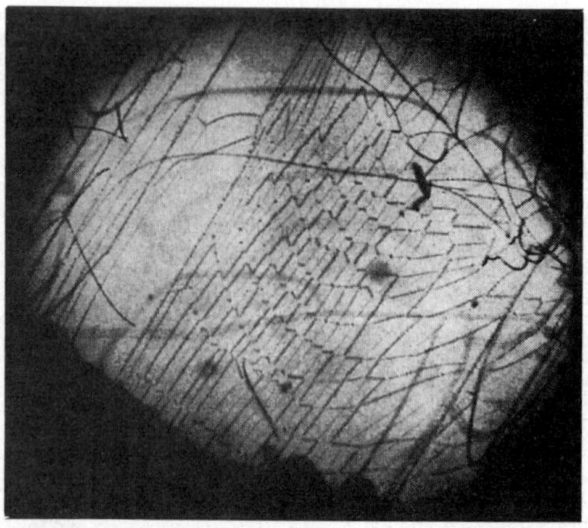

FIG. 10. Hexagonal network of dislocations at *B*5 in Fig. 8. Diameter of field is about 2.5 mm.

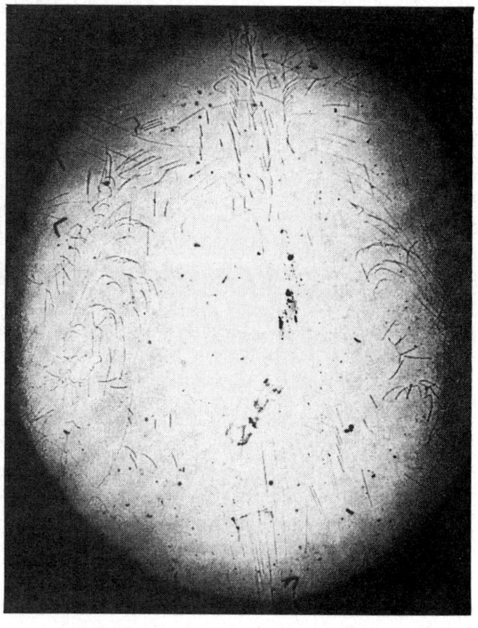

FIG. 11. Dislocations in slice 8 below twin. Only about half of the dislocations in slice 6 have been propagated into this region. Most of the others were removed at the twin. Minimum diameter is about 1.2 cm.

FIG. 9. View of etch pits on external surface of slice 7. Vertical groups represent pileups. High concentration of pits in diagonal line indicates position of twin plane. Periodic horizontal shadings represent the amount of crystal withdrawn in one rotation. Spacing between outer rows of pits is about 0.5 mm.

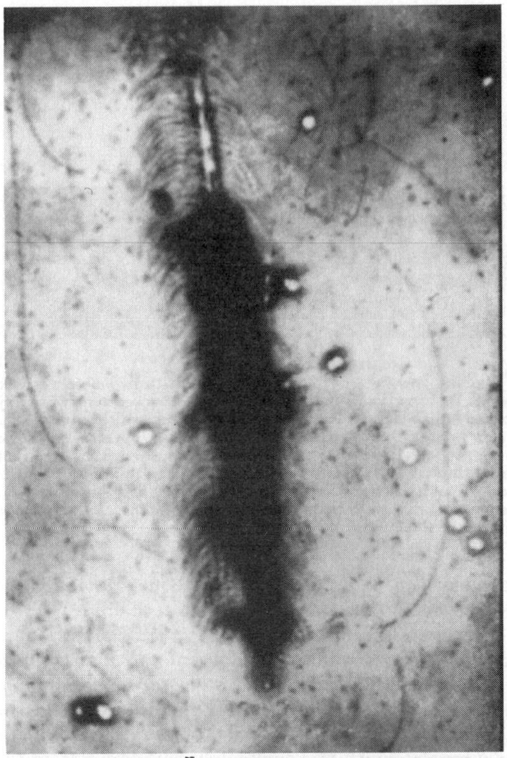

FIG. 12. Generation of dislocation loops from surface damage. A dislocation-free crystal was scribed (dark region in center) and heated in the arrangement used for making meltbacks. Loops expanded into the surrounding region. No loops form if the scribed region is etched away before heating. Width of field is about 0.25 mm.

The region near the arrow at left in Fig. 13 is shown at higher magnification in Fig. 14. Many twins, detectable on the surface, appear in Fig. 14 as a series of crystallographically oriented lines. Traces of the twin planes can be identified internally after decoration because of dislocations which lie parallel to them as in Fig. 6. In addition, a number of dislocations can be seen extending down into the region where the epitaxy was good, whence they are propagated by growth and multiplied by thermal stresses. Although the original crystal was not completely free from dislocations, most of those in Figs. 13 and 14 can be traced back to the region of poor epitaxy.

The incoherent structure is probably caused by contaminants at the surface such as an oxide layer or conceivably by a polycrystalline silicon layer formed by condensation from the vapor. Generation of dislocations by this process is important only at the seed under normal growth conditions. However, specks of solid matter either floating on the surface or suspended in the melt might cause a similar effect at any time during growth.

B. Dislocations Generated in the Main Volume of the Crystal

Another twinned crystal gives further information about the origin of dislocations when growth is well under way. In this specimen two closely-spaced twins lie parallel to the [110] growth axis as sketched in Fig. 15(a), beginning at the surface of the crystal several millimeters below the splice. Since there is an even number of twins, the orientation of the crystal on either side of the twins is the same. The scalloped external shape of the upper part resulted from abrupt increases in the temperature of the melt which were required in order to prevent solidification from a cold spot at the wall of the crucible. Upon etching this crystal in (1:3:10) it was discovered that all of the dislocation etch pits were confined to one side of the twins.

Figure 15(b) shows decorated dislocations in a longitudinal slab cut perpendicular to the twins. Only two small loops (see arrows) are to be found in the lower part of the slab. It is likely that these came from screws which "leaked" through the twin barrier, since they can move on any {111} plane. In contrast, there are in the upper part a number of long [110] dislocations

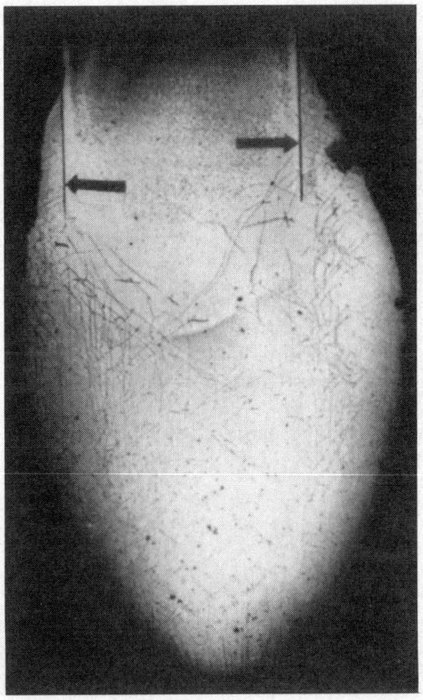

FIG. 13. A decorated meltback which demonstrates the effect of poor epitaxy. The arrows indicate the surface of the original bar. Surface tension caused liquid silicon to climb up the sides of the bar, where it solidified before proper wetting could take place. Most of the dislocations in the lower region came directly or by plastic generation from the region of poor epitaxy. Maximum diameter is about 5 mm.

propagated by growth, as well as large concentrations of tangled lines. These appear to have been generated by multiplication processes under thermal stresses following the abrupt changes in melt temperature.

"Spontaneous" generation from the surface is notably absent in the lower part of the specimen in Fig. 15. Since surface damage is unlikely to occur in growth by the Czochralski method, no deformation is expected from this source.

The absence of spontaneous internal generation of dislocation loops is also noteworthy. Seitz[9] has pointed out that with a sufficiently high vacancy supersaturation in a growing crystal, aggregates might form and eventually collapse into disks bounded by dislocations of Taylor-Orowan character. Continued condensation on the edge of such a disk nearest the interface would result in the formation of a pair of parallel edge dislocations running perpendicular to the interface. Prismatic dislocations can be formed under special conditions described in Sec. VC. If prismitic dislocations do form by vacancy aggregation in as-grown silicon, their diameter can be no greater than about 2 microns, the limit of resolution of the decoration technique.

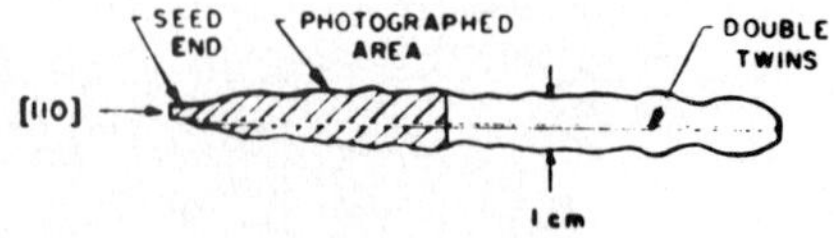

(a)

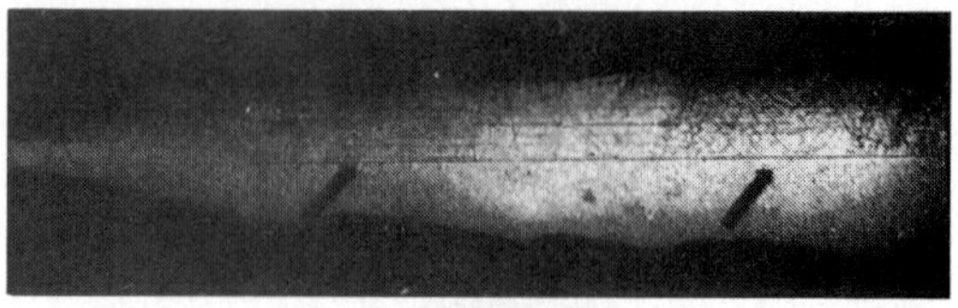

(b)

FIG. 15. Dislocations in a [110] crystal with two closely spaced twins. Deformation from thermal stresses has occurred repeatedly on only that side of the twins which contains dislocations. The other side has only two small loops (marked by arrows). These were probably screws, which can move on any glide plane,that came through the twins from the other side. Other lines on lower part of specimen are scratches on the surface. No "spontaneous" generation of dislocations occurred either internally or at the surface of this half of the crystal.

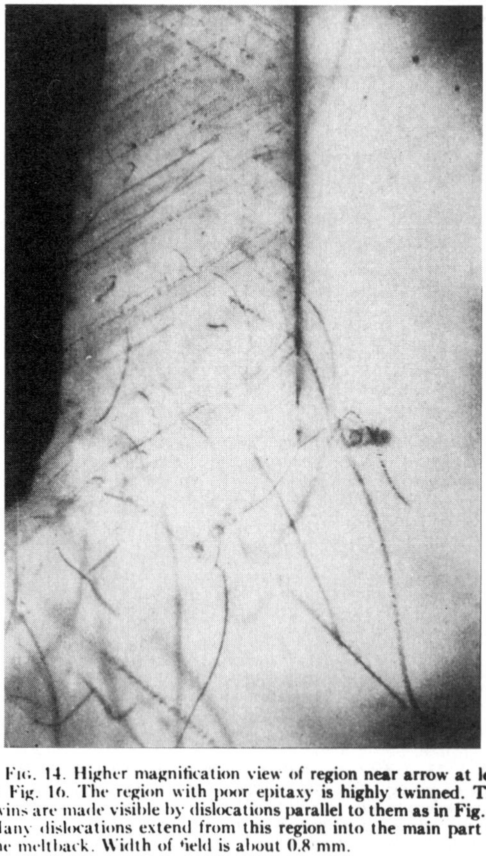

FIG. 14. Higher magnification view of region near arrow at left in Fig. 16. The region with poor epitaxy is highly twinned. The twins are made visible by dislocations parallel to them as in Fig. 6. Many dislocations extend from this region into the main part of the meltback. Width of field is about 0.8 mm.

From the specimen in Fig. 15 it can be seen that thermal stresses which are sufficient to cause appreciable plastic strain when dislocations are present cause no plastic strain under identical conditions but in the absence of dislocations. A similar observation was made on a crystal which was completely withdrawn from the melt during growth and re-inserted a few seconds later. A decorated slice from this specimen is shown in Fig. 16. The line indicated by the arrows identifies the interface between the material grown prior to withdrawal and that grown afterward. The crystal was free from dislocations above this line. None formed from the thermal shock upon re-insertion. In a crystal containing a few dislocations, treatment such as this specimen received results in the appearance of a large density of dislocations. Freedom from dislocations of a part of the crystal in Fig. 16 including the region of thermal shock was confirmed by A. R. Lang using his x-ray technique.[4]

From the specimens in Figs. 15 and 16 one observation deserves further emphasis: dislocations were generated only from other dislocations. This greatly simplifies the problem of growing crystals with high perfection.

C. Concerning Dislocations Generated by Segregation of Impurities

The bottom tip of a crucible grown crystal or of a meltback frequently shows evidence of poor structure. A photograph of a typical "sprout" which has been etched lightly is shown in Fig.17. Examination by infrared transmission of an undecorated sprout reveals a filamentary segregated phase shown in the upper part of Fig. 18. The lower part of this figure shows bire-

[9] F. Seitz, Phys. Rev. 79, 890 (1950).

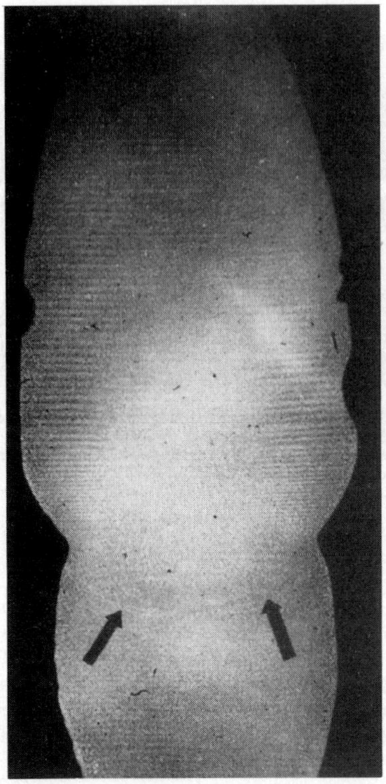

FIG. 16. A decorated slice from a dislocation-free crystal that received a severe thermal shock—extraction from the crucible for several seconds and re-insertion. The rows of copper specks, possibly nucleated by oxygen or vacancy clusters, have a spacing which corresponds to the amount of material withdrawn in one revolution, and delineate the successive interface positions. Maximum diameter is 1.7 cm. The position of the interface on re-insertion is indicated by the arrows. No dislocations were generated by the shock.

fringence in the region of the filaments. Figure 19 is a transmission electron micrograph of a filament, made on a polished specimen about 2 microns thick. Morphologically similar filaments of segregated material are found throughout the volume of the last several grams of a crystal withdrawn from a melt into which a small single crystal of silicon carbide had been placed. Measurements of weight change of the SiC indicated a solubility of 2 to 5×10^{-5} atom fraction in the liquid.[10]

Filaments with the same general appearance have been found in Ge-doped crystals. Other impurities may also produce a similar effect, and indeed impurities in the silicon carbide crystals used may have been responsible for the observations. This is considered to be unlikely, however, because the total impurity content in the SiC dissolved was probably no more than 10^{-8} atom fraction of the total silicon.

[10] R. N. Hall, J. Appl. Phys. 29, 914 (1958).

The volume of the "sprout" in undoped crystals varies from 1 to 50 mm^3 from specimen to specimen. In general, it is of order of one percent of that found in the SiC-doped crystals, which would suggest a lower limit of concentration of the segregating impurity of 10^{-6} to 10^{-7} atom fraction in the average crystal.[11]

Segregated impurities in the "sprout" can affect the dislocations further up the crystal because of differential thermal contraction. The high strain seen by birefringence in Fig. 18 is capable of causing plastic deformation in the region above the sprout if there are dislocations present. This probably accounts for the increased concentration of dislocations at the lower end of many crystals. In specimens in which all of the dislocations have been eliminated, no generation of dislocations occurs in the bulk of the crystal as a result of segregation at the tip. However, there is some evidence from etch pit studies that generation does occur in the immediate vicinity of the filaments.

Tiller[12] has postulated that segregation of solutes on a microscopic scale throughout the growth of a crystal causes the introduction of dislocation lines at the bounding surfaces of the segregate. He calculated that 10^3 to 10^6 dislocations per cm^2 might be expected to form by this process, depending upon impurity content and growth conditions. Goss *et al.*[13] have observed a macroscopic effect analogous to this caused by fluctuations in the freezing rate in Si-doped Ge.

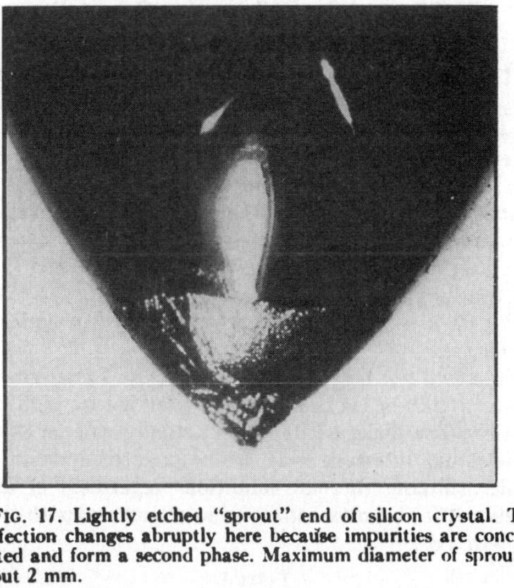

FIG. 17. Lightly etched "sprout" end of silicon crystal. The perfection changes abruptly here because impurities are concentrated and form a second phase. Maximum diameter of sprout is about 2 mm.

[11] H. A. Papazian and S. P. Wolsky [J. Appl. Phys. 27, 1561 (1956)] reported mass spectrometric evidence of carbon in silicon with a concentration around 10^{19} cm^{-3}. This figure appears to be much higher than expected from Hall's measurements, and from the observation that segregation occurs. The discrepancy is not understood.

[12] W. A. Tiller, J. Appl. Phys. 29, 611 (1958).

[13] Goss, Benson, and Pfann, Acta Met. 4, 332 (1956).

No evidence of Tiller's mechanism has thus far been found in the main bulk of silicon crystals which were either undoped or which contained boron at concentrations up to about 10^{-4} atom fraction. The effect of more strongly segregated impurities has not been studied.

V. CONSIDERATIONS INVOLVED IN IMPROVING PERFECTION

A. Preparation of the Seed

The initial dislocation concentration immediately after the commencement of withdrawal of the crystal is determined by the following effects, which have been described in Sec. IV.

(1) Propagation by growth of dislocations initially present in the seed.
(2) Generation of dislocations by thermal stresses in the seed from dislocations already present and propagation of these by growth.
(3) From residual surface damage in the seed.
(4) From poor epitaxy of the newly crystallized material.

These sources can be minimized by care in selection and preparation of the seed, use of a small cross section at the tip, and by allowing sufficient time for complete melting of the original surface of the seed where it contacts the liquid.

B. Effect of Crystallographic Orientation on Plastic Generation

The preferred crystallographic orientations minimize the number of plastically generated dislocations which expand from a source in the solid down to the growing interface. For a crystal of given diameter, the larger the minimum angle between the growth axis and {111} planes, the smaller will be the probability that dislocations formed by thermal stresses will expand, intersect the interface and be propagated. Thus ⟨100⟩ and ⟨111⟩ orientations are more favorable than ⟨110⟩ or ⟨112⟩. Table I lists four low index directions in order of preference.

It should not be concluded from Table I that growth along a ⟨100⟩ or ⟨111⟩ axis will in itself assure high perfection. The dislocations which actually emerge at the solid-liquid interface may be propagated indefinitely under suitable thermal conditions regardless of axis. Figure 20(b) is an example of this in a crystal with ⟨100⟩ growth axis.

TABLE I.

Crystal axis	Smallest angle between axis and a {111} glide plane
⟨100⟩	35.26°
⟨111⟩	19.48°
⟨112⟩	0° (one set of {111} planes)
⟨110⟩	0° (two sets of {111} planes)

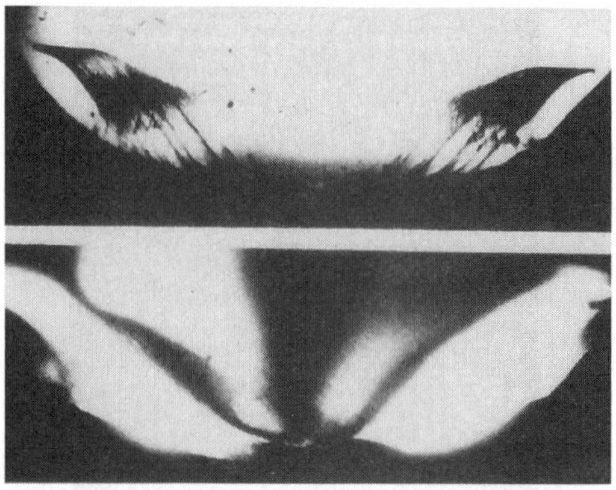

FIG. 18. (a) Infrared transmission of an undecorated sprout, sowing filaments of a segregated impurity. Separation of tips of clusters is about 3 mm. (b) Photograph of the specimen in (a) between crossed polarizers.

The number of dislocations generated by plastic flow will depend upon the nature of thermal stresses while the temperature of the crystal is in the plastic range. Billig[14] has analyzed this problem for the growth of germanium and silicon crystals. However, Figs. 15 and 16 indicate that thermal stresses cause plastic flow only when dislocations capable of motion are present. A moderate number of dislocations can be tolerated in the early stages of growth provided that there is a

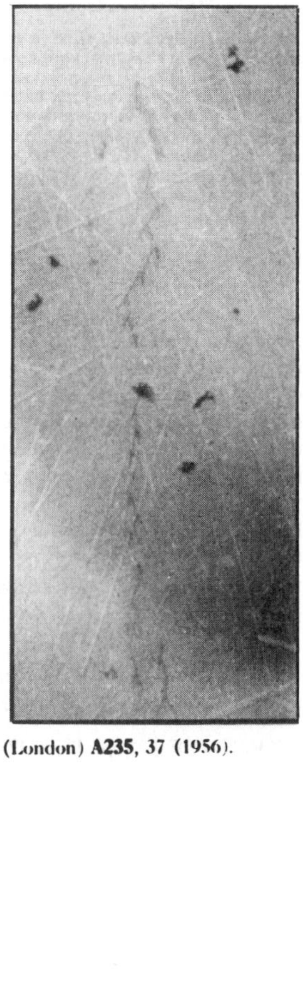

FIG. 19. Transmission electron micrograph of a branched filament of segregated material in sprout. Other lines are surface scratches, produced in preparing specimen. Length of filament is about 30 μ.

[14] E. Billig, Proc. Roy. Soc. (London) A235, 37 (1956).

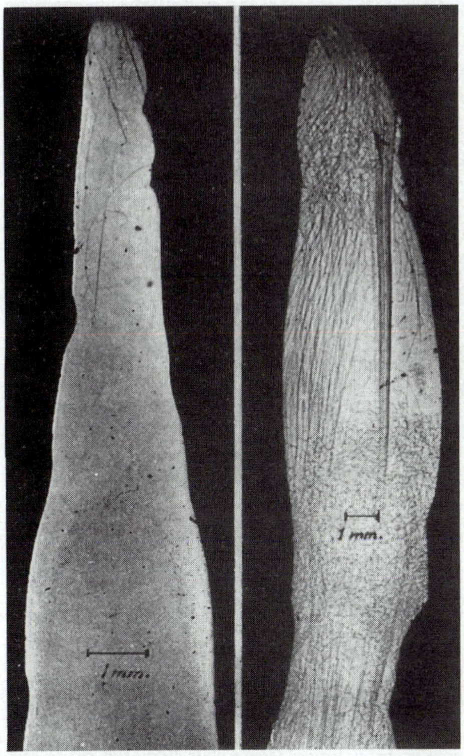

FIG. 20. Dislocations near the seed end of two pedestal crystals illustrating the effect of different growing conditions. (a) Initial withdrawal rate about 3 cm per minute to maintain small diameter and high temperature gradient. All dislocations have been removed in about 5 mm. Note the "island" of copper specks at lower end. (b) Initial withdrawal rate about 4 mm per minute. Diameter increases rapidly, dislocations propagate and multiply by thermal stresses.

mechanism for removing them. When none remain, radial thermal gradients and the shape of the solid-liquid interface no longer influence the dislocation density.

C. Effect of Temperature Gradient and Rate of Growth

Climb of dislocations, caused by a supersaturation of vacancies, provides a mechanism for removing the dislocations which are present in the early stages of growth. The excess vacancy concentration is related to the temperature gradient and to the rate of growth. It is not possible to say *a priori* how the gradient alone will affect the diffusion of vacancies from the liquid into the solid at very small growth rates.[15] The continuous withdrawal of the crystal, however, causes a "quenching-in" of vacancies in the solid when a temperature gradient exists near the solid-liquid interface. This occurs if the vacancies which are present in equilibrium concentration at the solid-liquid interface are not given sufficient time to diffuse to the surface.[9,16] The resulting supersaturation can be relieved by the climb of dislocations or by the condensation of the vacancies into aggregates, as discussed by Frank.[17] Higher rates of growth and larger temperature gradients lead to greater supersaturations.

At the present time there is insufficient quantitative information about vacancy concentrations and diffusion coefficients at fixed temperatures or in thermal gradients to allow the number of excess vacancies to be calculated. However, studies of the perfection of pedestal-grown crystals are qualitatively consistent with the statements made about rate of growth and thermal gradient. The perfection depends critically upon the way in which the initial stages of growth occur. This is illustrated in Fig. 20, which shows decorated dislocations in longitudinal slabs of two different specimens grown under nearly identical conditions. In Fig. 20(a), the diameter of the first part of the crystal is kept small, which is accomplished in this method by a rapid initial withdrawal rate (about 3 cm per minute); the dislocations are completely removed after about 5 mm of growth. The small diameter results in a larger temperature gradient in the first case because of lower efficiency of heating the withdrawn crystal in the electromagnetic field. In Fig. 20(b) the diameter increases rapidly below the splice; the dislocations persist and multiply as growth proceeds. The withdrawal rate where the diameter of the specimens is comparable is approximately 4 mm per minute in both cases. The first specimen, for which the initial growth rate and thermal gradient were both large relative to the second, is quickly freed of dislocations, whereas the second has a large number of dislocations. This behavior is always observed in crystals grown in this manner.

The comparison of the specimens in Fig. 20 is consistent with the idea that a high thermal gradient and high rate of growth produces a vacancy supersaturation. This in turn favors climb of dislocations with an edge component; a pure edge dislocation can be driven completely out of the crystal. It is important to note, however, that under the same conditions a screw dislocation will not be translated in a direction perpendicular to its axis. When the excess of vacancies becomes as large as 1% of the equilibrium concentration, a screw will climb into a helix.[18,19] Growth along a ⟨110⟩ direction has the disadvantage that a screw dislocation which happens

[15] A. D. LeClaire, Phys. Rev. **93**, 344 (1954). The author is indebted to F. S. Ham for discussions of this problem.

[16] A. G. Tweet [J. Appl. Phys. **29**, 1520 (1958)] has reported evidence of a supersaturation of vacancies in germanium crystals grown in a high temperature gradient.

[17] F. C. Frank, *Deformation and Flow of Solids* (Springer-Verlag, Berlin, 1956), p. 73.

[18] Amelinckx, Bontinck, DeKeyser, and Seitz, Phil. Mag. **2**, 355 (1957).

[19] J. Weertman, Phys. Rev. **107**, 1259 (1957).

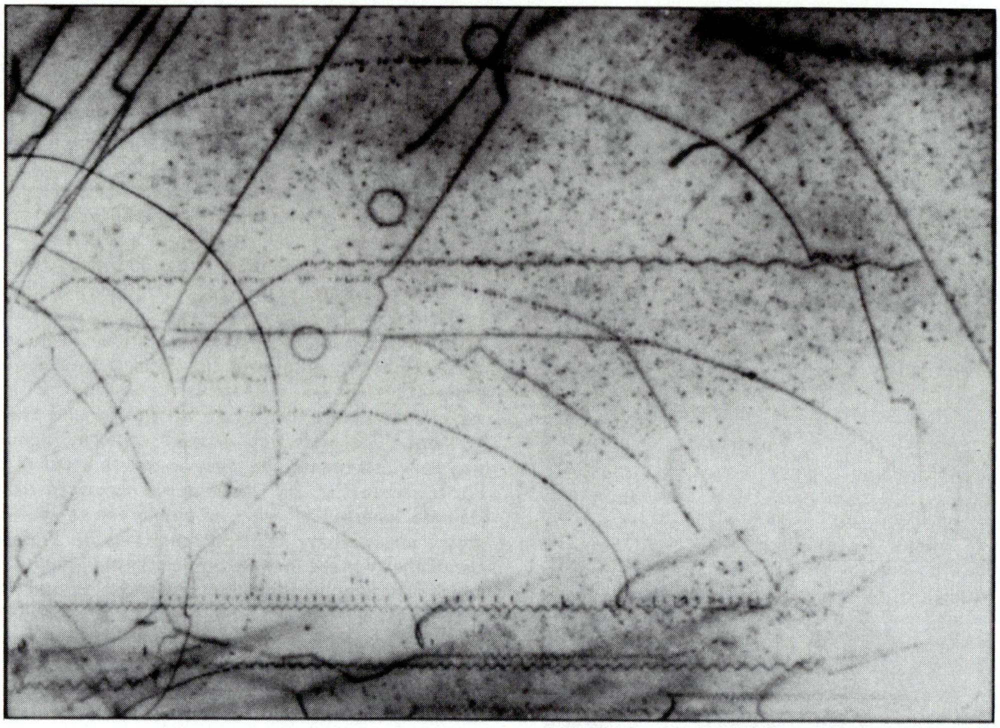

FIG. 21. Climb of dislocations following simultaneous diffusion of copper and gold at 1200°C. Dislocations in screw orientations form tightly wound spirals parallel to ⟨110⟩ orientations. A series of prismatic loops probably formed from a glide dislocation can be seen near bottom. Large loops parallel to {111} plane probably had a different origin: they may be stacking faults bounded by partial dislocations. Diameter of large loops is about 50 μ.

to be oriented parallel to this axis cannot be cast off by climb.

A number of observations illustrate these arguments.

a. Long undeviated dislocations parallel to the growth axis are very common in [110] crystals, as can be seen in Figs. 4 and 15(b). Copper decoration of deformed crystals demonstrated that many such dislocations in a typical [110] crystal were in the screw orientation.

b. Tweet[16] has found helical dislocations with axes aligned parallel to the growth axis in [110] germanium crystals grown in a high temperature gradient and then brought to room temperature over a period of about 10 to 15 minutes.

c. A qualitative idea of the effect of an excess of point defects on the configuration of dislocations in silicon has been obtained by simultaneous diffusion of gold and copper into a specimen at about 1200°C.[20] The mechanism is not understood. It is possible that gold ions change the normal vacancy concentration.[21] Further experimental results are necessary to clarify the detailed mechanism.

For the purposes of the present investigation, several observations can be made from the specimen shown in Fig. 21: Helices with strictly ⟨110⟩ orientations are formed. From the analyses by Amelinckx *et al.*[18] and by Weertman[19] they were formed from nearly pure screw dislocations. The sequence of prismatic loops seen on edge near the bottom of the photograph was apparently formed from a glide dislocation, since their Burgers vector is ⟨110⟩. The large loops lie on {111} planes; these presumably have a different origin. They may be regions of stacking fault surrounded by partial dislocations.

Prismatic loops can be seen in the process of forming from a glide dislocation in Fig. 22. Successive loops are being cut off from a helix as a result of inter-turn repulsion and expansion of the helix with respect to the remainder of the dislocation. As the loops are cut off, their spacing increases because of mutual repulsion. A

[20] A preliminary account of these studies was presented at the Chicago Meeting of the American Physical Society, March 27, 1958. See Bull. Am. Phys. Soc. Ser. II, 3, 106 (1958). A discussion of the mechanism of generation of prismatic loops from a glide dislocation was published by William C. Dash, Phys. Rev. Letters 1, 400 (1958).

[21] F. A. Kröger and H. J. Vink [J. Phys. Chem. Solids 5, 208 (1958)] discuss the effect of impurities upon vacancy concentration in solids.

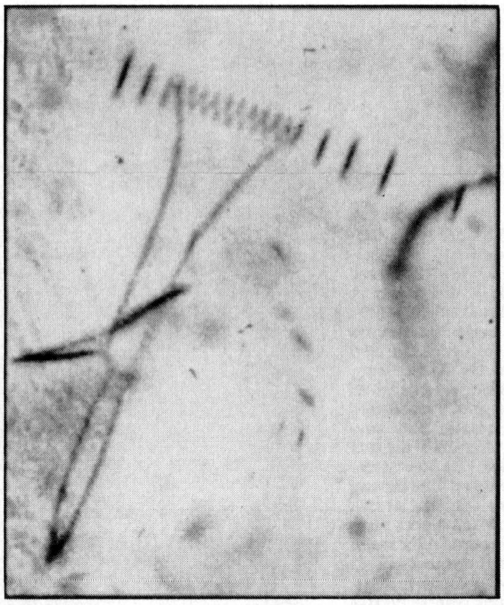

FIG. 22. Generation of prismatic loops from a glide dislocation following simultaneous copper and gold diffusion at 1200°C. Distance between outermost loops is 150 μ.

process such as this could account for the very regularly spaced prismatic loops in Fig. 21.

In summary, an excess of point defects tends to lock a screw dislocation parallel to the Burgers vector, whereupon it can propagate undeviated a long distance. With even a slight helicoidal shape it becomes difficult to move by glide. If the growth axis is not parallel to the Burgers vector, the screw will eventually grow out to the surface.

In one specimen with a [100] growth axis a single straight [100] dislocation over 10 cm long was found. In several other [100] crystals a few dislocations have persisted under conditions which favor climb. In order to be consistent with the ideas expressed here, the Burgers vector of these dislocations would have to be [100]. However, further information is required in order to be certain that the Burgers vector of the dislocations is [100]. No preferential alignment parallel to the growth axis has been found in [111] or [112] crystals grown under conditions which favor a vacancy excess.

The usual behavior encountered in crystals grown with an axis other than ⟨110⟩ is a continuous decrease in dislocation concentration with growth if excessive plastic generation is avoided. This was mentioned earlier in connection with the twinned specimen described in Sec. III. Many of the dislocations below the twin plane in that specimen were grown out to the surface in a short distance, as seen in the lower part of Fig. 4.

Another illustration of the gradual removal of dislocations during growth is shown in the specimen in Fig. 23. The long, smoothly curved lines in the center and on the right-hand side are confined largely to {111} planes. These were probably generated by glide several hundred degrees below the melting point. In contrast, those on the left-hand side show considerable evidence of climb. The zig-zag lines near the arrow are shown in the inset at higher magnification. They are irregular spirals with sections which are primarily edge alternating with sections which are primarily screw. The circumstances that led to the formation of these configurations are not known in detail. The curvature of the edge portions is indicative of a vacancy supersaturation of the order of 10^{-4}, as computed from the Bardeen-Herring climb formula[22] for an edge dislocation with a radius of 1 mm. The interpretation of this curvature quantitatively in terms of supersaturation is questionable, however, since steady-state conditions were not maintained.

VI. A PROCEDURE FOR GROWING DISLOCATION-FREE SILICON CRYSTALS

The results discussed in the preceding section suggest that by proper selection and preparation of the seed and by establishing growth conditions which favor the elimination of residual dislocations by climb, crystals largely free from dislocations may be grown. A procedure for achieving this in crucible- or pedestal-grown crystals is outlined below:

A seed crystal as free as possible from dislocations is desirable; a perfect crystal is not essential. Mechanical operations at room temperature required to prepare the seed do not affect the bulk perfection.[2] Surface damage, including relatively severe cracks from saw cutting, is readily removed by careful etching with (1:3:6) followed by a chemical polish with (1:3:0). A small diameter over all or a long taper to a small diameter at the tip of the seed is desirable in order to minimize thermal stresses upon splicing and to minimize the total number of dislocations at the interface. A ⟨111⟩ orientation is preferred, although in most cases a ⟨100⟩ orientation is also satisfactory.

When the seed is inserted into the melt, sufficient time and a high enough melt temperature should be provided to assure complete melting of the wetted surface and therefore removal of possible contaminants which might generate dislocations.

The diameter of the crystal during its initial growth should be kept as small as possible to provide a maximum opportunity for dislocations to grow out. This requires that the temperature of the melt be kept relatively high at first. The growth of the initial small diameter portion is maintained for a distance equal to several times its diameter.

The melt temperature can then be lowered to increase

[22] J. Bardeen and C. Herring, *Imperfections in Nearly Perfect Crystals*, edited by W. Shockley *et al.* (John Wiley and Sons, Inc., New York, 1952), p. 261.

the diameter of the crystal. No fundamental limitation on maximum diameter is expected; none has been found with the largest crystals thus far grown, namely 50 grams in weight with a maximum diameter of 2.2 cm.

When the initial stages have been carried out properly, the perfection is insensitive to fluctuations in diameter or to other details of further growth.

The specimen shown in Fig. 2 is a typical example of a dislocation-free crystal grown from a crucible. Numerous [100] and [111] crystals, as well as one with [110] orientation completely free of dislocations over at least 90% of their length have been grown from a crucible in this way.

Many [100] and [111] crystals grown by the pedestal method have likewise been found to be free from dislocations over most of their length. The orientation is especially important in this case because twins caused by poor epitaxy around the periphery of the seed commonly occur, but are easily cast off when the axis is not parallel to a {111} plane.

Several Ge crystals free of dislocations have been grown by a direct application of the above procedure. A CP–4 etch on {111} planes was used to determine the presence of dislocations.[23] This is not quite as satisfactory as a decoration process, since only the surface can be examined. However, Tweet's[16] results on Ge crystals grown under similar conditions give confirmation that an accurate determination of dislocation density can be made. There can be little doubt that the qualitative behavior of dislocations during growth of both germanium and silicon is the same.

VII. DISCUSSION

At the time of writing, approximately 20 silicon crystals free from dislocations of detectable size have been grown from a quartz crucible and a comparable number by the pedestal method. As mentioned earlier, dislocation loops less than 2 microns in diameter would escape detection by the methods used. Although the growth conditions (growth rate, temperature gradient, rotation, etc.) differ greatly between the two methods, these findings fit a comparatively simple pattern. With the exception of the external effects discussed above, plastic deformation accounts for the generation of all of the dislocations in a crystal grown as described. Climb caused by vacancy supersaturation modifies the distribution and provides a mechanism for eliminating dislocations. The seed preparation and initial growth must be carried out in a way which minimizes plastic flow and removes the residual dislocations. When this is done, the remainder of the crystal is free from dislocations despite considerable changes in growth variables. The withdrawn and re-inserted specimen in Fig. 16 demonstrates that a crystal entirely free of dislocations can be grown from a clean, dislocation-free seed.

[23] Vogel, Pfann, Corey, and Thomas, Phys. Rev. 90, 489 (1953).

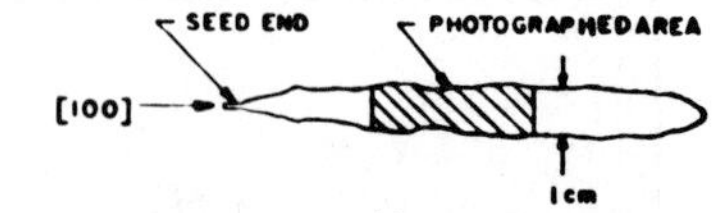

(a)

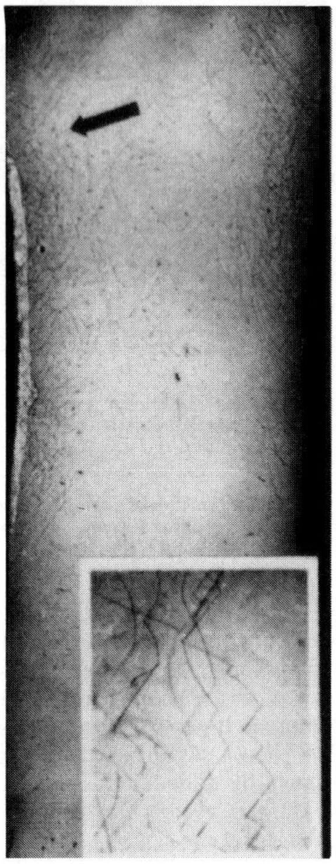

(b)

FIG. 23. Dislocations in a [100] specimen viewed in the [011] direction. A gradual improvement in perfection occurs with continued growth. The long, smoothly curved lines were probably formed by plastic flow several hundred degrees below the melt temperature. The zig-zag lines near the arrow, shown at higher magnification in the inset, are composed of sections which are alternately primarily edge and primarily screw. This is believed to indicate climb and glide in the region of the growing interface. Width of region shown in inset is about 0.4 mm.

Aggregation of vacancies might occur at places sufficiently removed from dislocations and from surfaces. The randomly distributed specks of copper found in the center of the pedestal-grown specimen in Fig. 20(a) might have been nucleated by clusters of vacancies which were too far from the surface to enable them to be removed. Some etching properties of the Ge crystals grown by Tweet[16] have a similar geometrical distribution to the copper specks in Fig. 20(a).

When all of the dislocations have been eliminated, there is no longer any advantage in maintaining growth conditions which favor climb. There may in fact be disadvantages if aggregation of vacancies is undesirably large. For this reason it may be necessary at this stage to use an after-heater and to cool slowly to room temperature. This would tend to remove a large fraction of the excess vacancies which otherwise might aggregate internally.

In view of the success of Frank's[24] screw dislocation mechanism for the growth of crystals, we may consider briefly its applicability to the present case. Frank's mechanism satisfactorily explains growth from vapor or solution under quasi-equlibrium conditions, where a supersaturation of 1% or less is sufficient to make ordinary crystals grow. The step formed on the surface where a screw dislocation emerges provides a self-perpetuating edge where atoms can be accommodated without the necessity of two-dimensional nucleation each time a layer is completed. In growth from the melt by the methods used in this investigation, near-equilibrium conditions are not maintained; a substantial temperature gradient exists in the solid. The interface can become supercooled by whatever amount is required to produce two-dimensional nucleation. It would be of interest to compare the temperature of the solid-liquid interface during growth of a dislocation-free crystal and of crystals with different numbers of dislocations. The effect of orientation on interface temperature would also be worthy of study.

The result of the present experiments can be helpful at least as a guide for improving the perfection of other crystals. Surface damage has been shown to be an important source of dislocations. This can be much more troublesome in crystals which deform readily at room temperature. Great care in handling the seed and the grown crystal is essential. The growth conditions required for the success of the climb mechanism of eliminating dislocations will vary from one material to another. For some substances, it may be necessary to grow at a slow rate with a low thermal gradient and small diameter; this would prevent too large a supersaturation of vacancies and subsequent generation of prismatic dislocations if such a process were found to be important. In crystals in which partial dislocations are found, the climb mechanism may be ineffective because a large surface energy of misfit would be created if if they were to move out of their glide planes.[22] However, for many substances it might be possible to use the procedure outlined for silicon to grow dislocation-free crystals with only such modifications as are required by dislocation geometry. Germanium is an example of a crystal for which no modification is necessary.

[24] For a discussion of this mechanism see Burton, Cabrera, and Frank, Phil. Trans. Roy. Soc. (London) A243, 299 (1951).

VIII. SUMMARY

The sources of dislocations in all phases of the growth of silicon crystals by the Czochralski method have been investigated by etching and copper decoration techniques. Poor epitaxy and surface damage in the seed are important sources at the commencement of growth. In the bulk of the crystal only plastic generation forms dislocations which propagate by growth. No prismatic loops of detectable size formed by vacancy aggregation are found. Segregation of some impurity, possibly silicon carbide, in the form of dendrites has been found at the tip of most crystals. When no grown-in dislocations are present, the dendrites have no effect on the bulk perfection.

If sufficient care is taken in the selection and preparation of the seed and in the initial stages of growth, the growing crystal will contain only those dislocations which have propagated by growth from the seed. Removal of these can be achieved by growing a small diameter portion wherein conditions which favor climb are maintained. Under these conditions, an edge or mixed dislocation is readily eliminated. A screw dislocation will become locked parallel to its axis and may form a helix in a sufficient vacancy supersaturation. To cast off screws it is important that all screw orientations make a finite angle with the growth axis. ⟨100⟩ and ⟨111⟩ axes are preferred for this purpose. When all dislocations have been removed, further generation does not occur despite considerable variation of growth conditions.

Germanium crystals have been grown free from dislocations by a direct application of the procedure outlined for silicon. It is believed that the procedure will prove to be of value for improving the perfection of other crystals as well.

ACKNOWLEDGMENTS

The author is greatly indebted to F. Hubbard Horn, who provided the author with a large number of silicon crystals over a period of several years. He is indebted also to L. J. Keifer, R. F. Reihl, and R. Zmijewski, who grew and prepared many other specimens for this investigation.

The x-ray investigation of dislocations in silicon by A. R. Lang of Harvard University and the electron microscopy by A. S. Holik are gratefully acknowledged.

The author also wishes to thank J. W. Mitchell for valuable discussions and criticism of the manuscript. W. W. Tyler and A. G. Tweet also contributed very helpful criticisms of the manuscript.

Facets and Anomalous Solute Distributions in Indium–Antimonide Crystals

By K. F. Hulme and J. B. Mullin
Ministry of Supply, Royal Radar Establishment,
Great Malvern, Worcestershire

[Received September 28, 1959]

We have found that, during the growth of InSb crystals from the melt, the presence of a planar crystallographic $\{111\}$ facet at the solid–liquid interface can profoundly affect the solute distribution in the growing solid. The effect is not due to a solute-enriched boundary layer existing because of inadequate stirring, but to a genuine difference in k^*, the distribution coefficient on and off a $\{111\}$ facet (k^* = ratio of solute concentrations in solid and liquid *at the interface*, under the given growth conditions; see eqn. 13, Burton *et al.* 1953). The difference can be large for Te, and for a residual donor impurity (which might also be Te).

Our evidence was obtained from crystals pulled from the melt by the Czochralski technique using rotation rates of ~ 100 r.p.m., pull rates of ~ 2 cm/hr and seed crystals oriented close to a $\langle 111 \rangle$ direction.

The ends of these crystals when parted from the residual melt by a sharp increase in pull rate often showed a planar facet on an otherwise curved surface. X-ray orientation determinations have shown that, with one exception so far, the facets are $\{111\}$ planes; we have observed a $\{100\}$ facet on a heavily twinned crystal, but have not attempted to determine the effect of {100} facets on solute distributions. The facet sizes ranged from ~ 2 mm to ~ 3 cm diameter, depending on the general interface curvature (the solid interface is convex in our case, at least in the final stages of crystal growth). If the seed is slightly off the ⟨111⟩ orientation the facet is off-axis (see fig. 1, Pl. 155); the rings on the end are thought to be associated with the way in which the rotating crystal parted from the melt rather than a true growth feature.

The autoradiograph shown in fig. 2 (Pl. 155) is a section parallel to the growth axis of a single crystal doped with radio-Te. The Te is concentrated on one side of the crystal: the straight lines present in the area of enhanced concentration were found to be parallel to a {111} plane, and are attributed to fluctuations in the growth conditions; they indicate that a {111} facet was present during growth at one side of the interface. The end of this crystal showed a facet at the appropriate side. The donor concentrations obtained by Hall constant measurements were $1{\cdot}5 \times 10^{19}$ and $2{\cdot}4 \times 10^{18}$ per cm^3 respectively in and out of the Te-enhanced region—thus Te is in true atomic solution in both regions. On the basis of previous measurements of distribution coefficients (Mullin 1958, Strauss 1959) and the concentration ratio of ~ 6 quoted above, we conclude that, for growth rates of ~ 2 cm/hr $k^* \sim 3$ on a {111} facet and $k^* \sim 0{\cdot}5$ off a facet—a striking difference, the values being on opposite sides of unity; the value of $\sim 0{\cdot}9$ obtained with polycrystalline material (Harman 1956, Hulme and Mullin 1957, Mullin and Hulme 1958) represents a weighted mean.

For a series of undoped crystals, regions were often found, in slices taken perpendicular to the growth direction, in which the donor concentrations were 6–15 times greater than the donor concentrations in adjacent regions of the slice. In two crystals where slices were taken close to the ends which showed {111} facets the area of high donor concentration corresponded in size and position to the facet. In these two cases the melt was vigorously swirled in the opposite direction to the crystal rotation, by means of a 400 cycle rotating magnetic field; the effect cannot, therefore, reasonably be ascribed to inadequate stirring. In two other crystals, a single twin grew, in which the growth direction was now almost ⟨511⟩; in slices showing both orientations the {111} area showed the usual high donor density region surrounded by a low donor density region whereas the twinned area, on which a {111} facet would not be expected to appear, was uniform and had low donor concentration. These observations indicate that k^* for the residual donor impurity is also markedly different on and off a {111} facet.

InSb belongs to the point group 43m and faces of the form {111} show etch pits in CP4, whereas faces of the form {111} do not (Allen 1957, Dewald 1957). All the observations quoted apply to crystals in which the face exposed to the melt did not show etch pits and was therefore {111}; reliable information on {111} facets is at present lacking.

As far as the authors are aware the possible importance of facets on segregation in melt-grown crystals has not been previously demonstrated although for Ge there have been indications (Burton, Kolb, Slichter and Struthers 1953, Burton, Prim and Slichter 1953, Hall 1953) of $\sim 10\%$ variations in k with growth direction. In crystal growth from aqueous solution the effect is well known (i.e. 'hour-glass' crystals, Buckley 1951). It must be attributed to differential adsorption on the interface and the values of k^* on {111} facets will be expected to depend markedly on growth rate, and perhaps on concentration. The values of k^* off a {111} facet might be expected to depend to a lesser extent on interface orientation, growth rate, and concentration. It would be interesting to know whether there are other examples of the effect in melt-grown crystals as clearly manifested as that involving Te in InSb, and whether {100} and other facets are important. This work will be published in greater detail together with further observations in due course.

Acknowledgments

It is a pleasure to acknowledge the experimental contributions of O. Jones and W. H. E. Wilgoss and the assistance of J. Wright, J. Elcox, M. Crofts and M. Stevens, and also valuable discussions with Dr. W. Bardsley.

This letter is published by permission of the Controller, H.B.M. Stationery Office.

References

Allen, J. W., 1957, *Phil. Mag.*, **2**, 1475.
Buckley, J. E., 1951, *Crystal Growth* (London : Chapman & Hall), p. 416.
Burton, J. A., Prim, R. C., and Slichter, W. P., 1953, *J. chem., Phys.*, **21**, 1987.
Burton, J. A., Kolb, E. D., Slichter, W. P., and Struthers, J. D., 1953, *J. chem. Phys.*, **21**, 1991.
Dewald, J. F., 1957, *J. electrochem. Soc.*, **104**, 244.
Harman, T. C., 1956, *J. electrochem. Soc.*, **103**, 128.
Hall, R. N., 1953, *J. phys. Chem.*, **57**, 86.
Hulme, K. F., and Mullin, J. B., 1957, *J. Electron. Contr.*, **3**, 160.
Mullin, J. B., and Hulme, K. F., 1958, *J. Electron. Contr.*, **4**, 170.
Mullin, J. B., 1958, *J. Electron. Contr.*, **4**, 358.
Strauss, A. J., 1959, *J. appl. Phys.*, **30**, 559.

VAPOR-LIQUID-SOLID MECHANISM OF SINGLE CRYSTAL GROWTH

R. S. Wagner and W. C. Ellis
Bell Telephone Laboratories, Inc.
Murray Hill, New Jersey

(new method: growth "catalysis" from impurity; whiskers, epitaxial, and large crystals; Si; E)

(Received 4 February 1964)

Detailed studies of the morphology and growth of silicon whiskers[1] have led to a new concept of crystal growth from the vapor, which we call here the vapor-liquid-solid (VLS) mechanism. From these and subsequent studies, in which Si whiskers were grown by the disproportionation of SiI_2 or by the hydrogen reduction of $SiCl_4$, three important facts emerged: (a) silicon whiskers do not contain an axial screw dislocation;[2] (b) an impurity is essential for whisker growth;[3] (c) a small globule is present at the tip of the whisker during growth.

From fact (a) and related evidence, it became clear that growth from the vapor did not occur by the Frank[4] screw dislocation mechanism. From facts (b) and (c), and much additional evidence, the VLS mechanism emerged. In this mechanism, the role of the impurity is to form a liquid alloy droplet of relatively low freezing temperature. The liquid droplet is a preferred site for deposition from the vapor, which causes the liquid to become supersaturated with Si. The whisker grows by precipitation of Si from the droplet. Since the whisker grows from the liquid, a screw dislocation is unnecessary.

Growth of seeded whiskers of Si using gold as an impurity occurs as follows: A small particle of Au is placed on a {111} surface of a Si wafer and heated to 950°C, forming a small droplet of Au–Si alloy as shown in Fig. 1*a*. A mixture of hydrogen and $SiCl_4$ is introduced as described by H. C. Theuerer.[5] The liquid alloy acts as a preferred sink for arriving Si atoms or, perhaps more likely, as a catalyst for the chemical process involved. The Si enters the liquid and freezes out, with a very small concentration of Au in solid solution, at the interface between solid Si and the liquid alloy. By a continuation of this process the alloy droplet becomes displaced from the substrate crystal and "rides" atop the growing whisker, as shown in Fig. 1*b*. The growth direction is <111>, and the side faces of the whisker are usually {211} but sometimes {211} and {110}. The whisker grows in length by this mechanism until the Au is consumed or until the growth conditions are changed.

VLS growth of Si whiskers can occur over a wide range of cross-sectional dimensions, as shown by the 1000-Å whisker and the 0.2-mm needle in Fig. 2*a* and 2*b*. In these examples, VLS growth was interrupted before the Au was consumed. Similar results were obtained with Pt, Ag, Pd, Cu, or Ni either by placing a particle on the Si substrate or by co-deposition. VLS growth of twinned Si ribbons having a <211> or a <110> growth direction and {111} main faces[6] has been observed.

The selection of a proper impurity for VLS growth depends on a number of factors such as, formation of a liquid alloy at the deposition temperature, vapor-liquid-solid interfacial energies, distribution coefficient and inertness to the reaction products. The term impurity is used in a broad sense. For VLS growth of compound crystals, for example GaAs, an excess of one of the component materials can act as a liquid-forming impurity. In some cases a combination of two or more impurities can be used.

The VLS growth mechanism explains many observations of the effect of impurities in crystal growth from the vapor. Crystals of α-Al_2O_3 (ref 7) and

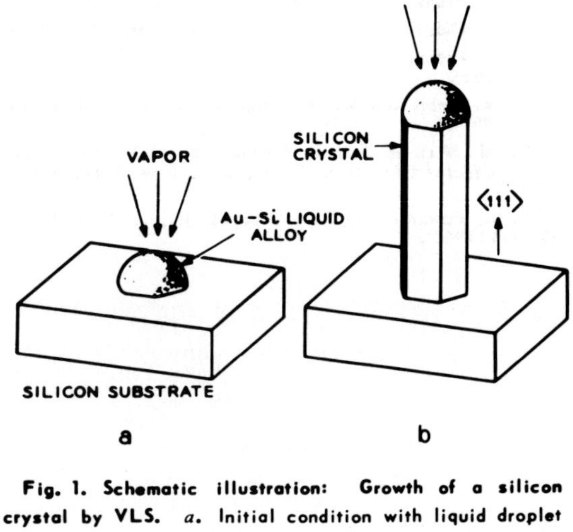

Fig. 1. Schematic illustration: Growth of a silicon crystal by VLS. *a*. Initial condition with liquid droplet on substrate. *b*. Growing crystal with liquid droplet at the tip.

SiC (ref 8), which have been shown to have rounded terminations, may have grown by the VLS mechanism. In the growth of BeO whiskers, which also show rounded terminations, Edwards and Happel[9] suggested that a droplet of molten Be was present at the tip of the growing whisker. However, they also postulated a solid shell of BeO enclosing the liquid Be, diffusion of oxygen through this shell and the need for a crystalline defect, presumably a screw dislocation. None of these features is a requirement of the VLS mechanism.

The proposed mechanism has widespread application to the growth of both filamentary and macroscopic crystals and of epitaxial layers. Controlled growth can be obtained through appropriate use of impurities in patterns or films on substrate surfaces and on single-crystal seeds of many substances. *P-N* junctions and heterojunctions can be made. Dislocation-free crystals can be grown.

W. G. Pfann contributed importantly to this work in numerous stimulating discussions. We are also grateful to H. C. Theuerer for valuable guidance in setting up the conditions for the $SiCl_4$ reduction and to R. D. Heidenreich and K. A. Jackson for helpful suggestions in the electron microscope studies.

1. R. S. Wagner, W. C. Ellis, K. A. Jackson, and S. M. Arnold (for publication in *J. Appl. Phys.*).
2. R. S. Wagner and W. C. Ellis, *J. Metals* **15**, 76 (1963).
3. E. S. Greiner, J. A. Gutowski, and W. C. Ellis, *J. Appl. Phys.* **32**, 2489 (1961).
4. F. C. Frank, *Discussions Faraday Soc.* **5**, 48 (1949).
5. H. C. Theuerer, *J. Electrochem. Soc.* **108**, 649 (1961).
6. R. S. Wagner and R. G. Treuting, *J. Appl. Phys.* **32**, 2490 (1961).
7. W. W. Webb and W. D. Forgeng, *J. Appl. Phys.* **28**, 1449 (1957).
8. K. M. Merz in *Silicon Carbide—A High Temperature Semiconductor* (Pergamon Press, Inc., New York, 1960), p 73.
9. P. L. Edwards and R. J. Happel, Jr., *J. Appl. Phys.* **33**, 943 (1962).

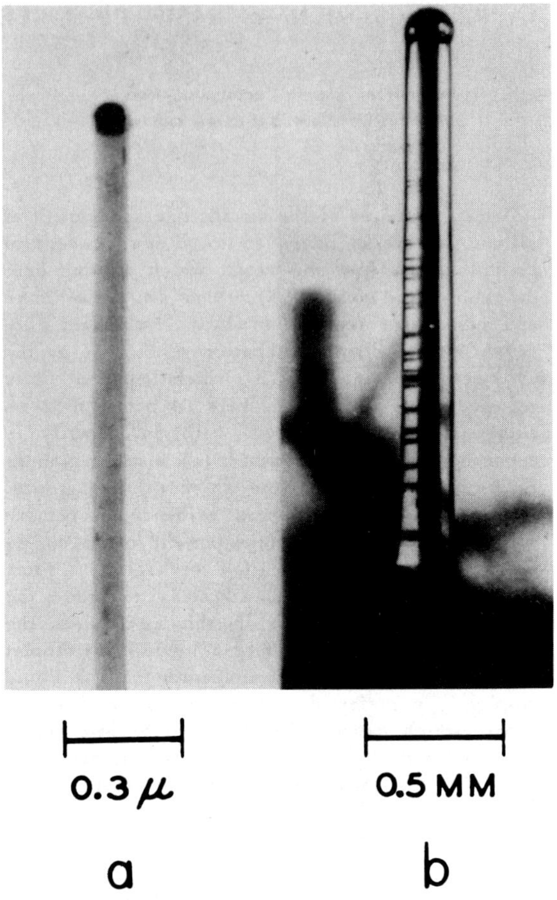

Fig. 2. Silicon crystals showing solidified gold-silicon alloy at tip. *a*, Transmission electron micrograph of a 1000-Å whisker. *b*. Photograph of a crystal seeded on a {111} substrate. This is a twelve-sided needle with alternating {211} and {110} faces.

Journal of Crystal Growth 68 (1984) 111–122
North-Holland, Amsterdam

A CRITICAL APPRAISAL OF GROWTH MECHANISMS IN MOVPE

G.B. STRINGFELLOW

Department of Materials Science and Engineering, University of Utah, Salt Lake City, Utah 84112, USA

The metalorganic vapor phase epitaxial (MOVPE) growth process will be considered by first examining, individually, each of the four fundamental aspects of the overall reaction: (1) thermodynamics, (2) homogeneous gas phase reactions, (3) mass transport, and (4) surface kinetic processes. These will first be examined in general, and then an attempt will be made to understand the MOVPE process in terms of these fundamental concepts using data for specific III/V systems as examples. Thermodynamics yields information concerning the basic driving force for both the crystal growth process itself and undesirable parasitic reactions occurring homogeneously in the vapor phase and on the reactor walls upstream from the substrate. Thermodynamic factors often control the solid composition of III/V alloys. The primary homogeneous gas phase reactions, pyrolysis of the reactants and adduct formation, possibly accompanied by elimination reactions which lead to polymer formation on the walls, will be examined. The vast difference in behavior between systems using trimethyl–versus triethyl–group III sources will be explored for the growth of Ga and In containing III/V compounds and alloys. In addition, the pyrolysis of both MO source molecules and the group V hydrides will be examined, especially relative to the determination of solid composition. For many systems, at ordinary growth temperatures, the MOVPE growth rate is controlled by diffusion through the gas phase. In this case, for $V/III \gg 1$, the temperature dependence of growth rate and the group III distribution coefficients for mixing on the III sublattice ($A_xB_{1-x}C$) are particularly simple; thermodynamics controls solid composition, i.e., at the interface, the solid is nearly in equilibrium with the vapor. The results obtained for the alloy system GaAsSb with $V/III \ll 1$ will be explored in detail. In this regime, under certain conditions, the MOVPE growth process is found capable of producing metastable alloys. Surface kinetics may control the MOVPE process at relatively low growth temperatures. The major factors observed to date seem to relate to AsH_3 and PH_3 pyrolysis at the growing interface. The detailed surface reaction mechanisms are nearly totally unknown.

1. Introduction

The MOVPE technique originated from the early work of Manasevit [1]. At a time when liquid phase epitaxy (LPE) and chloride VPE were already well developed for the growth of high-quality GaAs, GaP, and alloys such as $GaAs_{1-x}P_x$ and $Al_xGa_{1-x}As$, MOVPE was first used for heteroepitaxial growth of III/V semiconductors on substrates such as sapphire. Device quality material was not obtained until homoepitaxial GaAs with 77 K mobilities of 120,000 $cm^2/V \cdot s$ was demonstrated by Seki et al. [2]. This led to serious work in several laboratories around the world, cultimating in the successful use of MOVPE for the production of III/V semiconductors for use in many sorts of devices such as injection lasers, solar cells, field-effect transistors, and other devices [3,4]. This rapid leap from the first demonstration of device quality material to a heavy concentration on the devices, as grown by MOVPE, left a definite paucity of knowledge concerning the MOVPE process itself. This lack of knowledge becomes evident with each new materials system explored. Invariably, what is thought to be an essentially straightforward extension of existing technology turns up unexpected problems. An example is the use of MOVPE for the growth of In containing III/V semiconductors. Homogeneous gas phase reactions which caused no serious problems and were, in fact, not even considered for the growth of Ga and Al containing semiconductor materials, were found to completely dominate the growth process for In containing materials.

The purpose of this review paper is to attempt to fit together the pieces of a puzzle, the fundamental growth processes controlling MOVPE, into the best picture possible, given the presently available data. The objective is to consolidate the data to give some understanding of the processes controlling MOVPE in general. Many pieces of the puzzle are missing, so an attempt to develop a coherent picture necessarily involves some speculation. However, the effort may provide (1) a useful guide to the user of MOVPE systems and (2) a clearer idea of the most important missing pieces which should be systematically explored.

2. Fundamental aspects of MOVPE

A schematic overview of the MOVPE process for the growth of a general III/V quaternary alloy $(III_1)_x(III_2)_{1-x}(V_3)_y(V_4)_{1-y}$ or, more conveniently, $A_xB_{1-x}C_yD_{1-y}$, is shown in fig. 1. Four zones are distinguished: the source or input zone, the mixing zone where homogeneous gas phase reactions occur, the boundary layer where the gases become progressively hotter as they diffuse toward the substrate and the substrate surface where the actual crystal growth reaction occurs. The processes occurring in each of these zones, except the source zone, will be discussed briefly in a general way in this section. In the next section, data for specific MOVPE systems will be discussed in terms of the concepts developed in this section. For a more thorough discussion of the general processes occurring during MOVPE, the reader is referred to refs. [3–5].

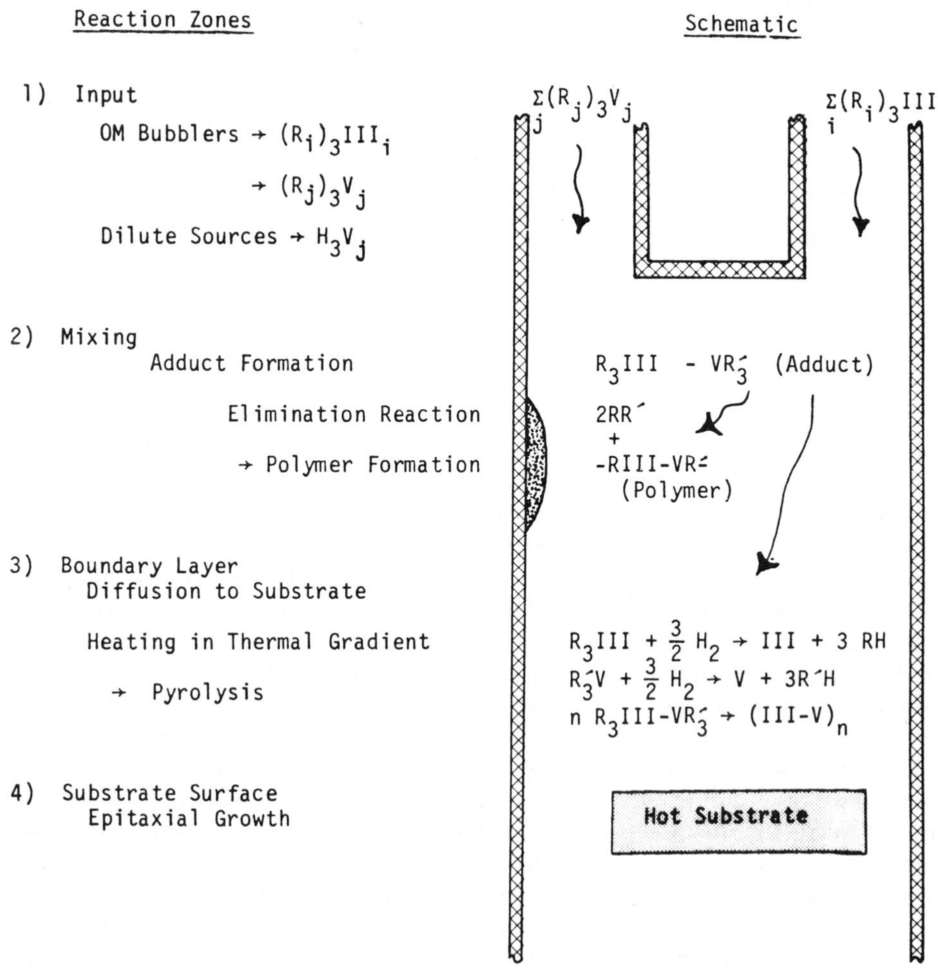

Fig. 1. Schematic illustration of the processes involved in MOVPE growth.

2.1. Thermodynamics

In the MOVPE process, a nonequilibrium situation is intentionally created where the input gas phase has a higher concentration of reactants than would exist in equilibrium with the substrate at the growth temperature. Thus, the first consideration in understanding the process is thermodynamics. At equilibrium, for each component the chemical potentials, μ_i, must be equal in the vapor and solid phases. When the system is not at equilibrium, the thermodynamic driving force to restore equilibrium is $\Delta\mu$. The maximum quantity of solid which can be produced is simply the amount which would establish equilibrium, sometimes referred to as the supersaturation. Thus, the maximum growth rate is fundamentally limited by thermodynamics and the total rate at which the supersaturated gas is passed through the reactor.

Except at very high temperatures, the growth rate is considerably lower than that calculated from thermodynamics. The kinetics of the individual growth processes are not fast enough to allow equilibrium to be established throughout the system. Often, equilibrium *is* established at the growing surface, but not in the gas phase far from the substrate. Under normal conditions, the rate of each step in the growth process is proportional to the chemical potential difference driving that particular step. In most cases, the rate of a particular step, the rate-limiting step, determines the overall growth rate. In this case, the growth rate is directly proportional to the difference in chemical potential between the input gas phase and the gas in equilibrium with the solid being grown, $\Delta\mu$.

The second major consequence of thermodynamics is often the control of solid composition for the growth of III/V alloys. The gas phase is considered to be ideal, i.e.,

$$\mu_i = \mu_i^0 + RT \ln(p_i/p_i^0) \tag{1}$$

where R and T have their usual significance and p_i is the partial pressure of the ith component. The superscript 0 in this case refers to the pure component. An accurate description of the thermodynamics of the solid phase must deal with its nonideality; i.e., for the solid

$$\mu_i = \mu_i^0 + RT \ln(a_i) \tag{2}$$

where a_i is the activity, often defined as the product of concentration, x_i, and activity coefficient, γ_i. Two models are frequently used for the treatment of nonideality of the solid: the regular solution model [6], or the DLP model [7]. Using either model, the activity coefficient is calculated in terms of the "interaction parameter",

$$\ln \gamma_i = (1 - x_i)^2 \Omega/RT. \tag{3}$$

The interaction parameter, Ω, is purely an empirical constant in the regular solution model, but is calculated in terms of the difference in lattice parameter in the DLP model,

$$\Omega_{AC-BC} = 5 \times 10^7 (a_{AC} - a_{BC})^2 / [(a_{AC} + a_{BC})/2]^{4.5}. \tag{4}$$

Two examples make the value of this approach clear. For the system AlAs–GaAs, where both components have nearly the same interatomic spacing, the solid solution is ideal. For the system InP–InSb, where the two components are very different in size, the system has a large deviation from ideality which gives rise to a miscibility gap, i.e., the two compounds do not form solid solutions over a certain composition range. As will be discussed below, when thermodynamic equilibrium is established at the growing interface, thermodynamics allows the determination of the solid composition which will be grown from the vapor of a given composition at a specified temperature.

2.2. Homogeneous gas phase reactions

After the group III alkyls and group V alkyls and/or hydrides are mixed, homogeneous gas phase reactions may occur to form addition compounds or adducts, denoted in fig. 1 $R_3III-VR'_3$. The group III alkyls are Lewis acids; the group V sources, either alkyls or hydrides, are Lewis bases. A rather weak bond is formed between the two to form the Lewis acid-base complexes [8]. The adducts have somewhat lower vapor pressures than the group III and group V alkyls themselves, but the real problem is that RR′ molecules are sequentially eliminated from the adduct eventually resulting in RIII–VR′, since the last RR′ is more strongly bound to the adduct. This remaining complex is highly reactive, and since it has an unsatisfied bond at each end, forms polymeric $(\mathrm{RIII{-}VR'})_n$ which deposits on the reactor walls upstream from the substrate. This parasitic deposition process is a major problem when triethylalkyls are used. It results in low growth rates and inhomogeneous alloy composition. The problem is especially severe for the growth of In containing materials.

2.3. Diffusion

The desired reaction, which leads to crystal growth, is simply the decomposition of the adduct, or the individual group III and group V source molecules, either in the heated layer of gas (boundary layer) through which the molecules must pass to reach the substrate or on the substrate surface itself. We use the term boundary layer as a convenience to describe the part of the laminar gas stream adjacent to the substrate through which the molecules diffuse in a time period of several seconds. A real, stagnant boundary layer does not exist (Rosenberger [9], Giling [10]).

As mentioned, individual R_3III or R'_3V molecules exist since the association to form the adduct is not normally very strong. These may either partially or totally pyrolize during diffusion through the boundary layer. For the growth of III/V compounds when the ratio of group V to group III partial pressures in the input gas stream (the V/III ratio) is high, the flux of the group III element through the "boundary layer" may limit the growth rate, as will be discussed in section 3. The flux is written [11]

$$J_{\mathrm{III}} = D_{\mathrm{III}}\left(p^0_{\mathrm{III}} - p_{\mathrm{III}}\right)/RTd_{\mathrm{b}}, \tag{5}$$

where D_{III} is the group III diffusion coefficient in the gas stream and is proportional to T^2, p^0_{III} is the partial pressure of the group III element in the input gas stream, and p_{III} is the equilibrium partial pressure at the growing interface; d_{b} is the boundary layer thickness.

2.4. Surface kinetics

As discussed above, thermodynamic forces drive the epitaxial process. However, the growth rate is often less than the thermodynamically allowed maximum growth rate, i.e., it is limited by kinetics. As will be seen, diffusion is often the slowest process in the series of steps involved in MOVPE, and hence limits the growth rate. The other kinetic processes are adsorption at the surface, surface reactions, attachment at an atomic step on the surface, and then perhaps at a kink on the step (often referred to as a "half-crystal" site). The incorporation process often involves the release of a product molecule which must desorb from the surface and diffuse away. In principle, any of these steps may dominate the growth rate. For example, in VPE systems involving Cl, the Cl often adsorbs at kinks, thus inhibiting a critical step in the growth process. In this case, the growth rate is surface-reaction-rate limited. The MOVPE process is normally limited by surface kinetics only at very low temperatures; hence, very little is known about the details of the surface processes in MOVPE.

In table 1, the effects of several growth variables on the growth rate are tabulated for the cases where thermodynamics, diffusion, and surface kinetics limit the growth rate. The flow velocity, keeping the partial pressures fixed, affects the thermodynamically limited growth rate by passing more nutrient through the reactor. It also decreases the boundary layer thickness and so increases the growth rate in the diffusion limited case. Naturally, increasing the partial pressure of the reactants increases the growth rate in all cases. Increasing the temperature increases the growth rate when it is limited by surface kinetic processes; however, for exothermic processes such as we are dealing with, increasing the growth temperature

Table 1
Determination of growth rate limiting step

	Flow velocity	Partial pressure	Temperature	Orientation
Thermodynamics	×	×	↓	–
Diffusion	×	×	–	–
Surface kinetics	–	×	↑	×

decreases the extent of reaction at equilibrium and so slows the growth rate when limited by thermodynamics. Temperature has only a slight effect on growth rate when it is limited by diffusion. The effect of substrate orientation is, of course, only important when the growth process is limited by surface kinetic processes.

3. MOVPE results

3.1. Gas phase reactions

The first aspect of the homogeneous gas phase reactions to be examined is the pyrolysis of both alkyls and hydrides in the boundary layer. For TMGa in H_2, Leys and Veenvliet [12] and Nishizawa and Kurabayashi [13] used IR spectroscopy to identify the gas molecules present in the boundary layer at temperatures above 550 °C. They found only CH_4, indicating that the TMGa is completely decomposed by homogeneous reaction in the vapor phase before reaching the interface. All of the group III alkyls TEAl, TEGa, TEIn, TMAl, TMGa, and TMIn are probably decomposed homogeneously in the boundary layer. This is also probably true for the group V alkyls TESb and TMSb. However, the group V hydrides and alkyls involving As and P are much more stable. The hydrides are less stable than the alkyls, and the As compounds are less stable than the P compounds, but even AsH_3 decomposition is believed not to occur in the vapor phase, but to be catalyzed by the III/V solid surface [3,14,15]. The alkyls and hydrides themselves are not direct sources of the group III and V elements, but must decompose early in the process to liberate the nutrient elements. As an example of the pyrolysis of the group V sources, new experimental data are available for the thermal decomposition of PH_3 [16]. PH_3 was passed through a 6 mm diamter, 60 cm long SiO_2 tube. The tube was heated and the

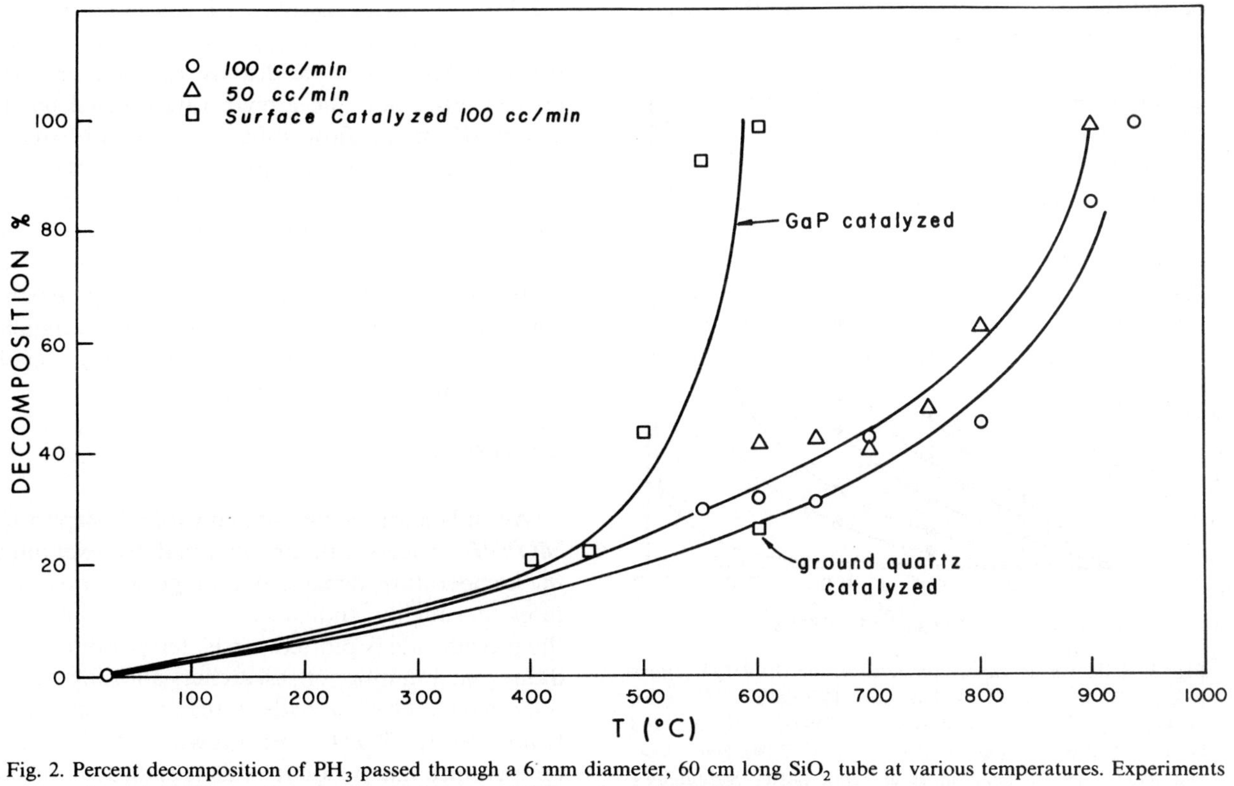

Fig. 2. Percent decomposition of PH_3 passed through a 6 mm diameter, 60 cm long SiO_2 tube at various temperatures. Experiments were performed at different flow rates and with ground SiO_2 and ground GaP to catalyze the pyrolysis.

exit gases were analyzed for total PH_3 content. The fraction of PH_3 decomposing on the tube walls at low total flow rates is shown in fig. 2. At 800 °C, only 1/2 of the PH_3 is found to decompose even at these extremely low flow velocities. Even less would decompose in either an ordinary MOVPE reactor tube, or in a conventional cracking furnace often used to increase the efficiency of PH_3 use in low-pressure reactors [17]. The effect of the III/V surface is clearly seen. Powdered GaP in the tube leads to complete pyrolysis of the PH_3 even at 600 °C. Powdered SiO_2 has little or no effect. The difference in pyrolysis rates is found to control the composition of alloys of the type GaAsP and InAsP as seen in fig. 3. At low temperatures, the PH_3 pyrolysis rate is so slow relative to that for AsH_3 that very little P is incorporated into the layer. At higher temperatures, the rate of PH_3 pyrolysis increases, leading to a higher P content of the solid.

In addition to the desirable pyrolysis reactions, adduct formation with the subsequent formation of low vapor pressure polymers on the reactor

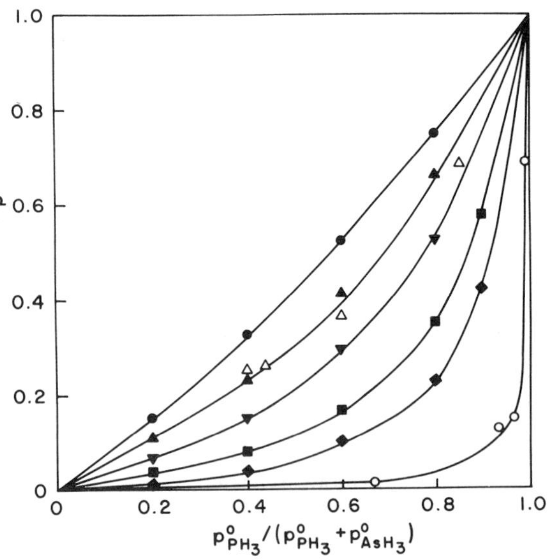

Fig. 3. Solid versus vapor composition for the III/V alloys $InAs_{1-x}P_x$ at 600 °C (Fukui and Horikoshi [25]) (○), $GaAs_{1-x}P_x$ at 750 °C (Ludowise and Dietze [29]) (△), and $GaAs_{1)x}P_x$ at 650 °C (◆), 700 °C (□), 750 °C (▼), 800 °C (▲) and 850 °C (●) (Samuelson et al. [30]). (After Stringfellow [11].)

walls also occurs in MOVPE systems, particularly those using triethyl-group III sources. Several researchers [3,4] have observed that growing GaAs using TEGa plus AsH_3 results in much lower growth rates than obtained using TMGa. Similarly, many researchers have observed severe parasitic predeposition problems when TEIn is used for the growth of In containing III/V materials. This has led to the adoption of more complex growth techniques involving the use of low pressure reactors [18] or adduct forms of the MO In source [18,19]. More recently, great success in avoiding the parasitic reactions has been achieved using TMIn as the In source [20–23]. Early work of Didchenko et al. [24] indicates that the TMIn–PH_3 adduct forms and the elimination reaction occurs below room temperature. However, when TMIn from a solid source held at 17 °C is allowed to mix with PH_3 at room temperature, no evidence of either adduct or polymer deposition on the SiO_2 walls is observed [16]. This had led to the growth of InP [21], GaInP [20], and GaInAs [22,23] with high growth efficiencies and uniform alloy composition in atmospheric pressure reactors using TMIn and hydrides as the sources. The growth efficiency, the growth rate divided by the group III molar flow rate, is a measure of the freedom from parasitic prereactions. Values for InP, GaAs, and GaInAs grown using triethyl and trimethyl sources are listed in table 2. The values of growth efficiency are much higher using trimethyl-group III sources than using triethyl sources, even when the latter are used in conjunction with the low-pressure technique to avoid parasitic prereaction problems.

3.2. Diffusion

An indication of the rate controlling step in the MOVPE process can be obtained by examining the temperature dependence of growth rate. The most thoroughly studied system is GaAs. In fig. 4, the growth rate is plotted versus temperature using data from a number of researchers all using TMGa plus AsH_3. Over a wide range of temperature, from 550 to 750 °C, the growth rate is nearly temperature independent. This is indicative of diffusion limited growth, as seen in table 1. In addi-

Table 2
Growth efficiency for triethyl versus trimethyl-group III sources

System	η (μm/mol)	Source	Pressure (atm)	Reference
GaAs	2×10^3	$TEGa + AsH_3$	1	Kuo et al. [22]
	1.6×10^4	$TMGa + AsH_3$	1	
InP	3.8×10^3	$TEIn + PH_3$	1	Fukui and Horikoshi [40]
	4.5×10^2	$TEIn + PH_3$	LP	Razeghi et al. [41]
	7.9×10^2	$TMIn–TEP + PH_3$	1	Moss and Evans [18]
	6.9×10^3	$TMIn + PH_3$	1	Hsu et al. [21]
GaInAs	7.6×10^2	$TEIn + TEGa + AsH_3$	LP	Razeghi et al. [41]
	2.0×10^4	$TMGa + TMIn + AsH_3$	1	Kuo et al. [22]

$$\eta = \frac{\text{Growth rate } (\mu\text{m/min})}{\text{Controlling flow rate (mol/min)}} \left(\frac{\mu\text{m}}{\text{mol}}\right).$$

tion, thc growth rate has been found to be independent of substrate orientation [24]. The growth rate is also found to be independent of AsH_3 flow rate when the V/III ratio is much larger than unity and linearly proportional to the TMGa flow rate, as expected for diffusion limited growth from eq. (5). In this temperature range, the chemical potential drop across the interface is small, the driving force is mainly expended on moving Ga through the boundary layer. In other words, the system is near thermodynamic equilibrium at the interface. This situation is shown schematically in fig. 5. The input gas is highly supersaturated but equilibrium is established at the solid–vapor interface. Since the input vapor phase has a very high supersaturation, one of the two components must be totally depleted at the interface. Since the V/III ratio is large, the Ga partial pressure will be nearly 0 at the interface [11]. The same situation will prevail for all group III elements at the interface during the growth of $A_xB_{1-x}C$ alloys with mixing on the group III sublattice. Thus, the group III distribution coefficient will be controlled by diffu-

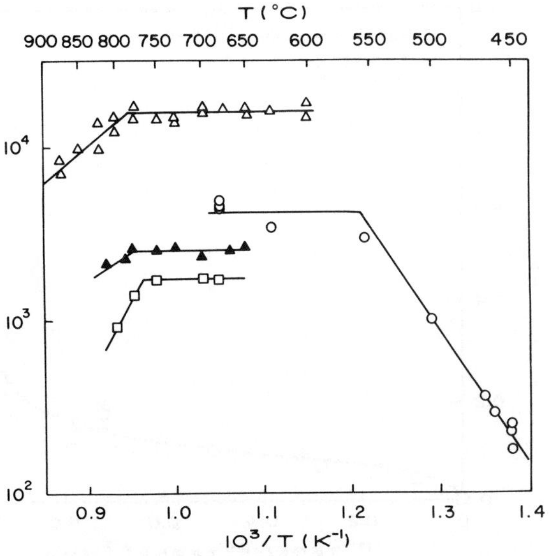

Fig. 4. Temperature dependence on GaAs growth rate (normalized by the TMGa molar flow rate). Data were obtained from Manasevit and Simpson [31] (△), Gottschalch et al. [32] (▲), Leys and Veenvliet [12] (□), and Krautle et al. [33] (○).

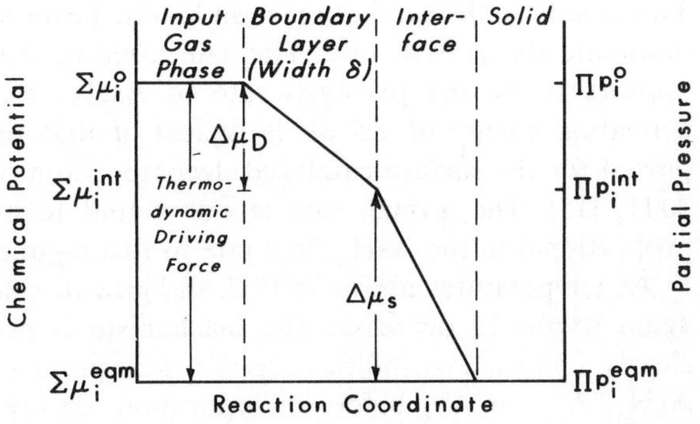

Fig. 5. Schematic diagram of chemical potential versus reaction coordinate, showing the drop in chemical potential required for each step in the growth sequence to keep all rates equal. The sum of individual chemical potentials can alternatively be thought of as products of partical pressures of the reactants.

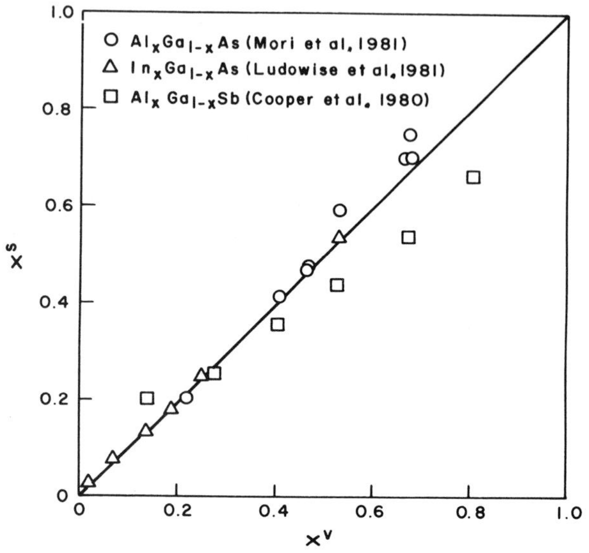

Fig. 6. Solid versus vapor composition for III/V alloys $Al_xGa_{1-x}As$ (data from Mori and Watanabe [34] (○)), $In_xGa_{1-x}As$ (data from Ludowise et al. [35] (△)), and $Al_xGa_{1-x}Sb$ (data from Cooper et al. [36] (□)).

sion, and since D depends little upon the species, will be nearly unity for all of these systems, as shown in fig. 6. In the normal range of growth temperatures, both growth rate and group III distribution coefficients are controlled by diffusion.

The data of Krautle et al. [33] in fig. 4 show that at low temperatures, the GaAs growth rate begins to decrease with decreasing temperature. This clearly indicates that reaction kinetic begin to dominate the growth rate. The rate limiting step appears to be the pyrolysis rate of AsH_3. The activation energy of 1.5 eV is typical of that reported for the surface catalyzed decomposition of AsH_3 [15]. The growth rate is also found to be proportional to the AsH_3 flow rate in this regime.

At temperatures above 750 °C, the growth rate again begins to decrease. The mechanism is not clearly known. Possibilities are the desorption of AsH_3, As_2, or As_4 before incorporation, desorption of Ga, or a thermodynamic limitation as discussed above. Another possibility is that GaAs is nucleated homogeneously in the gas phase at high temperatures with the tiny particles driven away from the interface by the Soret effect.

Since equilibrium is established at the interface in the diffusion limited growth regime, thermodynamics controls the distribution coefficients in alloy systems where mixing is on the group V sublattice, V/III > 1, and the rate of pyrolysis of the source molecules does not limit their incorporation rate [11]. An example is the system $InAs_{1-x}Sb_x$. The data of Fukui and Horikoshi [25], obtained for a V/III ratio of > 1, are plotted in fig. 7. The results of a simple thermodynamic calculation with no adjustable parameters which assumes equilibrium to be established at the growing interface and total decomposition of the TEIn, TESb, and AsH_3, is plotted as the solid line. The nonideality of the solid was taken into account using the DLP model described in the previous section. The calculated results agree with the experimental data extremely well, indicating that thermodynamics does indeed control solid composition even though diffusion controls the growth rate.

A more complex and interesting system is $GaAs_{1-x}Sb_x$. Initial experiments of Cooper et al. [26], shown in fig. 8, indicate a range of solid composition over which alloys apparently cannot

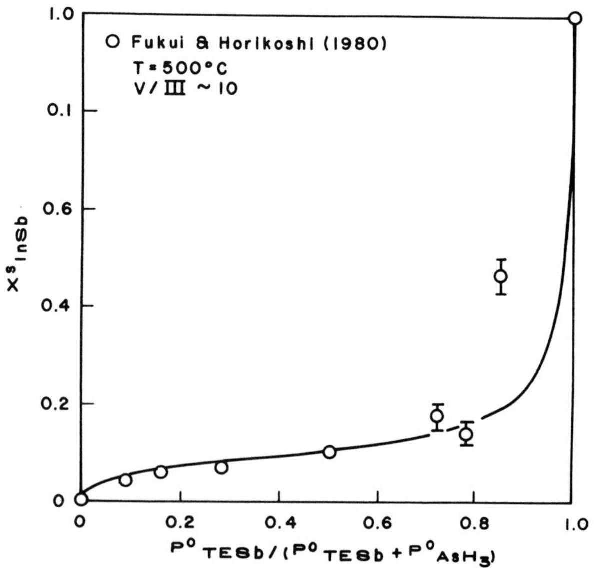

Fig. 7. Solid versus vapor composition for the alloy $InAs_{1-x}Sb_x$. The data are from the work of Fukui and Horikoshi [25]. The solid line was calculated using the DLP model with no adjustable parameters. (After Stringfellow [11].)

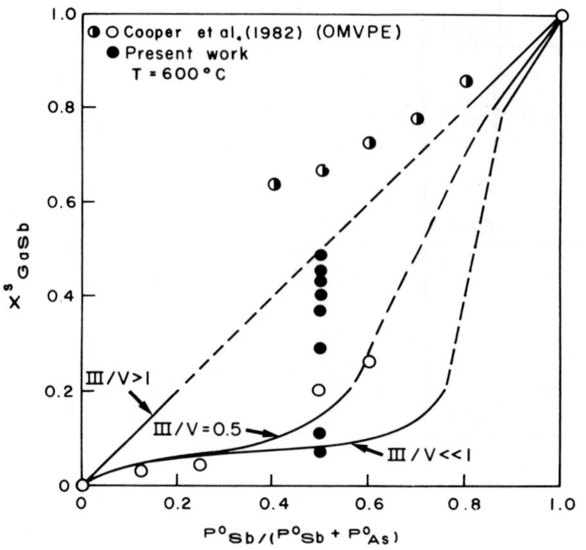

Fig. 8. Solid versus vapor composition for the alloy $GaAs_{1-x}Sb_x$. The data are from the work of Cooper, et al., [26] III/V = 0.5 (○), III/V = 2.0 (◑), and the work of Stringfellow and Cherng [27] (●). The curves were calculated for various III/V ratios. The broken sections of each curve represent the calculated regions of solid immiscibility. (After Stringfellow and Cherng [27].)

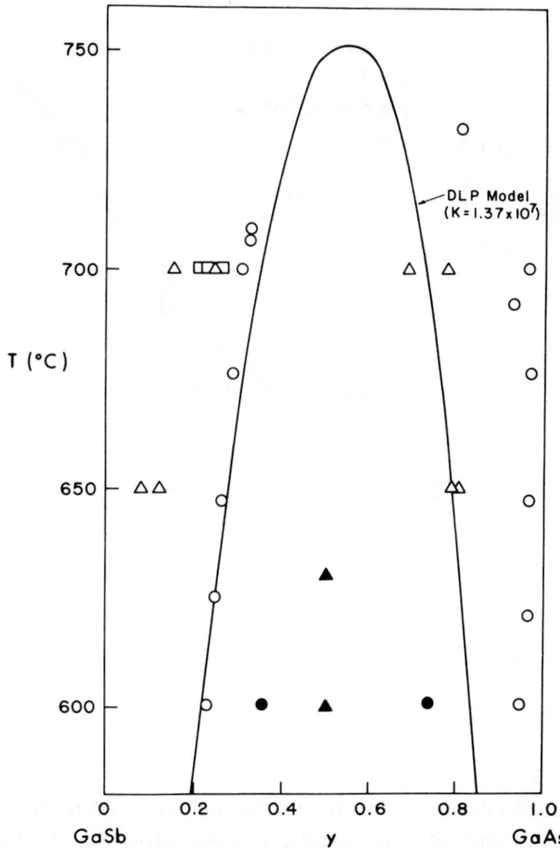

Fig. 9. Binodal curve for the system $GaAs_{1-x}Sb_x$. Data points are from the work of Pessetto and Stringfellow [37] (△), Gratton et al. [38] (○) Takanaka et al. [39] (□), Cooper et al. (MOVPE) [26] (●) and Stringfellow and Cherng [27] (▲) (MOVPE).

be grown at 600 °C. Thermodynamic calculations, performed as described above [11,27] yield the lines in fig. 8. For a V/III ratio of $\gg 1$, the Ga is essentially used up at the interface as for the growth of GaAs described above; however, very little of the As and Sb are used up at the interface. They are essentially undepleted, although they have pyrolyzed and presumably formed Sb_4 and As_4. The higher stability of GaAs relative to GaSb, and the nonideality of the solid, leads to the incorporation of more As than Sb into the solid, i.e., the Sb distribution coefficient is small, in agreement with the experimental data. The large positive deviation from ideality in this system, due to the large difference in lattice parameter in the DLP model, leads to a region of immiscibility in the solid. The calculated extent of the miscibility gap at 600 °C is indicated by the broken line in fig. 8. Alloys with $0.8 > x > 0.2$ cannot be grown at 600 °C by LPE, as shown in fig. 9, and is difficult by MOVPE when the V/III ratio is > 1. However, for V/III < 1, the situation is reversed and essentially all of the As and Sb are incorporated into the solid. This leads to an Sb distribution coefficient of unity as shown in fig. 8. In this case, metastable alloys in the region of solid immiscibility can readily be grown by MOVPE. This is shown in fig. 8 and also in the solid phase diagram presented in fig. 9. The effect of III/V ratio on solid composition is shown in fig. 10. It is seen that the Sb distribution coefficient is unity for values of III/V ratio of > 1, and progressively smaller as III/V is decreased until an asymptotic value is reached. The data are in excellent agreement with the corresponding solid curve calculated assuming equilibrium to be established at the growing interface. The calcu-

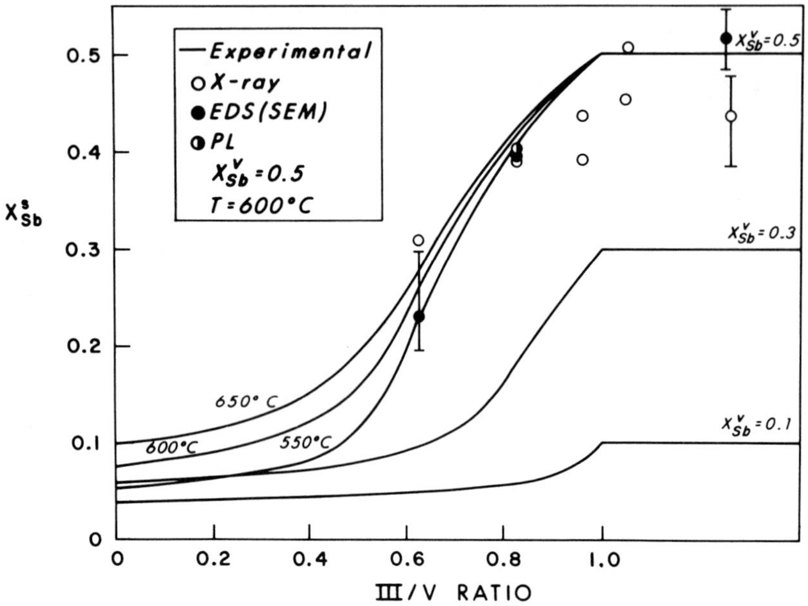

Fig. 10. GaSb concentration in the solid versus ratio of Ga to total group V in the vapor, Sb mole fraction in the vapor and temperature. The calculations, indicated by the solid lines, were performed assuming complete decomposition of all reactants and equilibrium at the interface. The experimental results were obtained at 600 °C and Sb/V = 0.5, using TMGa, TMSb and AsH_3 as the reactants [28]. (After Cherng et al. [28].)

lated curves also indicate the influence of temperature and Sb concentration in the vapor on the Sb concentration in the solid. These predictions are in agreement with experimental observations [28]. Metastable $GaAs_{0.5}Sb_{0.5}$ layers lattice matched to the InP substrate have excellent morphologies, and superficially appear to be normal III/V alloys. However, other properties are somewhat different than the best quality alloys grown in other, more ideal, III/V alloy systems [28]. The samples are always p-type with no intentional doping. The mobilities for $p = 10^{17}$ cm^{-3} are very low, in the range of 20–30 $cm^2/V \cdot s$. The X-ray half-widths are somewhat broader than for homogeneous alloys and the 300 and 4 K photoluminescence (PL) spectra are rather broad. In fig. 11, the PL half-width measured at 4 K, normalized by the composition dependence of band gap, is plotted versus the growth temperature divided by the critical temperature for the onset of solid phase immiscibility. The occurrence of the PL broadening is clearly induced by the nonideality of the solid. Thus, even though we are able to grow metastable

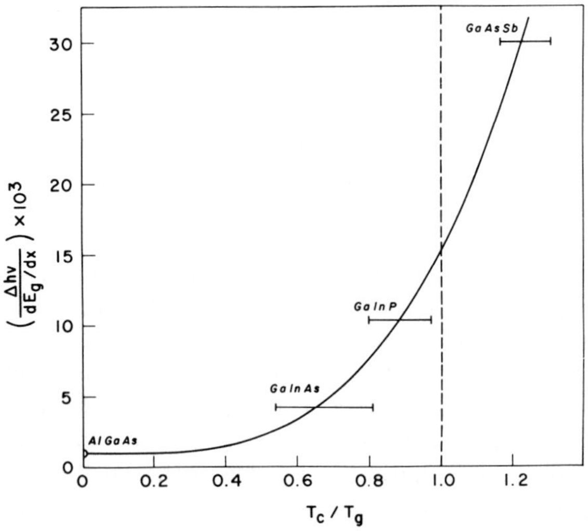

Fig. 11. 4K photoluminescence half-width, normalized by dE_g/dx, versus critical temperature divided by the growth temperature for several alloys grown lattice matched to the appropriate substrates by MOVPE. The solid line was drawn simply to pass through the data points. (After Cherng et al. [28].)

alloys by MOVPE, it is not clear how useful they will be for devices, since there appears to be a significant amount of compositional inhomogeneity or clustering in the solid. However, GaInAsP alloys grown by MOVPE appear perfectly suitable for laser devices, so no conclusion can be reached at the present time.

4. Summary

Several fundamental aspects of the MOVPE process have been examined briefly. The major controlling elements appear to be thermodynamics, homogeneous gas phase reactions, and diffusion of nutrients in the gas phase to the growing interface. Thermodynamics provides the driving force for the growth process and in many cases controls the solid composition. Homogeneous gas phase reactions control solid composition when the source molecules are unable to completely decompose before reaching the interface. The parasitic reactions involving formation of low vapor pressure polymers on the reactor walls upstream from the substrate also depend on the formation of adduct molecules and subsequent elimination reactions which occur homogeneously in the gas phase. These harmful reactions can be avoided using trimethyl–group III sources, rather than the more common triethyl–group III sources, by using low-pressure techniques and by using nonpolymer-forming adduct group III sources.

The properties obtained in MOVPE III/V semiconductors are excellent, similar to those obtained using the more developed LPE and MBE techniques. High mobilities, long lifetimes, and abrupt interfaces necessary for the most advanced devices have been obtained by MOVPE in several alloys systems. Indeed, it may be said that MOVPE is the most versatile of all III/V semiconductor growth techniques. MOVPE grown materials have been used in the fabrication of state-of-art devices including FETs, lasers, and solar cells. Because the MOVPE technique appears well suited for large-scale commerical production processes, it appears destined for a leading role in the growth of III/V materials and device structure in the future. The practical use of MOVPE is moving forward rapidly; however, more effort must be expended on exploring and understanding the fundamental aspects of MOVPE. As indicated in this paper, many basic processes occurring during MOVPE are not completely understood. In order to effectively design equipment and processes for the production of III/V materials and device structures, these basic processes will need to be better understood.

Acknowledgements

This work has been partially supported by the Department of Energy (contract number DE-AT03 81ER 10934) and by the Army Research Office (contract number DAAG29-83-K-0153). The GaAsSb results were obtained under DOE support and the GaInAs results under ARO support.

References

[1] H.M. Manasevit, Appl. Phys. Letters 11 (1968) 156.
[2] Y. Seki, K. Tanno, K. Iida and E. Ichiki, J. Electrochem. Soc. 122 (1975) 1108.
[3] G.B. Stringfellow, in: Lightwave Communication Technology, Ed. W. T. Tsang, to be published.
[4] G.B. Stringfellow, Rept. Progr. Phys. 45 (1982) 469.
[5] G.B. Stringfellow, in: Proc. 5th Intern. Summer School on Crystal Growth, Davos, 1983, to be published.
[6] M.B. Panish and M. Ilegems, in: Progress in Solid State Chemistry, Vol. 7, Eds. H. Reiss and J.O. McCaldin (Pergamon, New York, 1972) pp. 39–83.
[7] G.B. Stringfellow, J. Crystal Growth 27 (1974) 21.
[8] G.E. Coates, M.L.H. Green and K. Wade, Organometallic Compounds: The Main Group Elements, Vol. 1, 3rd ed. (Methuen, London, 1967).
[9] F. Rosenberger, Fundamentals of Crystal Growth (Springer, Berlin, 1979).
[10] L.J. Giling, J. Electrochem. Soc. 129 (1982) 634.
[11] G.B. Stringfellow, J. Crystal Growth 62 (1983) 225.
[12] M.R. Leys and H. Veenvliet, J. Crystal Growth 55 (1981) 145.
[13] J. Hishizawa and T. Kurabayashi, J. Electrochem. Soc. 130 (1983) 413.
[14] I.A. Frolov, P.B. Boldyrevskii, B.L. Druz and E.B. Sokolov, Inorg. Mater. 13 (1977) 632.
[15] I.A. Frolov, E.M. Kitaev, B.L. Druz and E.B. Sokolov, Russian J. Phys. Chem. 51 (1977) 591.
[16] C. Larsen and G.B. Stringfellow, unpublished results.
[17] J.P. Duchemin, J.P. Hirz, M. Razeghi, M. Bonnet and S.D. Hersee, J. Crystal Growth 55 (1981) 64.

[18] R.H. Moss and J.S. Evans, J. Crystal Growth 55 (1981) 129.
[19] K.W. Benz, H. Renz, J. Weidlein and M.H. Pilkuhn, J. Electron. Mater. 10 (1981) 185.
[20] C.C. Hsu, R.M. Cohen and G.B. Stringfellow, J. Crystal Growth 62 (1983) 648.
[21] C.C. Hsu, R.M. Cohen and G.B. Stringfellow, J. Crystal Growth 63 (1983) 8.
[22] C.P. Kuo, R.M. Cohen and G.B. Stringfellow, J. Crystal Growth 64 (1983) 550.
[23] M. Sacilotti, A. Mircea and R. Azoulay, J. Crystal Growth 63 (1983) 111.
[24] R.R. Saxena, C.B. Cooper,M.J. Ludowise, S. Hikado, V.M. Sardi and P.G. Borden, J. Crystal Growth 55 (1981) 58.
[25] T. Fukui and Y. Horikoshi, Japan. J. Appl. Phys. 19 (1980) L53.
[26] C.B. Cooper, R.R. Saxena and M.J. Ludowise, J. Electron Mater. 11 (1982) 1001.
[27] G.B. Stringfellow and M. J. Cherng, J. Crystal Growth 64 (1983) 413.
[28] M.J. Cherng, R.M. Cohen and G.B. Stringfellow, J. Electron. Mater., to be published.
[29] M.J. Ludowise and W.T. Dietze, J. Electron. Mater. 11 (1982) 59.
[30] L. Samuelson, P. Omling, H. Titze and H.R. Grimmeiss, J. Physique 43 (1982) C5-323.
[31] H.M. Manasevit and W.I. Simpson, J. Electrochem. Soc. 116 (1969) 1968.
[32] V. Gottschalch, W.H. Petzke and E. Butter, Kristall Tech. 9 (1974) 209.
[33] H. Krautle, H. Roehle, A. Escobosa and H. Beneking, J. Electron. Mater. 12 (1983) 215.
[34] Y. Mori and N. Watanabe, J. Appl. Phys. 52 (1981) 2792.
[35] M.J. Ludowise, C.B. Cooper and R.R. Saxena, J. Electron. Mater. 10 (1981) 1051.
[36] C.B. Cooper, R.R. Saxena and M.J. Ludowise, Electron. Letters 16 (1980) 892.
[37] J.R. Pessetto and G.B. Stringfellow, J. Crystal Growth 62 (1983) 1.
[38] M.F. Gratton, R.G. Goodchild, L.Y. Juravel and J.C. Wooley, J. Electron. Mater. 8 (1979) 25.
[39] N. Takanaka, M. Inoue, J. Shirafuji and Y. Inuishi, J. Phys. D11 (1978) L91.
[40] T. Fukui and Y. Horikoshi, Japan. J. Appl. Phys. 19 (1980) L395.
[41] M. Razeghi, M.A. Poisson, P.P. Larivain and J.P. Duchemin, J. Electron Mater. 12 (1983) 371.

Journal of Crystal Growth 99 (1990) 482–490
North-Holland

SURFACE DIFFUSION AND RELATED PHENOMENA IN MBE GROWTH OF III–V COMPOUNDS

T. NISHINAGA, T. SHITARA and K. MOCHIZUKI *

Department of Electronic Engineering, The Faculty of Engineering, The University of Tokyo, 7-3-1 Hongo, Bunkyo-ku, Tokyo 113, Japan

and

K.I. CHO

Electronics and Telecommunications Research Institute, P.O. Box 8 Daedog Danji, Daejeon, Chungnam, Korea

Surface diffusion in MBE is studied taking GaAs and $In_zGa_{1-z}As$ as examples. First, the mode transition between 2D nucleation and step flow in MBE on vicinal surfaces is studied theoretically and experimentally. The principal idea of the theory is to assume that the transition occurs when the surface supersaturation on the step terrace becomes identical with the critical supersaturation for 2D nucleation. This allows the diffusion length of Ga to be caluculated at the experimental critical temperature for the mode transition. It is found that the diffusion length increases as the temperature is decreased, due to the increased residence time, and that the diffusion length on (111)B is longer than that on (001) using the assumption of equal formation energy of 2D nuclei for both surfaces. Then the theory is applied to help understand the dependence of the $In_zGa_{1-z}As$ composition on the growth temperature, the substrate orientation and the degree of misorientation. The theory is in good agreement with the present experiments and it is concluded that surface diffusion is one of the most important and essential processes controlling MBE growth and the impurity incorporation.

1. Introduction

Understanding the elemental processes involved in MBE growth is essential for controlling the growth on an atomic scale. Surface diffusion is one of the most important rate limiting growth processes in MBE, but very little is known about the atomic details of surface diffusion or of the various physical parameters characterising the process such as diffusion length, residence time, activation energy and so on. Neave et al. have found that in the MBE growth of GaAs on a substrate slightly misoriented from (100), RHEED oscillations appear at a low growth temperature but disappear at high temperature [1]. This has been explained by them as follows. When the growth temperature is low, 2D nucleation is formed between the atomic steps which lie in parallel on the misoriented substrate, on the other hand, when the growth temperature increases, all the growing atoms and molecules have a large surface mobility and they diffuse to the step edges to promote growth without forming 2D nucleations. By measuring the critical temperature of the appearance and disappearance of the RHEED oscillations they tried to determine the diffusion coefficient of Ga. In their treatment, they assumed that at this critical temperature, the diffusion length took the same value as the interstep distance on the misoriented substrate. However, the definition of the diffusion length so far given in the MBE community is not unique and somewhat confused. The diffusion length is given by

$$\lambda = \sqrt{D_s \tau}, \tag{1}$$

where D_s and τ is the diffusion coefficient and the life time for the diffusing atoms or molecules respectively. The origin of the confusion lies in the

* Central Research Laboratory, Hitachi Ltd., 1-280 Higasi-koigakubo, Kokubunji, Tokyo 185, Japan.

0022-0248/90/$03.50 © Elsevier Science Publishers B.V. (North-Holland)

different definitions of τ. In the BCF theory, τ has been defined as the residence time before de-adsorption [2,3]. On the other hand, under the usual III–V MBE growth condition the residence time of the group III element is very long and almost all of the group III atoms are incorporated into the crystal without re-evaporation. Hence, the capture rate of the migrating atoms at the growth site determines the life time, and hence the diffusion length. Then, the diffusion length is a function of the density of atomic steps. If there are no steps on the growing surface, 2D nucleation is required for growth. Then, the diffusion length becomes a function of the surface concentration of the growing atoms since the probability of the nucleation and hence the step density now is the function of the adatom concentration. In their work Neave et al. took τ as the time for monolayer coverage. Van Hove and Cohen [4] made similar experiments varying the interstep distance, by varying the degree of misorientation and they found the change of the critical temperature. They obtained the diffusion coefficient from experiments using eq. (1) also with monolayer coverage. However, there is no physical meaning of diffusion length for the period of the monolayer coverage. In the sense of their measurements, τ should be the average time for the 2D nucleation to occur. In other words, if the adatoms can diffuse to the step before forming 2D nucleation, one cannot see the 2D nucleation occurring between the steps and hence no RHEED oscillation might be observed. In the extreme case that the supersaturation is very high and the number of atoms in the critical nuclei is unity, one can take a collision time as the time for 2D nucleation ot occur. Then the critical condition for the transition between the presence and the absence of the RHEED oscillation is

$$\lambda_0 = \sqrt{D_s \tau_{coll}}, \qquad (2)$$

where λ_0 is the interstep distance and τ_{coll} is the collision time. In the present paper, our method of obtaining the diffusion length is reviewed and is applied to find the diffusion length of Ga in the MBE of GaAs. Finally, the change in alloy composition as a function of the growth temperature and the misorientation angle is studied using the present surface diffusion theory.

2. Theoretical consideration

2.1. Surface diffusion on vicinal surfaces

Fig. 1 illustrates schematically the vicinal surface. Growing atoms impinge in the form of a molecular beam and arrive on the surface on which they migrate until they are captured at the kink of the growth step. If the adatom concentration is too low to create 2D nucleations between the steps, the adatom concentration on the terrace between the steps is given according to BCF theory in the form:

$$n_s(y) = J\tau_s + (n_{step} - J\tau_s)\frac{\cosh(y/\lambda_s)}{\cosh(\lambda_0/2\lambda_s)}, \qquad (3)$$

where J, τ_s, n_{step} and λ_s are, respectively, the flux of growing atoms, the residence time on the surface, the surface concentration of the atoms at the step and the surface diffusion length [5]. In this treatment, the surface diffusion equation is solved under the assumption that the velocity of the step is infinitely slow compared with the diffusion velocity. This assumption is valid since on the vicinal surface with the misorientation angle of 1°, the step velocity is nearly 100 Å/s, while the average velocity of the diffusing atoms is of the order of 10^3 Å/s. If the residence time is large and

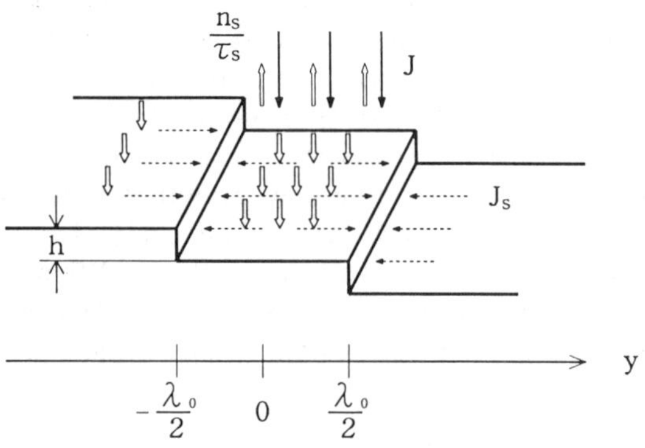

Fig. 1. Schematic illustration of vicinal surface.

the diffusion length is much larger than the inter-step distance, $n_s(y)$ takes a parabolic form as [3]:

$$n_s(y) = n_{step} + (J\lambda_0^2/8D_s)\left[1 - (2y/\lambda_0)^2\right]. \quad (4)$$

The surface flux of diffusing atoms to the step, J_s, is given by

$$J_s(y) = -D_s\,dn_s(y)/dy. \quad (5)$$

With eq. (5), one gets the flux at the step as

$$J_s(\tfrac{1}{2}\lambda_0) = (J - n_{s0}/\tau_s)\lambda_s \tanh(\lambda_0/2\lambda_s), \quad (6)$$

where n_{s0} is the surface equilibrium concentration of the growing atoms.

2.2. Critical condition for the mode transition between 2D nucleation and step flow

Eq. (4) shows that the adatom concentration and hence the supersaturation ratio becomes a maximum in the center between the two steps. If the maximum supersaturation ratio exceeds the critical value for the 2D nucleation, one sees the birth and spread of the 2D nucleation in the center of the terrace. Fig. 2 shows schematically the case for 2D nucleation assuming that the chemical equilibrium is established at the growth step.

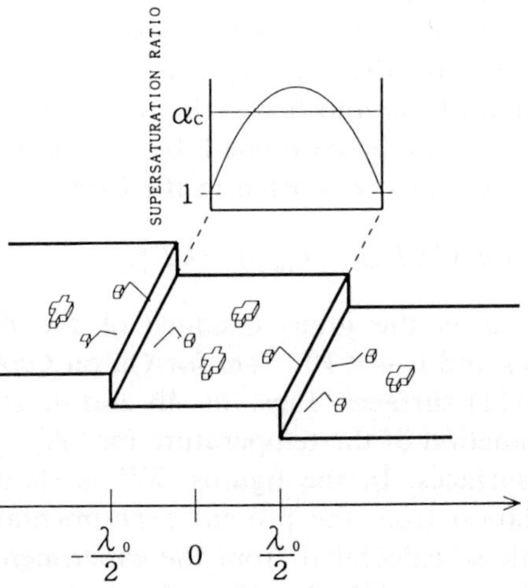

Fig. 2. Supersaturation ratio of the growing atoms on the terrace of an atomic step. Here, the supersaturation in the center of the terrace exceeds the critical supersaturation for 2D nucleation.

The critical [6] and the maximum supersaturation ratios are given respectively by

$$\alpha_{crit} = \exp\left[\Omega\pi h\sigma^2/(65 - \ln 10^{12})k^2T^2\right], \quad (7)$$

$$\alpha_{max} = (J\lambda_0^2/8D_s n_{step}) + 1, \quad (8)$$

where Ω, h and σ are the atomic volume, step height and surface free energy to create the 2D nucleus. Here, we assume then to observe 2D nucleation by RHEED oscillations, one 2D nucleation per 100 Å^2 must exist. Since the critical supersaturation ratio is not a strong function of this number, we can take this as an approximation. Now, at the critical condition for the mode transition, one gets

$$\alpha_{crit} = \alpha_{max}, \quad (9)$$

a form which gives information on the surface diffusion.

For evaluating D_s with eq. (9), one should know J, σ, and n_{step}. Of these J, the flux of the growing species, can be determined by measuring the period of the RHEED oscillations. One of the somewhat difficult points in the present method lies in determining σ. There exists almost no experiment to evaluate it. This is mainly because it depends on the reconstruction of the side wall surface of the nuclei, which is unknown at this moment. Hence, we tentatively choose $\sigma = \frac{1}{2}n_0\phi$ where n_0 is the average number of the breaking bound on the side wall and ϕ is the breaking energy per bond.

The evaluation of n_{step} is also difficult. In the present treatment, chemical equilibrium at the step edge is postulated as the first step, which allows us to determine n_{step} by employing the mass action law assuming the residence time of the growing atom is known. For instance, in the single component system the equilibrium pressure of the growing species should be known as a function of temperature from the mass action law. Then, n_{s0}, the equilibrium surface concentration, which should be equal to n_{step} under the present assumption, is given by

$$n_{s0}/\tau_s = P/\sqrt{2\pi mkT}, \quad (10)$$

where P and m are the equilibrium pressure and

mass of the growing atom. If τ_s is known, one can determine D_s from eqs. (7)–(10). However, there is no reliable experiment which gives the value of τ_s. Hence, we have to be satisfied for now by determining $D_s\tau_s$ which is equal to λ_s^2. In other words, the present method gives in effect not D_s but λ_s, which is the average diffusion length during the residence time on the growing surface.

In the case of the two-component system such as III–V and II–VI compound semiconductors, the diffusion equation should be solved with the boundary conditions assuming chemical equilibrium at the step and equations similar to eqs. (7)–(10) [5].

3. Experimental results and calculations

3.1. Surface diffusion length of Ga on GaAs (001) and (111)B surfaces

Fig. 3 shows schematically the three-dimensional view of the (001) surface. In the experiments, (001) substrates 1°–4° misoriented toward [110], [$\bar{1}$10] and [100] orientations are employed. For simplicity, the above orientations are named "A", "B" and "C" hereafter. MBE growth was

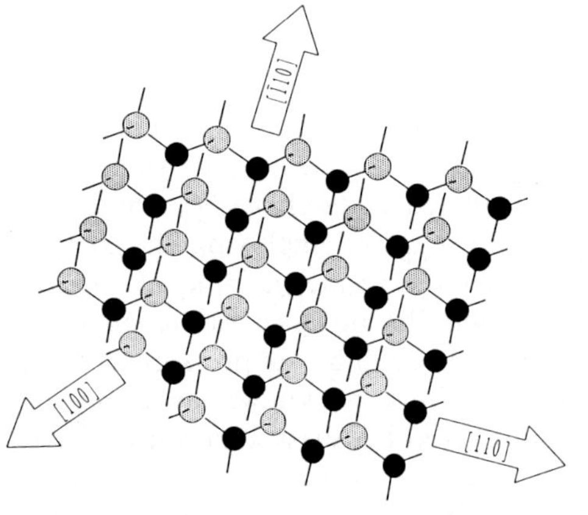

Fig. 3. Three-dimensional view of the GaAs (001) surface. The arrows denote the directions of the misorientation from the (001) surface.

performed with an ULVAC MBC-300 system and the critical temperature for the mode transition was measured with those substrates for various growth conditions. After removal of the native oxide by heating to 600°C under an incident As_4 flux, a buffer layer thicker than 10 nm was grown at around 580°C, to make the surface smoother. The As_4/Ga incident flux ratio was varied from 0.80 to 11.2, and the incident flux of Ga was changed from 1.2×10^{14} to 1.2×10^{15} atoms/cm^2 · s. Reflection electron diffraction (20 kV) was used and the intensity of the specular spot was measured at an orthogonal azimuth to the inclination direction.

The experiments showed that:(1) the critical temperature decreased as the angle of misorientation was increased, (2) the critical temperature increased as the Ga flux was increased, and (3) different critical temperatures were found for different orientations of the misorientations. Points (1) and (2) are well understood by the concept described in the previous section.

To obtain n_{s0}, one needs the chemical equilibrium constant of the reaction,

$$\mathrm{Ga(v)} + \tfrac{1}{4}\mathrm{As_4(v)} \rightleftarrows \mathrm{GaAs(s)}, \tag{11}$$

where v and s denote the vapor and solid respectively. In this treatment, we employed the equilibrium constant obtained by Heckingbottom [7]. Under the growth condition of excess arsenic pressure, the rate determining process is the surface diffusion of Ga and hence the diffusion length of Ga, λ_s^{Ga}, can be evaluated by the above treatments, λ_s^{Ga} can be written in the form of

$$\lambda_s^{Ga} = a \exp[(E_{des} - E_{diff})/2kT], \tag{12}$$

where a is the jump distance of the diffusion process and is 4×10^{-8} cm for Ga on GaAs (100) and (111) surfaces. Figs. 4a, 4b and 4c show λ_s^{Ga} as a function of the temperature for "A", "B" and "C" surfaces. In the figures, λ_s^{Ga} is shown after calculation from the present experimental results with those calculated from the experiments given by Ohta et al. [8]. For all surfaces, λ_s^{Ga} increases as the temperature is decreased. This means that the diffusion energy is smaller than the desorption energy, and hence as the temperature is decreased

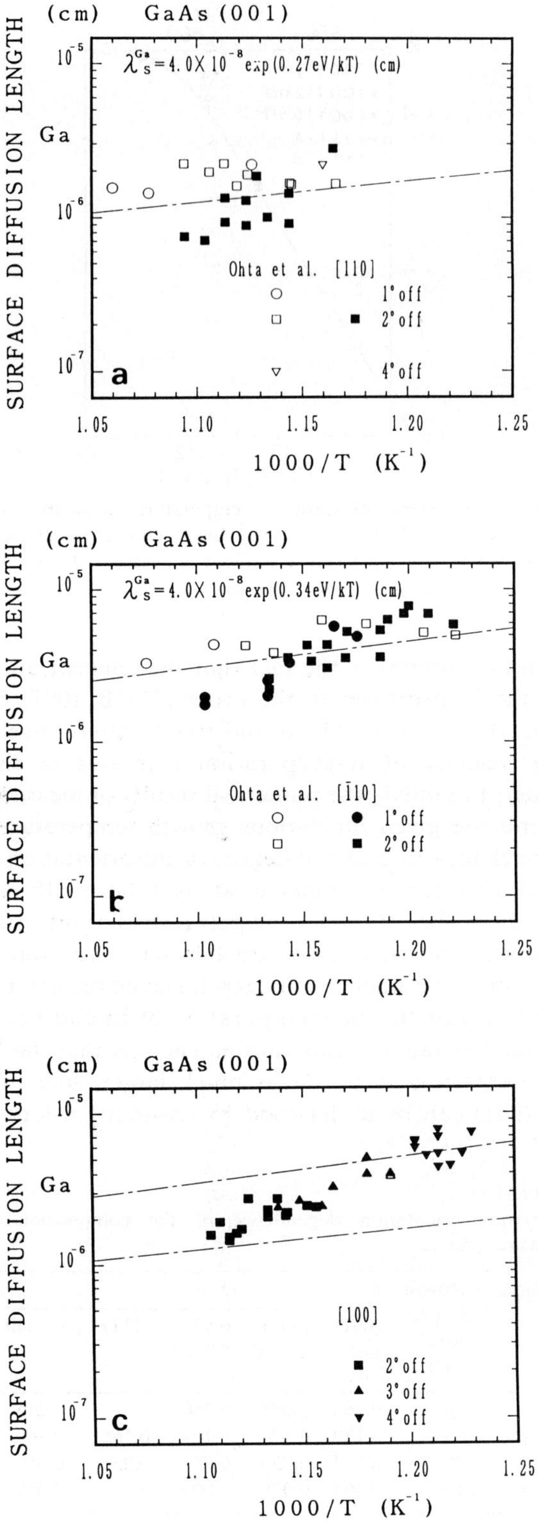

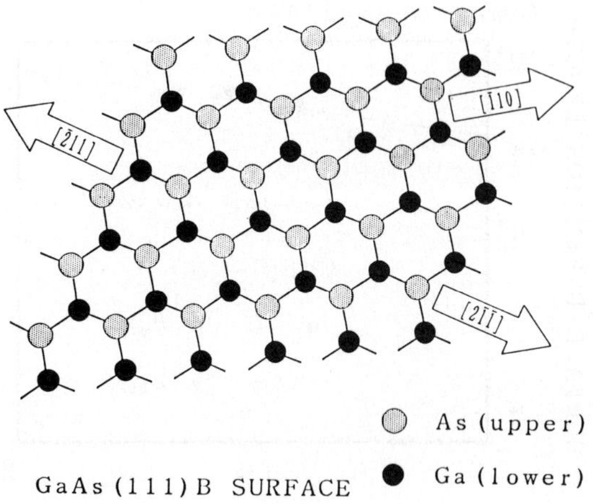

Fig. 5. Schematic picture of a GaAs (111)B surface. The arrows denote the directions of tilting from (111)B surface.

the residence time becomes large so that the atoms migrate a long way on the growing surface. In fig. 4, one sees a different energy for the diffusion length which is equal to $\frac{1}{2}(E_{des} - E_{diff})$. For A and B surfaces, the energies are respectively 0.27 and 0.34 eV, and for the C surface the value lies between these two energies. To obtain λ_s^{Ga}, we have used $\phi = 1.4$ eV, the bond energy of Ga and As. The calculated activation energy depends on ϕ and hence we must stress the fact that the energy obtained in this calculation is the tentative one when we assumed the bond energy of Ga and As being 1.4 eV and 2D nuclei of disk shape.

In the next step, GaAs (111)B substrates and those with misorientation were employed. The schematic illustration of the (111)B surface is shown in fig. 5, in which the directions of the misorientation are also shown. The substrates with the misorientation toward [$\bar{1}$10], [2$\bar{1}\bar{1}$] and [$\bar{2}$11] are denoted respectively as "D", "E" and "F". The As_4/Ga flux ratio was chosen to be nearly 2 and the growth rate was changed to get a different critical temperature for the mode transition. The

Fig. 4. The diffusion length calculated from the experimental temperature of the mode transition assuming complete equilibrium at the growth step: (a) on "A", (b) on "B" and (c) on "C" surfaces. The diffusion length calculated from the experiment by Ohta et al [8] is also shown in the figure for comparison.

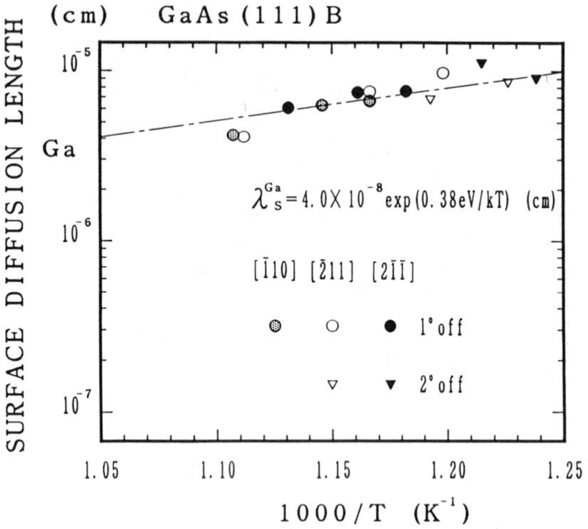

Fig. 6. The calculated surface diffusion length on (111)B.

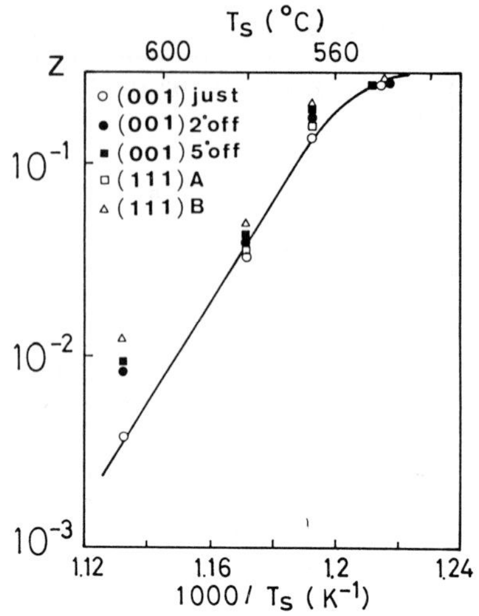

Fig. 7. Dependence of substrate temperature on an the solid composition of $In_zGa_{1-z}As$. The beam equivalent pressure measured by the ion gauge was fixed as follows: $P_{In} = 1.3 \times 10^{-5}$ Pa, $P_{Ga} = 2.7 \times 10^{-5}$ Pa and $P_{As_4} = 1.5 \times 10^{-3}$ Pa.

critical temperature for the mode transition was lower for (111)B than for (001) with the same degree of misorientation although the interstep distance of the former surface was slightly larger than the latter. This means that 2D nucleation on the (111)B surface occurs with more difficulty than on (001) surface. The calculated diffusion length for the (111)B surface is shown in fig. 6, and the activation energy for the diffusion length is determined as 0.38 eV. This is slightly larger than the values on the (001) surface.

3.2. Composition of $In_zGa_{1-z}As$ on vicinal surfaces

$In_zGa_{1-z}As$ was grown by MBE on Cr–O doped GaAs substrates with (001), (111)A and (111)B surfaces (< ±0.5) and with 2° and 5° misorientations from the (001) surface toward [110] [9]. After the removal of an oxide layer, a GaAs buffer layer of 150 nm was grown to produce a smooth surface. Then the growth of $In_zGa_{1-z}As$ was started at a rate of 1 Å/s. The thickness of the grown layer was maintained 1.1 μm throughout the experiment. The alloy composition was measured by EPMA (electron probe X-ray microanalyzer). The results of the measurements are shown in fig. 7. As clearly seen the concentration of In decreases markedly as the growth temperature is increased. This is due to the increase in In re-evaporation from the growing surface. Another point of interest is the fact that the concentration of the In decreases in the order (111)B, (001) 5° off, (001) 2° off, (111)B and (001). Alternatively, the velocity of re-evaporation increases in this order. In table 1, the numerical results of measurements are given for various growth temperatures. The change in z as the degree of misorientation is increased can be understood as follows. If one increases the off angle, one gets a smaller interstep distance and, hence, the larger In concentration in the solid, the smaller interstep distance results in a shorter time for the incorporation of In and hence in the low rate of evaporation. The fact that the In concentration in (111)B is much larger than that in (001) can be understood by assuming a longer

Table 1
Substrate orientation dependence of the composition of $In_zGa_{1-z}As$

Sample No.	Growth temper-ature (°C)	z				
		(001) just	(001) 2° off	(001) 5° off	(111)A	(111)B
IN-1	550	0.260	0.268	0.260	–	0.275
IN-2	565	0.139	0.176	0.194	0.165	0.200
IN-3	580	0.034	0.039	0.043	0.035	0.050
IN-4	610	0.004	0.008	0.009	–	0.012

diffusion length of In on (111)B than that on (001). This assumption is consistent with the experiments described previously in section 2, namely with the fact that the diffusion lengths of Ga on (111)B are longer than on (001).

To understand the reason for the different In incorporation rates for different degrees of misorientation, surface diffusion theory is applied. Surface diffusion fluxes of the diffusing species to the step are given by

$$J_s^{Ga}(\tfrac{1}{2}\lambda_0) = \left(J_{Ga} - \frac{P_e^{Ga}}{\sqrt{2\pi m_{Ga} kT}} \right) \times \lambda_s^{Ga} \tanh(\lambda_0/2\lambda_s^{Ga}), \tag{13}$$

$$J_s^{As}(\tfrac{1}{2}\lambda_0) = \left(4J_{As_4} - \frac{2P_e^{As_4}}{\sqrt{2\pi m_{As_4} kT}} - \frac{2P_e^{As_2}}{\sqrt{2\pi m_{As_2} kT}} \right) \times \lambda_{As} \tanh(\lambda_0/2\lambda_{As}), \tag{14}$$

$$J_s^{In}(\tfrac{1}{2}\lambda_0) = \left(J_{In} - \frac{P_e^{In}}{\sqrt{2\pi m_{In} kT}} \right) \times \lambda_s^{In} \tanh(\lambda_0/2\lambda_s^{In}). \tag{15}$$

P_e^{Ga}, $P_e^{As_4}$ and P_e^{In} are the equilibrium pressures for the species denoted by the superscripts. According to the mass action laws one gets:

$$K_{Ga-As_4} = \frac{a_{GaAs}}{P_e^{Ga}(P_e^{As_4})^{1/4}},$$

$$Ga(v) + \tfrac{1}{4}As_4(v) \rightleftarrows GaAs(s), \tag{16}$$

$$K_{Ga-As_2} = \frac{a_{GaAs}}{P_e^{Ga}(P_e^{As_2})^{1/2}},$$

$$Ga(v) + \tfrac{1}{2}As_2(v) \rightleftarrows GaAs(s), \tag{17}$$

$$K_{In-As_4} = \frac{a_{InAs}}{P_e^{In}(P_e^{As_4})^{1/4}},$$

$$In(v) + \tfrac{1}{2}As_4(v) \rightleftarrows InAs(s), \tag{18}$$

where a_{GaAs} and a_{InAs} are the activities which are given by

$$a_{GaAs} = (1-z)\exp(\alpha_{InAs-GaAs} z^2/RT), \tag{19}$$

$$a_{InAs} = z \exp\left[\alpha_{InAs-GaAs}(1-z)^2/RT\right], \tag{20}$$

in the regular solution approximation, $\alpha_{InAs-GaAs}$ in the interaction parameter and 12.6 kJ/mol is used for it in the present calculation [10].

Macrostoichiometric requirements give

$$J_s^{In}(\tfrac{1}{2}\lambda_0) + J_s^{Ga}(\tfrac{1}{2}\lambda_0) = J_s^{As}(\tfrac{1}{2}\lambda_0), \tag{21}$$

By solving the above equations, one can get the alloy composition,

$$z = \frac{J_s^{In}(\tfrac{1}{2}\lambda_0)}{J_s^{In}(\tfrac{1}{2}\lambda_0) + J_s^{Ga}(\tfrac{1}{2}\lambda_0)}.$$

as a function of the In fraction arriving in the flux.

In numerical calculations, the following equilibrium constants were employed,

$$K_{Ga-As_4} = 8.73 \times 10^{-17} \exp(4.76 \times 10^4/T), \tag{22}$$

$$K_{Ga-As_2} = 4.46 \times 10^{-20} \exp(5.52 \times 10^4/T), \tag{23}$$

$$K_{In-As_4} = 3.48 \times 10^{-16} \exp(3.95 \times 10^4/T), \tag{24}$$

As for the diffusion lengths of Ga And As, the following values are used [3,11,12],

$$\lambda_s^{Ga} = 4.0 \exp(3.48 \times 10^3/T)\ [\text{Å}], \tag{25}$$

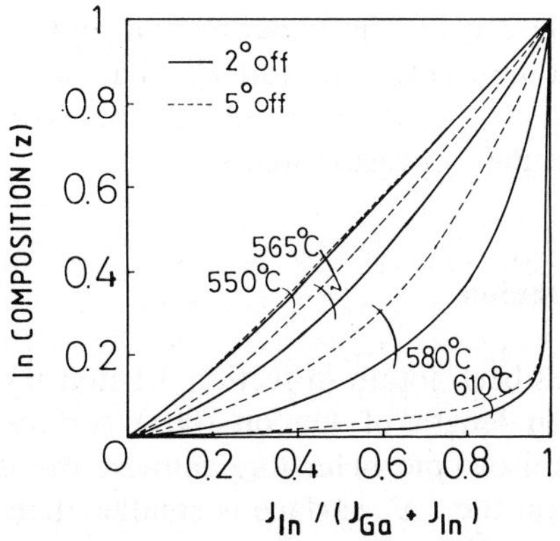

Fig. 8. Calculated results for the dependence for the $In_zGa_{1-z}As$ solid composition on the incident flux ratio. The solid line indicates (100) 2° off, and the dashed one (100) 5° off. J_{As_4} and $J_{As_4}/(J_{In}+J_{Ga})$ were kept at 1.25×10^{19} m^{-2} and 5.7.

Table 2
Calculated results for the solid composition of $In_zGa_{1-z}As$ on substrates tilted from (100); λ_s^{In} was chosen as the fiting parameter; the values in parentheses are the experimental results listed in table 1

Sample No.	Growth temperature (°C)	λ_s^{In} (Å)	z	
			2° off	5° off
IN-1	550	120	0.215 (0.268)	0.219 (0.260)
IN-2	565	32	0.132 (0.176)	0.167 (0.194)
IN-3	580	5	0.032 (0.039)	0.060 (0.043)
IN-4	610	1	0.007 (0.008)	0.012 (0.009)

$$\lambda_s^{As} = 1.7 \exp(8.12 \times 10^2/T) \; [\text{Å}], \qquad (26)$$

$$\lambda_s^{In} = 4.2 \times 10^{-30} \exp(5.69 \times 10^4/T) \; [\text{Å}]. \qquad (27)$$

In the above equations, the diffusion length of As_2 are assumed to be the same as that of As_4 and λ_s^{In} is determined so that this gives a good agreement between theory and experiment. The calculated In composition is shown in fig. 8 as a function of the In fraction in the total flux. This figure shows that z decreases rapidly as the growth temperature is increased and it decreases as the degree of misorientation is increased. These tendencies are in good agreement with the experiments.

Table 2 gives the experimental and the calculated In concentration and λ_s^{In}. The agreement in z is satisfactory if one thinks of the experimental error in the z measurements.

4. Discussion

It has been found in section 3.1 that the surface diffusion length of Ga on (001) surfaces shows some anisotropic behavior, namely, the diffusion length on the "A" surface is smaller than that on the "B" surface. The first conclusion which could be derived is that some anisotropy exists in the surface diffusion coefficient of Ga. This has already been pointed out by Ohta et al. [8]. However, there could be another possibility. In the above calculation, a chemical equilibrium is assumed to be established at the growth step. On the other hand, Pukite et al. [13] have reported the step edge on the "B" surface is atomically rough while that on the "A" surface is atomically smooth. If this is the case, the chemical equilibrium at the step edge on the "A" surface may not be established and there could be some supersaturation at the step. The recalculated diffusion length on the "A" surface assuming a supersaturation ratio of 3.5 at the step edge is given in fig. 9. The figure shows that now $\frac{1}{2}(E_{des} - E_{diff})$ takes the value of 0.34 eV which is identical to that on the "B" surface. Hence, the anisotropy in the diffusion coefficient does not provide a unique explanation for the anisotropy in the mode transition temperature.

According to the present experiment, the diffusion length of Ga on a GaAs (111)B surface is found to be much longer than that on a (001) surface. However, this conclusion applies on the assumption that the formation energy for 2D nucleation is the same for both surfaces. It could be that 2D nucleation on (111)B is much more difficult than on (001) because the side surface free energy of the 2D nuclei on (111)B might be larger than that on (001). If this so, the longer diffusion length on (111)B is not a unique conclusion.

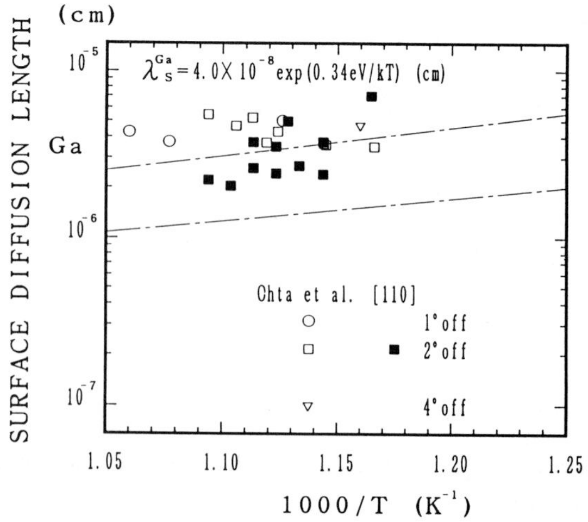

Fig. 9. The diffusion length of Ga on an "A" surface re-calculated with a supersaturation ratio of 3.5 at the step edge.

As mentioned in the previous section, the In concentration in $In_zGa_{1-z}As$ grown on (111)B is always larger than in layers grown on (001). This means that the diffusion length of In on (111)B is much longer than that on (001), assuming the step density on both surfaces is about the same. This assumption is reasonable since the steps on these surfaces are supplied from 2D nucleation, the creation rate of which is determined by the flux of impinging atoms. If nucleation on (111)B is more difficult than on (001), the average number of 2D nuclei is larger for (001), which would result in a high density of steps and hence should lead to a high In concentration on (001) surfaces. But this is not the case. Although, the above discussion is valid only for In on a GaAs surface, Ga on GaAs might behave in a similar way to In. This would be strong evidence for the previous conclusion that the surface diffusion length of Ga on (111)B is much longer than that on (001) surface.

5. Conclusion

The surface diffusion length of Ga on GaAs substrates is determined by measuring the critical temperature for the mode transition between 2D nucleation and step flow. At the critical temperature, the interstep distance is equated with the diffusion length, for the formation of 2D nuclei rather than for monolayer growth. This gives a longer diffusion length for de-adsorption as the growth temperature is increased. The measured diffusion length of Ga on (001) misoriented towards [110] is concluded to be intrinsic for a (001) surface, which is given as

$$\lambda_s^{Ga} = 4.0 \times 10^{-8} \exp(0.34 \text{ eV}/kT) \text{ [Å]}. \quad (28)$$

On a (111)B surface, the diffusion length is of the form,

$$\lambda_s^{Ga} = 4.0 \times 10^{-8} \exp(0.38 \text{ eV}/kT) \text{ [Å]}. \quad (29)$$

MBE growth of $In_zGa_{1-z}As$ has been carried out on GaAs substrates with various misorientations. It is found that z decreases markedly as the growth temperature is increased, and increases as the degree of misorientation is increased. These changes are explained using surface diffusion theory, as they have their origin in the re-evaporation of In on the growing surface.

Acknowledgements

The authors thank Mr. F. Yanagawa and Mr. K. Hirata of NTT LSI Laboratories for their help in measuring the alloy composition and valuable discussion. They are also indebted to Ms. M. Washiyama for her help throughout the experimental work. This work was supported in part by the Scientific Research Grant-in-Aid No. 62104002 for Special Project Research on "Alloy Semiconductor Physics and Electronics", from the Ministry of Education, Scicncc and Culture, the Mitsubishi Foundation and the Special Coordination Fund for Promoting Science and Technology on Physical, Chemical and Biological Phenomena under Microgravity Environment.

References

[1] J.H. Neave, P.J. Dobson, B.A. Joyce and J. Zhang, Appl. Phys. Letters 47 (1985) 100.
[2] W.K. Burton, N. Cabrera and F.C. Frank, Phil. Trans. Roy. Soy. London A243 (1951) 299.
[3] T. Nishinaga and K.I. Cho, Japan. J. Appl. Phys. Letters 27 (1988) L12.
[4] J.M. Van Hove and P.I. Cohen, J. Crystal Growth 81 (1987) 13.
[5] T. Shitara and T. Nishinaga, Japan. J. Appl. Phys. 28 (1989) 1212.
[6] J.P. Hirth and G.M. Pound, in: Condensation and Evaporation, Nucleation and Growth Kinetics (Pergamon, Oxford, 1963).
[7] R. Heckingbottom, J. Vacuum Sci. Technol. B3 (1985) 572.
[8] K. Ohta, T. Kojima and T. Nakagawa, J. Crystal Growth 95 (1988) 71.
[9] K. Mochizuki and T. Nishinaga, Japan. J. Appl. Phys. 27 (1988) 1585.
[10] M.B. Panish and M. Ilegems, in: Progress in Solid State Chemistry, Vol. 7, Eds. H. Reiss and J.O. McCaldin (Pergamon, New York, 1972) p. 79.
[11] C.T. Foxon and B.A. Joyce, Surface Sci. 50 (1975) 434.
[12] T. Nishinaga, T. Shitara and K.I. Cho, in: Record on 7th Alloy Semiconductor Physics and Electronics Symp., Kyoto, 1988, p. 57.
[13] P.R. Pukite, G.S. Petrich and P.E. Cohen, J. Crystal Growth 95 (1988) 269.

Zum Problem des Kristallwachstums.

Von

M. Volmer.

(Eingegangen am 10. 6. 22.)

Lange Zeit hindurch glaubte man in dem Prinzip von Curie und Wulff, nach welchem jeder Kristall bestrebt ist, eine solche Form anzunehmen, dass seine freie Energie der Oberfläche ein Minimum ist, eine Grundlage für eine allgemeine Theorie des Kristallwachstums zu haben. Dass dieses Prinzip aber tatsächlich ohne Bedeutung ist, geht, wie besonders Valeton[1]) neuerdings betont, bereits aus den viel älteren Ausführungen von W. Gibbs hervor, wonach bei makroskopischen Kristallen, an welchen allein die Beobachtungen gemacht wurden, das Gleichgewicht in bezug auf die Kristallform völlig indifferent ist, da der Einfluss des von der Oberflächenenergie herrührenden Gliedes im Ausdruck für das thermodynamische Potential bei solchen Kristallen verschwindend klein ist.

Trotzdem wird die Theorie von Curie nur ungern aufgegeben[2]), und zwar wohl deshalb, weil damit dieses Forschungsgebiet zunächst eines jeden leitenden Grundprinzips völlig beraubt ist.

Man hat versucht durch kinetische Vorstellungen[3]) in speziellen Fällen Aufschluss über die Ursache der verschiedenen Wachstumsgeschwindigkeiten eines Kristalls in verschiedenen Richtungen zu

[1]) Valeton, Verh. d. sächs. Ges. d. W., Leipzig 1915, S. 1. Die darüber hinausgehende Kritik der Curieschen Auffassung durch Valeton dürfte aber nach Ansicht des Verf. nicht berechtigt sein.

[2]) P. Ehrenfest, Ann. d. Physik **48**, 360 (1915); Born und Stern, Über die Oberflächenenergie der Kristalle und ihren Einfluss auf die Kristallgestalt, Berl. Akad. Ber. 901 (1919).

[3]) Valeton, Physik. Zeitschr. **21**, 606 (1920).

erhalten, doch kann hieraus kein allgemeines Prinzip abgeleitet werden[1]).

In der vorliegenden Arbeit werden einige Konsequenzen aus neueren Beobachtungen gezogen, in deren Verfolgung sich ein neuer Weg zu bieten scheint, der aus den Schwierigkeiten herausführen kann. Um die Ideen in konkreter Weise wiederzugeben, war es notwendig, an verschiedenen Stellen teils Annahmen zu machen, die noch bestätigt oder möglicherweise auch modifiziert werden müssen, teils rohe Schätzungen von Grössen vorzunehmen, deren Kenntnis zur Zeit noch fehlt. Dadurch erhält die ganze Darlegung den Charakter eines vorläufigen Entwurfes, dessen Mitteilung aber dadurch gerechtfertigt erscheint, dass der Grundgedanke erhalten bleibt, wenn auch im einzelnen wesentliche Änderungen vorgenommen werden sollten.

Die Resultate einiger vorhergehenden Arbeiten sind folgende[2]):

1. Bei der Bildung von *Hg*-Kristallen aus übersättigtem Dampf bei niedrigem Drucke wurde festgestellt, dass das Wachsen der Kristalle nicht dadurch geschieht, dass die ankommenden Moleküle[3]) einfach an den nächsten freien Gitterpunkten angelagert werden, sondern dass sich die Moleküle zum Kristall erst im kondensierten Zustand ordnen.

2. Es lassen sich Gründe angeben, welche es sehr unwahrscheinlich erscheinen lassen, dass dieses Wachsen im kondensierten Zustand dadurch erfolgt, dass neue Moleküle sich in das fertige Gitter hineindrängen und so den Kristall auseinandertreiben.

3. Es wird deshalb geschlossen, dass die neu kondensierten Moleküle sich zunächst in einem beweglichen Zustand auf der Oberfläche des Kristalls befinden und hier gelegentlich zu kleinen neuen „zweidimensionalen“ Keimen zusammentreten, welche dann seitlich die auf der Oberfläche sich bewegenden Moleküle anlagern und zu vollständigen neuen Netzebenen auswachsen.

Diese Auffassung wird durch neue mikroskopische Beobachtungen an wachsenden Kristallen weiter gestützt. Die Versuchsobjekte waren:

a) *Hg*-Kristalle im *Hg*-Dampf bei niedrigem Druck,

b) elektrolytisch wachsende Kristalle von *Cd* und *Sn*,

c) PbJ_2-Kristalle, die beim Zusammentreffen von Bleinitrat und Jodkaliumlösung entstehen.

---

1) Volmer, Physik. Zeitschr. **22**, 646 (1921).

2) Zeitschr. f. Physik **7**, 13 (1921); **9**, 193 (1922).

3) Das Wort Molekül wird im folgenden ganz allgemein gebraucht, auch wenn es sich speziell um Atome oder Ionen handelt.

Stellt man bei 500 bis 1000 facher Vergrösserung auf eine der vollkommen eben erscheinenden Kristallflächen ein, so beobachtet man direkt, dass schnell nacheinander neue Schichten sich auf der Kristallfläche bilden, und zwar beginnt diese Schichtbildung an einer Stelle und breitet sich von da in konstanter Dicke schnell über die ganze Fläche aus. Insbesondere ist die gleichmässige Dicke der Schichten mit Sicherheit an den Interferenzfarben der dünnen Kristallblättchen von PbJ_2 zu erkennen. Der Beginn der Bildung einer neuen Schicht wird bemerkt an dem Auftreten eines anderen Farbtones an einer Stelle, dieser Fleck breitet sich seitlich aus, wobei innerhalb der Flächen rechts und links der stets scharfen Grenze die Farbtöne während der Verschiebung der Grenze konstant bleiben. Daraus folgt, dass das Wachsen einer Kristallfläche ein diskontinuierlicher Vorgang ist, indem nacheinander Schicht auf Schicht entsteht. Diese neuen Schichten können verschiedene Dicken haben, die nach dem Grad, in welchem sich der Farbton ändert, beurteilt werden können[1]). Die untere Grenze der auftretenden Schichtdicken ist nicht direkt beobachtbar, aber aus der völligen Analogie der Erscheinung mit der von Marcellin studierten kann geschlossen werden, dass sie wie bei einer Molekülschicht liegt. Je dünner die Schicht, um so schneller erfolgt ihre Ausbreitung. Bei Metallkristallen erweckt diese Ausbildung und Auswachsung der Schichten den Eindruck, als ob über die Oberfläche flüssige Metallschichten fliessen. Die sichtbar dünnsten Schichten eilen mit ausserordentlicher Geschwindigkeit über die Flächen, durch Überholung entstehen dickere Schichten, die sich sodann ganz langsam weiter vorschieben. Diese Tatsache findet sofort ihre Erklärung aus der unter 3. angeführten Auffassung des Vorganges.

Interessant dürfte ein Vergleich der hier an der Hand der Experimente erlangten Auffassung mit dem Bild sein, welches sich Gibbs[2]) von dem Vorgang des Kristallwachstums gemacht hat: „... wir können nicht annehmen, dass ein Körper von innerem Bau und äusserer Gestalt eines Kristalls durch einen völlig stetigen Vorgang oder einen, der in demselben Sinne wie Verflüssigung und Verdampfung zwischen

[1]) Diese beim Wachsen entstehenden Schichten sind genau der gleichen Art, wie solche, die von Marcellin [Ann. d. Physik **10**, 189 (1918)] beim Zerreissen von Glimmer erhalten wurden. Es ist mir besonders wertvoll, dass dies bestätigt wurde von Herrn Dr. Müller, welcher im hiesigen physikalischen Institut die Versuche von Marcellin wiederholt und weiter fortführt.

[2]) Gibbs, Thermodynamische Studien, S. 380—381; siehe auch die Fussnoten daselbst.

Flüssigkeit und Gas oder der entsprechende Vorgang zwischen einem amorphen festen Körper und einer Flüssigkeit stetig ist, wächst oder sich auflöst. Der Vorgang ist eher als periodischer anzusehen usw."

Betrachten wir einen Kristall im Gleichgewicht mit seinem gesättigten Dampf und nehmen wir den beweglichen Zwischenzustand der Moleküle beim Wachsen als bewiesen an, so ergibt sich sofort, dass der Kristall dauernd von einer adsorbierten Schicht seiner eigenen Moleküle umgeben ist. Es scheint, dass das Vorhandensein einer solchen Zwischenschicht auch unabhängig von den genannten Experimenten einfach aus der Tatsache folgt, dass an der Oberfläche des Kristalls van der Waalssche Kräfte vorhanden sind. Dieselben Gründe, die nach Hulshof[1]) und Bakker[2]) zur Annahme einer Übergangsschicht an der Grenze flüssig-gasförmig massgebend sind, dürften auch hier Geltung haben. Für die Existenz einer Adsorptionsschicht sprechen ausserdem die Beobachtungen von Marc[3]) über die Geschwindigkeit der Konzentrationsabnahme übersättigter Lösungen beim Hineinbringen der Kristalle. Dabei erhält er im ersten Moment eine verhältnismässig viel stärkere Abnahme, die er in dem obigen Sinn deutet.

Das thermodynamische Potential ist natürlich an allen Stellen der Adsorptionsschicht dasselbe wie im Dampf und im Kristall, die mittlere Dichte der Moleküle in der Adsorptionsschicht ändert sich jedoch mit der kristallographischen Natur der Fläche, weil das Adsorptionspotential für verschiedene Gitterebenen verschieden sein muss. Bezüglich der Adsorption fremder Stoffe liegen dafür direkte experimentelle Erfahrungen vor[3]). Es ist für die eigenen Molekeln zu schliessen aus der von Born und Stern an einem Modell berechneten Tatsache, die aber ohne Bedenken (auch für homeopolare Stoffe) verallgemeinert werden kann, dass die spezifische Oberflächenenergie [ungenauer Oberflächenspannung[4])] verschiedene Werte für verschiedenartige Kristallflächen hat. Die Oberflächenenergie ist aber ein Mass für die unabgesättigten Anziehungskräfte der in der Oberfläche liegenden Molekeln, auf die jede Adsorption zurückzuführen ist[5]). Es wäre für das folgende überaus wichtig, wenn an irgendeinem speziellen Modell z. B. *NaCl*, die Adsorptionspotentiale für *Na* und *Cl* berechnet

[1]) Hulshof, Ann. d. Physik **4**, 165 (1901).
[2]) Bakker, Zeitschr. f. physik. Chemie **28**, 708 (1899) bis **61**, 273 (1920).
[3]) Marc, Zeitschr. f. physik. Chemie **68**, 109 (1910); **75**, 710 (1911); **81**, 641 (1913).
[4]) Vgl. Gibbs, Thermodynamische Studien, S. 369, Fussnote.
[5]) Haber, Zeitschr. f. Elektrochemie **20**, 521 (1914); Langmuir, Phys. Rev. **6**, 79 (1915).

würden. Vorläufig wollen wir, um die Idee weiter durchführen zu können, die mittleren Adsorptionspotentiale proportional den spezifischen Oberflächenenergien, und weiter das Potential innerhalb der Absorptionsschichten konstant gleich A_1 bzw. A_2 setzen. Ferner behandeln wir diese mittleren Potentiale in erster Näherung als Temperatur unabhängig. Vernachlässigen wir die gegenseitige Beeinflussung der Molekeln innerhalb der Schicht, so ergibt sich für die mittleren Dichten vor zwei verschiedenen Netzebenen nach dem Bolzmannschen e-Satz:

$$\frac{c_1}{c_2} = e^{\frac{A_1 - A_2}{RT}}.$$

Die Gleichgewichtseinstellung in der Schicht kann nach dem Vorangehenden[1]) nicht nur durch Vermittlung des festen oder gasförmigen Zustandes, sondern auch durch direkten Ausgleich (Fliessen) innerhalb der Schicht und daher sehr schnell erfolgen; diese Erkenntnis ist wichtig und bildet die Grundlage für das weitere.

Die Gleichgewichtseinstellung zwischen Schicht und Kristall erfolgt dagegen nicht durch direkten ungeordneten Molekülübergang, sondern nur durch Aufbau oder Abbau von Netzebenen. Dies ist allerdings durch die Experimente bisher nur für den Aufbau bewiesen, kann aber wohl unbedenklich auf den in jeder Hinsicht reziproken Vorgang des Abbaues übertragen werden.

Die Geschwindigkeit, mit der im Gleichgewicht die wechselnden Vorgänge erfolgen, variiert von Fläche zu Fläche, doch ist insgesamt das Wachstum jeder Fläche 0.

Wir betrachten nun die Bildung und Auswachsung einer Netzebene als einen Vorgang in der Adsorptionsschicht, auf welche die darunter liegende Netzebene keinen direkten Einfluss ausübt. Die Unterlage bestimmt nur 1. die relative Moleküldichte und ermöglicht 2. eine Zusammenlagerung der Molekeln. Denn findet in der Schicht, die wir uns mit Langmuir im wesentlichen monomolekular vorstellen, ein Zusammenstoss statt, so kann die Energie von den Molekülen des Gitters aufgenommen werden, daher der Stoss unelastisch sein[2]).

Nach dieser Voraussetzung ergibt sich, dass die Geschwindigkeit von Neubildung und Wachstum der Netzebenen hauptsächlich von der

---

[1]) Zeitschr. f. Physik 7, 13 (1921).

[2]) Damit der Stoss der Moleküle unelastisch ist, d. h. die Moleküle zusammenbleiben, ist erforderlich, dass ein Mechanismus existiert, der die freiwerdende Energie abführt. Beim Stoss von Molekülen auf ihr festes Kondensat wird die Energie äusserst

Moleküldichte abhängig ist. Zur Angabe der speziellen Form der Abhängigkeit muss man sich zu besonderen Vorstellungen über den Mechanismus entschliessen. Nimmt man an, dass die Anlage einer Netzebene beginnt mit dem unelastischen Zusammenstoss zweier Moleküle und darauffolgender Anlagerung eines dritten usw., so ist die Geschwindigkeit zunächst proportional dem Quadrat der Dichte und schliesslich ihr selbst. Die Ermittlung dieser Abhängigkeit dürfte die diesbezüglich wichtigste Aufgabe sein. Wir setzen die Geschwindigkeit proportional c^n, wobei n mindestens Eins ist, so dass bis auf einen unbekannten sterischen Faktor a, der wahrscheinlich von der Grössenordnung 1 ist, das Verhältnis der Wachstumsgeschwindigkeiten gegeben ist durch

$$\frac{v_1}{v_2} = a\left(\frac{c_1}{c_2}\right)^n = a e^{n \frac{A_1 - A_2}{RT}} .$$

Dabei ist vorausgesetzt, dass die Einstellung der Dichteverteilung in der Schicht schnell gegenüber dem Gitteraufbau erfolgt, und infolgedessen sich auch um den ganzen Kristall dann einstellt, wenn die absoluten Werte nicht dem Gleichgewichtszustand entsprechen, d. h. wenn der Dampf weit übersättigt ist. Im allgemeinen wird das jedoch nicht zutreffen, insbesondere dann nicht, wenn noch fremde Moleküle adsorbiert sind. Auch bei einem in reinem Dampf wachsenden Kristall ist es nicht immer der Fall, sonst dürfte kein Einfluss der Stoffzufuhr auf die relativen Wachstumsgeschwindigkeiten eines Kristalls merklich sein [1]). Es wird nicht leicht sein, Beispiele experimentell zu realisieren, bei denen die Bedingung streng erfüllt ist; am ehesten wird es noch bei kleinen Kristallen möglich sein, die im übersättigten Dampf wachsen. Verläuft die Einstellung der Dichteverteilung nicht schnell gegen die Bildung von Netzebenen, so bedeutet dies einen teilweisen Ausgleich der Wachstumsgeschwindigkeiten. Tatsächlich sind bei grossen Kristallen die relativen Dimensionen nie so verschieden, wie sie sich im folgenden nach obiger Gleichung ergeben.

Diese durch rohe Annahmen erhaltene Beziehung erklärt

---

schnell auf eine grosse Molekülzahl des festen Körpers verteilt. Nach den Berechnungen von Langmuir [Phys. Rev. 8, 149 (1916)] ist unter Berücksichtigung der Wärmeleitung des Materials die Geschwindigkeit, mit der das geschieht, in allen Fällen so gross, dass praktisch elastische Ströme nie zu erwarten sind. Auf den vorliegenden Fall ist auch die spezielle Auffassung von Haber und Zisch [Zeitschr. f. Physik 9, 302 (1922)] anwendbar, wobei ein energiereicher, kurzdauernder Zwischenzustand angenommen wird.

[1]) Zeitschr. f. Physik 9, 193 (1922).

1. die Erfahrungstatsache, die auch aus der Curieschen Theorie folgte, dass die Flächen mit kleinen spezifischen Oberflächenenergien besonders häufig und ausgedehnt auftreten, der Grund ist hier aber der, dass sie am langsamsten wachsen, und zwar weil das Adsorptionspotential dieser Flächen am kleinsten ist. Entsprechend ergibt sich die Bravaissche Regel, weil dies für die dichtesten Netzebenen gilt.

2. Um das Verhältnis der relativen Wachstumsgeschwindigkeiten der Grössenordnung nach abschätzen zu können, machen wir die Annahme, dass A_1 die Adsorptionswärme für eine Netzebene mittlerer Dichte gleich der halben Verdampfungswärme λ ist[1]). Für das Verhältnis von $\frac{A_1}{A_2}$ setzen wir das Verhältnis der spezifischen Oberflächenenergien, welches von Born und Stern für einen Kristall vom Typus *NaCl* für die 011 bzw. 001 Fläche berechnet worden ist, nämlich:

$$\frac{\sigma_1}{\sigma_2} = 2{\cdot}7.$$

Dieses Verhältnis wird man für Schätzungszwecke auch auf andere Kristalle als ungefähr zutreffend annehmen dürfen.

Dann wird:

$$\frac{v_1}{v_2} \sim a \cdot e^{n \frac{\frac{\lambda}{2}\left(1 - \frac{1}{2{\cdot}7}\right)}{RT}} \sim a \cdot e^{n \frac{\lambda}{3RT}}.$$

Da der Schmelzpunkt von Kristallen nie erheblich über dem Siedepunkt liegt (in Bruchteilen der absoluten Temperatur ausgedrückt), so ist der kleinste Wert, den $\frac{v_1}{v_2}$ etwa annehmen kann, unter Benutzung der Troutonschen Regel:

$$\frac{v_1}{v_2} \sim e^3.$$

Mit sinkender Temperatur wächst das Verhältnis schnell: ein eigenartiges Ergebnis, welches der experimentellen Prüfung zugänglich ist.

Im allgemeinen wird also $\frac{v_1}{v_2} > e^3$ sein, immer vorausgesetzt, dass das Wachsen weit entfernt vom Gleichgewicht[2]) erfolgt und keine aus-

---

[1]) Die Temperaturabhängigkeit auch von λ bleibt für diese Überschlagsbetrachtungen unberücksichtigt.

[2]) Die bisherigen Messungen des Kristallwachstums sind mit Ausnahme des folgenden Beispiels nahe am Gleichgewicht ausgeführt worden und daher zur Ermittlung der Geschwindigkeitsgesetze für den einseitig verlaufenden Vorgang und zur Prüfung obiger Formel ungeeignet.

gleichenden Nebenumstände vorhanden sind. Für *Hg*-Kristalle, welche bei etwa -50° aus ihrem übersättigten Dampf entstehen, ergibt sich beispielsweise für $n = 1$ und $a = 1$

$$\frac{v_1}{v_2} \sim e^{\frac{15000}{3 \cdot 2 \cdot 223}} = 7 \cdot 10^4.$$

Tatsächlich entstehen unter solchen Umständen erfahrungsgemäss dünne Kristallblättchen[1]) oder Nadeln, deren Dimensionen in diesem Verhältnis etwa stehen so lange sie klein sind. Die Bildung solcher Kriställchen mit extrem verschiedenen Ausdehnungen konnte bisher auch nicht andeutungsweise erklärt werden.

Was den Gitterabbau anbelangt, so ist für die Häufigkeit, mit der der Übergang aus dem Gitter in die Schicht erfolgt, ein Faktor

$$e^{-\frac{Q}{RT}}$$

in erster Linie massgebend, wo $Q = \lambda - A_1$ bzw. $\lambda - A_2$ ist. So ergibt sich für das Verhältnis der Abbaugeschwindigkeiten entsprechend das massgebende Glied zu:

$$\frac{v'_1}{v'_2} \sim e^{\frac{A_1 - A_2}{RT}}.$$

Das Wachsen des Kristalls aus der Schmelze lässt sich im gleichen Sinne behandeln, und zwar handelt es sich hier nicht um Verdichtungen in der Grenzschicht, sondern zum Teil um Verarmung der Grenze an Molekülen, d. h. ein Kristall wird von seiner Schmelze in ungleicher Weise benetzt, und zwar die Flächen kleinster Adsorptionspotentials am schlechtesten. Letzteres kann man leicht beobachten: hat man eine Unterlage mit *Hg*-Kristallen besetzt und lässt langsam bis zum Schmelzpunkt erwärmen, so sieht man das an einer Stelle schmelzende *Hg* schnell kapillar die einzelnen Kristalle umfliessen, mit Ausnahme der Basisflächen. Auf diesen erscheint ein deutlicher Randwinkel gegen die Schmelze, der unter den beobachteten Bedingungen (hohes Vakuum) nicht von Verunreinigung verursacht sein kann. Die Verschiedenheit der kapillaren Ausbreitung der Schmelze über einen daraus entstehenden Kristall ist auch die Ursache für das Wachsen eines Kristalls über die Grenzen seiner Schmelze hinaus, z. B. beim Kristallisieren eines etwas unterkühlten Tropfens. Das Relief der Eisblumen entsteht auf gleiche Weise. Auch die mechanischen Wirkungen wachsender Kristalle werden verständlich[2]).

---

[1]) Zeitschr. f. Physik **7**, 13 (1921).

[2]) O. Lehmann, Molekularphysik, S. 344.

Über diese Dinge sowie über das interessante elektrolytische Wachsen von Kristallen soll später eingehend berichtet werden, doch mag bz. des letzteren schon angedeutet sein, dass in Übereinstimmung mit der Tatsache, dass die elektrolytischen Kristalle genau die gleichen Wachstumserscheinungen zeigen, wie die aus dem betreffenden Dampf wachsenden Kristalle auch hier die verschiedene Absorbierbarkeit der Metallatome an den verschiedenen Flächen in gleicher Weise massgebend ist. Der Vorgang rückt dadurch in nahe Verwandtschaft zu den Überspannungserscheinungen bei der Abscheidung von Wasserstoff an Metallelektroden.

Hamburg, Physik.-chem. Institut der Universität.

Zur Theorie des Kristallwachstums[1]).

Von

Iwan N. Stranski.

(Mit 6 Figuren im Text.)

(Eingegangen am 27. 7. 28.)

Es wird angenommen, dass die Kristalloberfläche nur unwesentlich vom Bau im Kristallinneren abweicht, und dass die Molekeln an der Oberfläche diejenigen Lagen einnehmen, welchen ein Energieminimum zukommt. Um das Wachstum bzw. Auflösen eines Kristalls herleiten zu können, müssen daher die Werte der Abtrennungsarbeiten, welche den verschiedenen Lagen an der Oberfläche zukommen, vorher bestimmt werden. Letzteres wird an einem *NaCl*-Kristall ausgeführt und gezeigt, dass sich die daraus zu ziehenden Folgerungen befriedigend mit den Tatsachen decken.

1. Das Kristallwachstum ist von den verschiedenen Autoren, die sich mit dessen Theorie befasst haben, aus hauptsächlich zwei wesentlich voneinander abweichenden Standpunkten aufgefasst worden.

Die einen[2]) nehmen an, dass es sich dabei um eine Frage handelt, welche rein thermodynamisch behandelt werden kann. Nach diesen

---

[1]) Diese Arbeit war in der vorliegenden Form schon im Sommer 1927 fertig und ist im Jahrbuch der Universität Sofia, **24**, phys.-math. Abt. **2**, 297 (1927/28), in bulgarischer Sprache veröffentlicht worden. Der darin vertretene Standpunkt wurde von mir auch anlässlich einer Arbeit von H. BRANDES, Z. physikal. Chem. **126**, 198. 1927, in einer Zuschrift vom 2. Okt. 1927 an die Redaktion derselben Zeitschrift zum Teil klargelegt. Inzwischen ist eine sehr ähnliche Arbeit von Herrn Prof. W. KOSSEL, Nachr. Ges. Wiss. Göttingen, mathem.-phys. Kl. 1927, 135, erschienen, von welcher ich leider erst aus dem Referat im Chem. Ztrblt. erfuhr. Da die Ergebnisse in meiner Arbeit auf selbständigem Wege erhalten worden sind und, wie es mir scheint, in manchem Punkte weiter gehen, halte ich es für gegeben, dieselbe schon jetzt ungeändert in deutscher Sprache erscheinen zu lassen, um sie dadurch allgemein zugänglich zu machen, und nicht erst im Rahmen einer umfassenderen Abhandlung, wie von mir zuerst geplant wurde. Hierbei möchte ich nicht unterlassen, auch auf die Arbeit von E. BRANDENBURGER, Z. Kristallogr. **66**, 120. 1927, hinzuweisen, welche einen Umriss einer Molekulartheorie des Kristallwachstums aus allgemeinen theoretischen Gesichtspunkten gibt.

[2]) P. CURIE, Z. Kristallogr. **12**, 651. 1887. G. WULFF, Z. Kristallogr. **34**, 512. 1901. A. RIETZEL, Z. Kristallogr. **49**, 172. 1911. H. LIEBMANN, Z. Kristallogr. **53**, 171. 1914. P. EHRENFEST, Ann. Phys. **48**, 360. 1915. M. BORN und O. STERN, Sitzber. Preuss. Akad. Wiss. 901. 1919. M. YAMADA, Physikal. Ztschr. **24**, 364. 1923. **25**, 52. 1924. J. BIEMÜLLER, Z. Physik **38**, 753. 1926.

strebt jeder Kristall einer bestimmten Form zu, welche bei den bestehenden Gleichgewichtsbedingungen die allein mögliche ist.

Die anderen[1]) beziehen sich auf eine Gleichung, die zuerst von J. W. GIBBS (1875—1878) hergeleitet wurde und wonach die Löslichkeit bzw. der Sublimationsdruck eines genügend grossen Kristalls aufhört, von der Oberflächenspannung abzuhängen. Daraus folgern sie, dass die Tracht und also auch das Wachstum eines Kristalls überhaupt nicht thermodynamisch herzuleiten ist, sondern dass sie reine Geschwindigkeitsfragen sind.

Schliesslich versuchen einige Autoren, mit M. VOLMER[2]) an der Spitze, einen Mittelweg einzuschlagen.

Eine eingehende Darlegung und Diskussion der verschiedenen Standpunkte wird an anderer Stelle erscheinen. Die Aufgabe der vorliegenden Arbeit ist, zu zeigen, dass man bei Zuständen, die nicht weit vom Gleichgewicht abstehen, sowohl das Wachstum, wie auch die Auflösung der Kristalle aus dem Prinzip des Energieminimums befriedigend herleiten kann.

Indem wir von der Vorstellung ausgehen, dass die Kristalloberfläche nur unwesentlich vom Bau im Kristallinnern abweicht, d. h., dass die Molekeln (Atome, Ionen) an der Oberfläche an bestimmte Ruhelagen gebunden sind, die weitgehend dem Gitter entsprechen, so werden wir in gewissen einfachen Fällen (zur Zeit nur bei einigen Ionenkristallen) verhältnismässig leicht die Abtrennungsarbeiten für jede mögliche Lage an der Oberfläche näherungsweise bestimmen können. Mit Abtrennungsarbeit soll dabei diejenige Arbeit bezeichnet sein, welcher es bedarf, um eine Molekel (Atom, Ion) von ihrem Platz an der Oberfläche bis ins Unendliche zu entfernen. Dann muss folgendes gelten: Die Molekeln, welche die grössten Abtrennungsarbeiten besitzen, werden am seltensten die Oberfläche verlassen, und umgekehrt, neue Molekeln werden am leichtesten an solchen Stellen angelagert,

[1]) A. BERTHOUD, J. chim. phys. **10**, 624. 1912. G. FRIEDEL, J. chim. phys. **11**, 478. 1913. J. J. P. VALETON, Ber. d. mathem.-phys. Kl. d. Sächs. Ges. Wiss. **67**, 1. 1915. Physikal. Ztschr. **21**, 606. 1920. Z. Kristallogr. **59**, 135, 335. 1923/24. **60**, 1. 1924. R. GROSS, Abhdlg. d. mathem.-phys. Kl. d. Sächs. Ges. Wiss. **35**, 137. 1918. G. MASING, Naturwiss. **10**, 899. 1920. P. NIGGLI, Z. angew. Chem. **110**, 55. 1920. K. SPANGENBERG, Z. Kristallogr. **59**, 383. 1923/24.

[2]) M. VOLMER und J. ESTERMANN, Z. Physik **7**, 13. 1921. M. VOLMER, Physikal. Ztschr. **22**, 646. 1921. Z. Physik **9**, 193. 1922. Z. physikal. Chem. **102**, 270. 1922. **115**, 253. 1925. M. VOLMER und A. WEBER, Z. physikal. Chem. **119**, 277. 1926. H. BRANDES, Z. physikal. Chem. **126**, 198. 1927.

welchen die grössten Abtrennungsarbeiten zukommen. Demnach besteht die Aufgabe, die Reihenfolge der Anlagerungen oder Abtrennungen der Molekeln an der Kristalloberfläche aufzusuchen, zunächst darin, die Abtrennungsarbeiten für eine Reihe von charakteristischen Lagen an der Oberfläche zu bestimmen.

Im folgenden soll an einem Ionenkristall vom $NaCl$-Typus als einfachstem Beispiel gezeigt werden, inwieweit das bisher entworfene Programm zu verwirklichen ist. Da von den Faktoren, welche das Kristallwachstum bedingen, nur die inneren berücksichtigt werden und alle anderen (Lösungsmittel, Materialzufuhr) fürs erste ausgeschaltet sind, so muss der zu untersuchende Kristall nur von seinem eigenen (verdünnten) Dampf umgeben sein und nur sehr wenig vom Gleichgewichtszustand abstehen. Es sei noch bemerkt, dass bei den Ausrechnungen der Abtrennungsarbeiten die Wärmebewegungen ebenfalls nicht berücksichtigt werden.

2. Bekanntlich kann bei den Ionenkristallen der Zusammenhalt der Ionen im Gitter mit grosser Genauigkeit nur auf die elektrostatischen Kräfte zwischen den Ionen und auf die BORNschen Abstossungskräfte zurückgeführt werden. Diese Einfachheit, welche im Kristallinnern herrscht, besteht jedoch nicht mehr an der Kristalloberfläche. Über die Abweichungen, welche an dieser auftreten können, sind bis jetzt zwei verschiedene Meinungen geäussert worden. E. MADELUNG[1]) hat den Fall durchgerechnet, dass die Ionen sich gleichbleiben, sowohl im Kristallinnern, wie an der Oberfläche. Nach ihm sind Abweichungen in der Lage der Ionen an der Oberfläche in bezug auf das Gitter zu erwarten, die im allgemeinen für Kationen und Anionen verschieden ausfallen müssen. J. BIEMÜLLER[2]) hat hingegen auf M. BORNS Anregung den Fall durchgerechnet, dass nur Ionendeformationen an dieser stattfinden, dass aber die Lage der einzelnen Ionen in bezug auf das Gitter unverändert bleibt.

Die Ionendeformation, die aus Symmetriegründen im Kristallinnern fast vollkommen fehlt, kommt an der Oberfläche wieder zum Vorschein, wenn auch nicht in dem Masse, wie bei den einfachen Molekeln (im Gaszustand), wo sie wegen der höchst einseitigen Einwirkung der Ionen aufeinander besonders stark auftreten muss. Die Abweichungen an der Oberfläche werden aber wahrscheinlich sowohl in Gitter- wie auch in Ionendeformationen bestehen. Man übersieht die

---

[1]) E. MADELUNG, Physikal. Ztschr. **20**, 494. 1919. [2]) J. BIEMÜLLER, Z. Physik **38**, 759. 1926.

Verhältnisse besser an Fig. 1. Sind die Ionen in der äussersten (ersten) Netzebene deformiert, so wird der Abstand zwischen der ersten und zweiten Netzebene kleiner ausfallen müssen, als der Netzebenenabstand im Kristallinnern, denn durch die Dipolbildung ist eine zusätzliche Anziehungskraft zwischen beiden Netzebenen entstanden. Die Bindung zwischen der ersten und zweiten Netzebene wird aber noch etwas dadurch verstärkt, da die abstossende Wirkung der vierten Netzebene auf die zweite nicht kompensiert wird. In der Figur sind diese Verhältnisse durch eine grössere Entfernung zwischen der zweiten und dritten und eine kleinere Entfernung zwischen der ersten und zweiten Netzebene veranschaulicht worden.

Eine Verzerrung ist aber auch in Richtung der Fläche selbst zu erwarten. Auf eine solche muss schon aus der verhältnismässig grossen

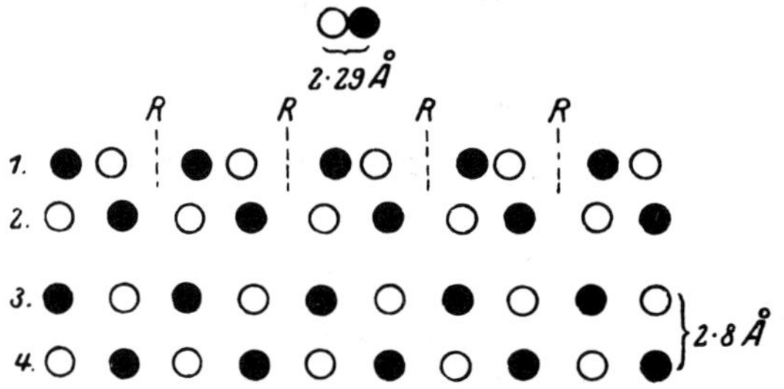

Fig. 1.

Differenz zwischen dem Ionenabstand im Kristallinnern und in einer Gasmolekel geschlossen werden. Der erste beträgt für Steinsalz etwa $2{\cdot}8 \cdot 10^{-8}$ cm, während der zweite unabhängig von jeder Deformation, schon wegen des Fehlens von anderen Ionen, kleiner sein muss[1]). Unter Berücksichtigung der Deformation haben M. Born und W. Heisenberg[2]) den Ionenabstand in der Gasmolekel *NaCl* zu etwa $2{\cdot}29 \cdot 10^{-8}$ cm errechnet. Ein Zusammenrücken aller Ionen an der Würfelfläche verhindern schon die tieferen Ionennetzebenen. Es bleibt nur anzunehmen, dass sich kleine Risse (die Stellen *R* in der Figur) bilden, die sich auf die äussersten Netzebenen beschränken und die die Zusammengehörigkeit der Ionen zu Molekeln schon hier andeuten.

Um eine genaue Ausrechnung der uns hier interessierenden Abtrennungsarbeiten zu verwirklichen, müsste man alle diese Wirkungen berücksichtigen, was zur Zeit kaum streng durchzuführen wäre. Ich

[1]) A. Reis, Z. Physik **1**, 294. 1920. [2]) M. Born und W. Heisenberg, Z. Physik **23**, 407. 1924.

habe das Problem auf folgendem vereinfachtem Wege zu lösen versucht. Mit BIEMÜLLER nehme ich an, dass das Gitter an der Oberfläche als undeformiert betrachtet werden kann. Die Abtrennungsarbeiten berechne ich aber dann allein aus dem elektrostatischen Anteil und aus dem Anteil der Abstossung. Ich mache also noch die Voraussetzung, dass der Anteil der Abstossungsarbeit, welcher von der (Gitter- und) Ionendeformation herrührt, durch die Deformation der anderen Ionen, welche durch das Entfernen des betreffenden Ions entblösst werden, gerade kompensiert wird. Selbstverständlich trifft dies nur näherungsweise zu. Hier ist auch die Annahme mit einbezogen, dass sich Kationen und Anionen vollständig gleich betragen.

Die auf eine derartige Weise berechneten Abtrennungsarbeiten von Ionen in einigen typischen Lagen am *NaCl*-Kristall sind in der Tabelle 1 zusammengestellt.

Tabelle 1.

Lage des Ions	$\varphi_1 \cdot \frac{\delta}{e^2}$	$\varphi_2 \cdot \frac{\delta}{e^2}$	$\varphi \cdot \frac{\delta}{e^2}$	$\varphi' \cdot \frac{\delta}{e^2}$
0	3·487(6)	— 0·387(7)	3·100	1·868
1	3·355(9)	— 0·316(6)	3·039	1·746
2	3·175(8)	— 0·248(2)	2·928	1·524
3	2·682(7)	— 0·184(7)	2·498	1·251
4	3·127(3)	— 0·252(6)	2·875	1·418
5	2·369(7)	— 0·187(7)	2·182	1·034
6	1·743(8)	— 0·193(8)	1·550	0·709
7	2·949(6)	— 0·185(1)	2·765	1·198
8	0·360(3)	— 0·134(9)	0·225	0·709
9	0·937(8)	— 0·132(3)	0·806	0·545
10	0·591(2)	— 0·064(5)	0·527	0·266
11	0·131(7)	— 0·070(9)	0·061	0·709
12	0·180(2)	— 0·067(5)	0·113	0·650
13	0·493(1)	— 0·064(5)	0·429	0·536
14	2·131(7)	— 0·129(7)	2·002	— 0·328
15	2·180(2)	— 0·126(4)	2·054	— 0·224
16	2·026(8)	— 0·126(4)	1·900	— 0·062
17	2·360(3)	— 0·193(7)	2·167	0·000
18	2·104(4)	— 0·190(3)	1·914	0·380
19	1·515(2)	— 0·129(7)	1·386	~ 0·381
20	2·321(3)	— 0·191(6)	2·130	~ 0·981
21	< 0·305(9)	— 0·138(4)	< 0·168	~ 0·593
22	> 0·408(8)	— 0·131(5)	> 0·277	~ 0·702
23	< 3·072(3)	— 0·256(0)	< 2·816	< 1·300
24	< 1·689(4)	— 0·197(2)	< 1·492	< 0·593
25	> 1·792(3)	— 0·190(3)	> 1·602	> 0·813
26	< — 1·362(8)	— 0·201(6)	< — 1·564	—
27	> 7·122(4)	— 0·186(0)	> 6·936	~ 2·981

φ: (0) > (1) > (2) > (4) > (7) > (3) > (5) > (17) > (20) > (15) > (14) > (18) > (16) > (6) > (19) > (9) > (10) > (13) > (8) > (12) > (11); (22) > (21); (25) > (24)

φ': (0′) > (1′) > (2′) > (4′) > (3′) > (7′) > (5′) > (20′) > (6′) = (8′) = (11′) > (12′) > (9′) > (13′) > (19′) ~ (18′) > (10′) > (17′) > (16′) > (15′) > (14′).

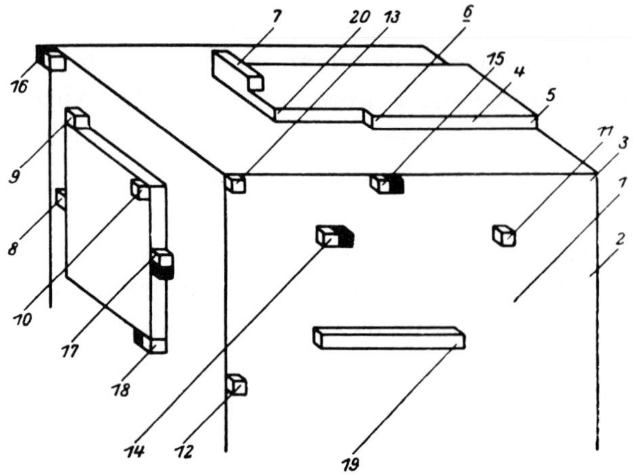

Fig. 2.

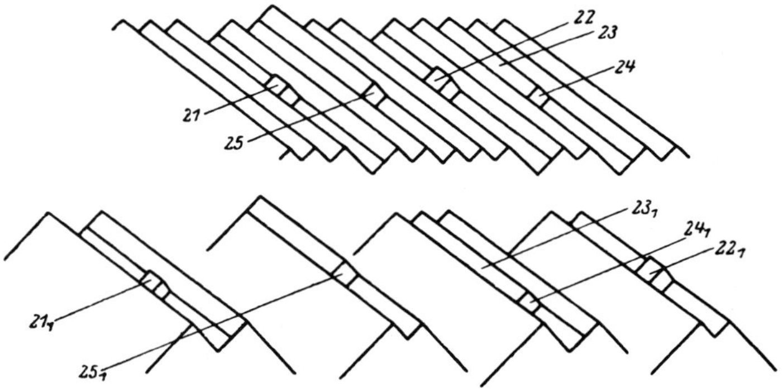

Fig. 3.

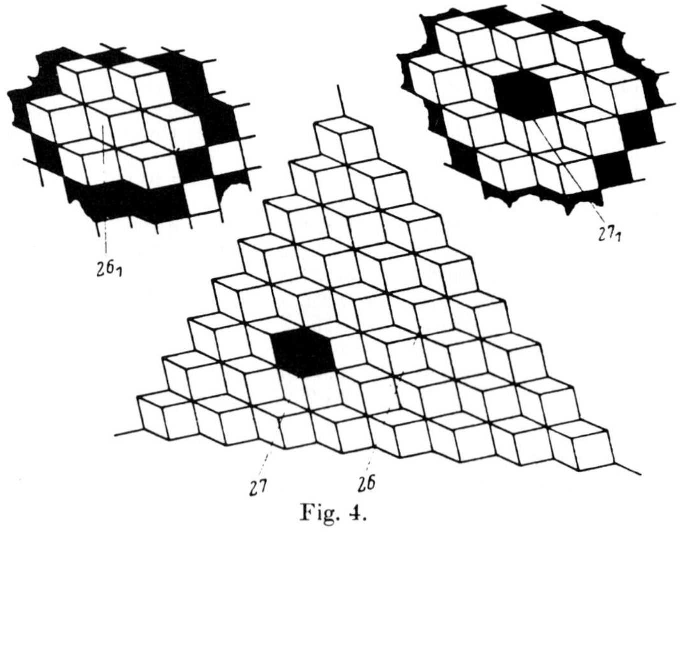

Fig. 4.

Die Zahlen in der ersten Spalte der Tabelle bedeuten die Lage des betreffenden Ions, welche aus den Fig. 2, 3 und 4 zu erkennen ist. Um die Lagen ersichtlicher zu machen, sind hier die Ionen als Würfel dargestellt.

φ_1 bedeutet den Anteil der Abtrennungsarbeit, der allein aus den elektrostatischen Kräften nach MADELUNG[1]) berechnet ist.

φ_2 ist entsprechend der Anteil der Abstossung. Hierbei werden nur diejenigen Ionen berücksichtigt, welche sich von dem betreffenden Ion in einem Abstand von $\frac{\delta}{2}$, $\frac{\delta}{2}\sqrt{2}$ und $\frac{\delta}{2}\sqrt{3}$ befinden (δ = Gitterkonstante), was für die hier erstrebte Genauigkeit vollkommen ausreicht. Nach BORN[2]) ist bei den Kristallen vom $NaCl$-Typus der Abstossungsanteil von der Gitterenergie, welcher einem einzelnen Ion zufällt, gleich

$$\frac{3{\cdot}487(6)\,e^2}{9\,\delta}.$$

Nach obigem setzen wir

$$\varphi_2 = -K\frac{r_0^9 \cdot e^2}{\delta}\left(\frac{n_0}{r_0^9} + \frac{n_1}{r_1^9} + \frac{n_2}{r_2^9}\right) = -\frac{3{\cdot}487(6) \cdot e^2}{9\,\delta},$$

wo n_0, n_1 und n_2 die Anzahl der Ionen in den Entfernungen $r_0 = \frac{\delta}{2}$, $r_1 = \frac{\delta}{2}\sqrt{2}$ und $r_2 = \frac{\delta}{2}\sqrt{3}$ bedeuten und K eine Konstante ist. Da für ein Ion im Kristallinnern $n_0 = 6$, $n_1 = 12$ und $n_2 = 8$ ist, so erhält man für K den Wert 0·52952. Für ein Ion in beliebiger Lage wird demnach

---

1) E. MADELUNG, Physikal. Ztschr. **19**, 524. 1918. Die hier gegebenen Werte lassen sich allein aus dem Zahlenbeispiel auf S. 531 derselben Arbeit errechnen. Als Beispiel sei die Rechnung für die Würfelecke (Lage 3) wiedergegeben:

$^1/_2 \cdot 2{\cdot}767(0) = 1{\cdot}383(5)$	für die (halbe) Reihe durch das Ion,
$^1/_2 \cdot 0{\cdot}228(6) = 0{\cdot}114(3)$ $^1/_4 \cdot 2{\cdot}767(0) = 0{\cdot}691(8)$	für die Nachbarreihen (die halben Reihen von der einen Seite + ein Viertel der Reihe durch das Ion),
$^1/_4 \cdot 0{\cdot}131(7) = 0{\cdot}032(9)$ $^1/_2 \cdot 0{\cdot}228(6) = 0{\cdot}114(3)$ $^1/_8 \cdot 2{\cdot}767(0) = 0{\cdot}345(9)$	für die Nachbarebenen (ein Viertel der Nachbarebenen von der einen Seite + die halben Reihen von der einen Seite + ein Achtel der Reihe durch das Ion).
$\varphi_1 \cdot \frac{\delta}{e^2} = 2{\cdot}682(7)$	

2) M. BORN, Atomtheorie des festen Zustandes, Berlin-Leipzig 1923, S. 746. Für die MADELUNGsche Konstante ist hier der von MADELUNG selbst errechnete Wert eingesetzt.

$$\varphi_2 = -\frac{e^2}{\delta} n_0 (5{\cdot}883 \cdot 10^{-2} + n_1\, 2{\cdot}6 \cdot 10^{-3} + n_2\, 4{\cdot}2 \cdot 10^{-4})$$

sein [1]).

φ ist die gesamte Abtrennungsarbeit: $\varphi = \varphi_1 + \varphi_2$. Die Werte sind in der vierten Spalte auf die dritte Dezimalstelle abgerundet.

Die mit 0 bezeichneten Werte beziehen sich auf ein Ion im Kristallinnern, weshalb die entsprechende Lage in den Figuren fehlt. Die mit 1 bis 20 einschliesslich bezeichneten Werte beziehen sich auf die Würfelfläche (100), von 21 bis 25 auf die Rhombendodekaederfläche (110) und die mit den beiden letzten Ziffern 26 und 27 bezeichneten Werte auf die Oktaederfläche (111). Die Zahlen in 21 bis 27 drücken nicht die gesuchten Werte aus, sondern sie beziehen sich auf die Lagen 21_1 bis 27_1 in den Figuren. Man ersieht ohne weiteres, in welcher Richtung die gesuchten Werte von den entsprechenden indizierten abweichen werden, was auch in der Tabelle durch Ungleichungszeichen kenntlich gemacht ist. Speziell für die Lagen 26 und 27 sei bemerkt, dass die zugehörenden φ_1-Werte für einen unendlich ausgedehnten Kristall $-\infty$ bzw. $+\infty$ sein müssen. Dies ersieht man aus der folgenden einfachen Überlegung: Fig. 5 soll einen Teil von einer unendlich ausgedehnten (111)-Fläche darstellen. Die Hälfte der Ionen von der äussersten Netzebene (die schwarzen) sind auf die aus der Figur zu ersehenden Weise entfernt worden. Dann wird φ_1 für das umringte Ion gleich $\frac{\varphi_1}{2}$ der Lage 0 oder, was dasselbe ist, gleich φ_1 der Lage 6 sein. Den Wert φ_1 für die Lage 26 erhalten wir nun, indem wir jetzt alle entfernten Ionen auf ihre Plätze zurückbringen und die dabei gegen die Abstossung durch das umringte Ion zu leistenden Arbeiten vom ersten Betrag abziehen. Ganz entsprechend erhalten wir den Wert φ_1 für die Lage 27, indem wir auch die übrigen (schwarzen) Ionen

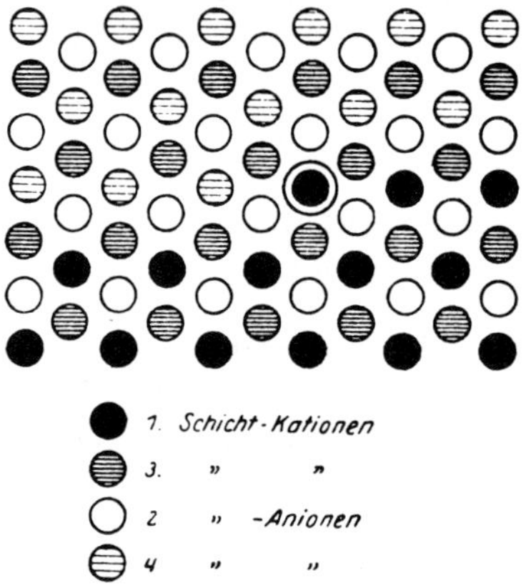

Fig. 5.

[1]) Für die Lage 3 wird beispielsweise $n_0 = 3$, $n_1 = 3$ und $n_2 = 1$ sein und daher $\varphi_2 \cdot \frac{\delta}{e^2} = -(3 \cdot 5{\cdot}883 \cdot 10^{-2} + 3 \cdot 2{\cdot}6 \cdot 10^{-3} + 4{\cdot}2 \cdot 10^{-4}) = -0{\cdot}1847$.

mit Ausnahme des umringten entfernen und die geleisteten Arbeiten durch die Abstossung durch dasselbe Ion jetzt zum ersten Betrag hinzuaddieren.

Ist unser Ionenkristall von seinem eigenen Dampf umgeben, so müssen wir der Tatsache Rechnung tragen, dass die Gasphase fast nur aus zweiionigen Molekeln besteht. Demnach müssen wir Trennungsarbeiten verwenden, die sich auf solche Molekeln beziehen. Es wäre vielleicht nicht uninteressant zu zeigen, dass man aus den Werten der Trennungsarbeiten für Ionenkomplexe, die aus beliebig vielen Ionen bestehen, zu dem gleichen Ergebnis gelangt, dass nämlich die Ionen fast nur als Komplexe, bestehend aus zwei entgegengesetzt geladenen Ionen, die Kristalloberfläche verlassen. Wie sich aus Tabelle 1 ergibt, bedürfen nur die allein stehenden Ionen über einer (100)- oder (110)-Fläche (die Lagen 8, 9, 10, 11, 12, 13, 21, 22 in den Figuren), wie auch die Ionen einer ausgebildeten (111)-Fläche (Lage 27) einer kleineren Abtrennungsarbeit. Diesen Lagen kommt aber keine weitere Bedeutung zu, denn sie können beim Wachstum nur dann auftreten, wenn die Gasphase aus einzelnen Ionen besteht, und beim Auflösen werden sie eben, soweit ihre Bildung zufällig zustande gekommen ist, schneller als alle anderen die Kristallfläche verlassen. Was schliesslich die Oktaederfläche betrifft, so ist ihr Zustandekommen nicht möglich (siehe weiter unten). Bei allen anderen Lagen erfordert das Austreten von einem Ionenpaar das Minimum an Arbeit. Zur Illustration seien die Werte für die Abtrennungsarbeiten gegeben (Tabelle 2), berechnet auf Grund der Annahme von unendlich harten Ionenkugeln (W. KOSSEL[1])), um ein bzw. zwei, drei, vier und sechs benachbarte Ionen aus einer ausgebildeten Würfelfläche (Lage 1) und aus dem Rand einer wachsenden (nicht zu kleinen) Würfelnetzebene (Lage 6) abzutrennen.

Dieses Resultat ist qualitativ richtig und die Reihenfolge der Werte würde durch eine genaue Rechnung, wie sie etwa HEISENBERG[2]) für die unter viel einfacheren Verhältnissen geschehenden Umsetzungen in der Gasphase durchführte, nicht geändert werden.

Der gesonderten Stellung der Abtrennungsarbeiten der aus zwei Ionen bestehenden Molekeln ist in der Tabelle 1 durch die fünfte Spalte Rechnung getragen. In dieser sind die Abtrennungsarbeiten (φ') für je eine solche Molekel in der zugehörigen Lage eingetragen. Bei den

[1]) W. KOSSEL, Ann. Phys. **49**, 229. 1916. [2]) W. HEISENBERG, Z. Physik **26**, 196. 1924.

Tabelle 2.

Lage	Anzahl der Ionen	Gegenseitige Lage der Ionen		$\varphi_1 \cdot \frac{\delta}{e^2}$
		an der Oberfläche	in der Gasphase	
1	1	○	○	3·356
1	2	○●	○●	**2·712**
1	3	○●○	○●○	4·068
1	4	○●○●	○●○●	4·090
1	4	○●○●	○● ●○	3·585
1	4	○● ●○	○● ●○	3·080
1	6	○●○ ●○●	○●○ ●○●	3·871
6	1	○	○	1·744
6	2	○●	○●	**1·488**
6	3	○●○	○●○	2·231
6	4	○●○●	○●○●	2·309
6	4	○●○●	○● ●○	1·804
6	6	○●○●○●	○●○ ●○●	2·331

Ausrechnungen ist aber für die potentielle Energie einer $NaCl$-Molekel der Wert $9{\cdot}68 \cdot 10^{-12}$ erg $= 2{\cdot}391 \frac{e^2}{\delta}$ (die Bildungsenergie der Molekeln aus den Ionen gleich 140 kcal pro Mol[1])) eingesetzt worden.

[1]) Vgl. M. Born und W. Heisenberg, Z. Physik **23**, 406. 1924. Ich möchte hier auf ein mir überraschend erscheinendes Ergebnis aufmerksam machen, welches man aus der Tabelle daselbst entnehmen kann, dass nämlich bei den heteropolaren Gasmolekeln die Deformationsenergie fast genau durch die Abstossung kompensiert wird. Bezeichnet man mit V_e die aus experimentellen Daten bestimmte Bildungsenergie der Molekeln aus den Ionen in kcal pro Mol, mit V_r dieselbe, berechnet unter Berücksichtigung der Deformation, mit V_b dieselbe, berechnet ohne Berücksichtigung der Deformation, und schliesslich mit V_k die nach Kossel zu berechnende $\left(V_k = V_b \frac{9}{8}\right)$, so erhält man folgende Tabelle. Man sieht, dass die Zahlen der 1., 2. und 4. Reihe sehr gut untereinander übereinstimmen. Freilich muss man aber, um V_k berechnen zu können, erst den Ionenabstand oder V_b ermitteln.

	NaF	$NaCl$	$NaBr$	NaJ	KF	KCl	KBr	KJ	RbF	$RbCl$	$RbBr$	RbJ	CsF	$CsCl$	$CsBr$	CsJ
V_e	165	138	133	121	149	123	118	108	123	118	112	103	135	109	102	94
V_r	161	139	133	126	140	124	120	113	122	119	115	110	129	115	110	105
V_b	147	121	114	105	126	108	103	96	110	103	99	93	113	99	94	89
V_k	165	136	128	118	142	123	116	108	124	116	111	104	127	111	106	100

Im folgenden werden wir die φ-Werte durch die eingeklammerten Ziffern der zugehörenden Lage bezeichnen; die φ'-Werte durch eingeklammerte Ziffern mit einem Strich versehen. Die Lagen selbst werden durch die blossen Ziffern bezeichnet sein.

Wie es sich zeigen wird, müssen wir beim Kristallwachstum die Bildung von Ionenstreifen und Ionenflächen — zweidimensionale Kristallkeime (VOLMER) — über die (100)-Fläche annehmen, die sich allmählich über die ganze Fläche ausbreiten. Es ist nun von Interesse zu wissen, ob oder bis wann es bei einem solchen Streifen oder Fläche leichter zur Abtrennung eines einzelnen Ionenpaars oder des ganzen Streifens bzw. Fläche kommen wird[2]). Aus dem hier vertretenen Standpunkt lässt sich prinzipiell leicht darauf antworten. Die Zahl der Ionen, aus denen ein Streifen über die Würfelfläche mindestens bestehen muss (wenn er sich in der Mitte derselben befindet), um ein Ionenpaar abtrennen zu können und nicht als ganzes selbst abgetrennt zu werden, ergibt sich zu

$$n \sim \frac{2 \cdot 1{\cdot}386 - 2{\cdot}391}{0{\cdot}061} \sim 7,$$

denn $1{\cdot}386 \frac{e^2}{\delta} = (19)$ ist die Abtrennungsarbeit eines Ions vom Streifenende, $2{\cdot}391 \frac{e^2}{\delta}$ entsprechend die Arbeit, welche man leisten muss, um eine heteropolare zweiionige Molekel in den einzelnen Ionen zu trennen, und $0{\cdot}061 \frac{e^2}{\delta} = (11)$ ist schliesslich die Abtrennungsarbeit eines alleinstehenden Ions über die Würfelfläche. Ganz entsprechend ergibt sich die Mindestzahl für die Ionen eines zweidimensionalen Keims über die Würfelfläche, bei welchem ein Ionenpaar abgetrennt werden kann, ohne den ganzen Keim mitzureissen, annähernd 17, 24 oder 29 je nachdem, ob das Paar aus einer Ecke, Kante oder aus der Mitte des Keims herausbefördert werden soll. Wie sich aus der folgenden Diskussion ergibt, sind diese Zahlen nur der Grössenordnung nach richtig und geben nur die unteren Grenzen an. Als obere Grenzen erhält man hingegen, indem man 1·941 an Stelle von 2·391 setzt, die Zahlen 14, 24, 31 und 36.

Es seien noch die Werte in der Tabelle 1 einer näheren Diskussion unterzogen. Diese Werte wurden auf Grund der Annahme

[2]) Eine Anlagerung oder Auflösung von ganzen „Gitterfetzen" wird auch von K. SPANGENBERG, Z. Kristallogr. **59**, 403. 1923/24, gelegentlich als möglich betrachtet.

ermittelt, dass der Deformationsanteil der Abtrennungsarbeit durch die Deformation, welche nach dem Entfernen der betreffenden Molekel (Ion) stattfindet, gerade kompensiert wird. Wie schon früher gesagt wurde, kann diese Annahme nur näherungsweise zutreffen. Auch in der Tabelle stossen wir auf Abweichungen, welche gerade in diesem Sinn zu deuten sind. Die gemachte Annahme muss nur für die Lage 6 genau zutreffen, da sich sowohl bei einer Anlagerung, wie auch bei einer Entfernung von Molekeln, nur diese Lage beliebig oft wiederholen lässt. Für Lagen, welchen eine grössere Abtrennungsarbeit als für 6 zukommt, wird die Deformation vor der Entfernung der Molekel durch die Deformation überkompensiert, welche nach der Entfernung stattfindet. Demnach müssen diese Abtrennungsarbeiten kleiner ausfallen als in der Tabelle. Beispielsweise ist ein Ion im Kristallinnern fast gar nicht deformiert (tatsächlich rechnen einige Autoren[1]) auch hier mit einer kleinen Deformation), aber nach seinem Entfernen werden dessen Nachbarn zweifellos eine beträchtliche Deformation erfahren müssen, welche unbedingt (0) bzw. (0′) verkleinern wird. Demgegenüber wird für Lagen, welchen eine kleinere Abtrennungsarbeit als für 6 zukommt, die Deformation vor der Abtrennung nicht kompensiert durch die nachher eintretende Deformation und die Abtrennungsarbeiten werden grösser sein als in der Tabelle. Am empfindlichsten werden dadurch die Werte der Abtrennungsarbeiten der Lagen 14, 15, 16 und 17 beeinflusst. Tatsächlich sind (14′), (15′) und (16′) in der Tabelle mit negativem Vorzeichen und (17′) Null. Dagegen ist es sicher, dass diese Werte, wenn auch klein, doch ein positives Vorzeichen haben müssen. Die obere Grenze dieser Werte können wir leicht erhalten, indem wir annehmen, dass die Ionen in diesen Lagen an der Oberfläche schon ebenso nah aneinander herankommen wie in der Gasmolekel. Darnach müssten sie um $0{\cdot}450\,\frac{e^2}{\delta}$ vergrössert werden. Da die Abweichungen ihr Maximum einerseits bei diesen Lagen (14, 15, 16, 17) und andererseits bei der Lage 0 erreichen, und deren Minimum bei 6 liegt, so lässt sich erwarten, dass dadurch nur die Differenzen zwischen den Werten der Tabelle verkleinert werden, dass aber die Reihenfolge am wahrscheinlichsten überall unverändert bestehen bleibt.

3. Im folgenden werden wir aus den ermittelten Abtrennungsarbeiten einige Folgerungen über das Wachsen und Auflösen der Kristalle vom $NaCl$-Typus ziehen.

[1]) Vgl. K. Fajans, Z. Kristallogr. **61**, 38. 1924/25.

Für das Wachsen oder Auflösen im Vakuum haben natürlich nur die φ'-Werte einen Sinn. Bei den Betrachtungen sollen aber zugleich auch die φ-Werte mitberücksichtigt werden, um so mehr, da sie zu den gleichen Ergebnissen führen.

Würfelfläche. Ganz unabhängig davon, ob die Molekeln der Gasphase aus einzelnen Ionen oder aus je zwei polar verbundenen Ionen besteht, gehört die kleinste Abtrennungsarbeit einer alleinstehenden Molekel an [(11), (12), (13) bzw. (14′), (15′), (16′)]. Darnach wird eine derartige Anlagerung ausserordentlich selten längere Zeit andauern. Die Trennungsarbeiten wachsen aber stark an, wenn sich an die ersten Ionen weitere Ionen dermassen anlagern, dass ein Ionenstreifen entsteht [(19) bzw. (19′)], und sie wachsen um fast noch einmal bzw. zweimal soviel an, wenn sich der Streifen zu einer Fläche ausbildet [(20) bzw. (20′)]. Das Kristallwachstum wird hier fast nur in dem Ausbreiten des einmal gebildeten zweidimensionalen Kcims über die ganze Würfelfläche bestehen. Dies folgt unmittelbar aus den Ungleichungen:

$$(9) > (8) > (12) > (11);\ (9) > (13)$$

bzw.

$$(18') > (17') > (16') > (15') > (14').$$

Aus den Ungleichungen

$$(4) > (7),\ (9) > (10) \text{ bzw. } (4') > (7')$$

kann man weiter ersehen, dass andere Randanlagerungen am Keim bedeutend weniger wahrscheinlich sind.

Wie mit dem Wachsen die Abtrennungsarbeiten einem Maximum zustreben, das erst dann erreicht ist, wenn die äusserste Netzebene (der wachsende Keim) vollständig ausgebildet ist, kann man sehr gut aus einem Vergleich der Abtrennungsarbeiten der an der Kante einer Netzebene stehenden Ionen bzw. Molekeln ersehen. Wenn der Keim noch aus einem einzigen aber schon genügend langen Ionenstreifen besteht, so sind die entsprechenden Werte $\varphi \frac{\delta}{e^2}$ bzw. $\varphi' \frac{\delta}{e^2}$ gemäss der

Tabelle [(19) bzw. (19′)] . . . . 1·386 bzw. 0·381.

Wächst der Ionenstreifen an der Seite einer Fläche,
so vergrössern sich diese Werte [(6) bzw. (6′)] auf 1·550 bzw. 0·709,
an der Ecke der Fläche selbst [(20) bzw. (20′)], auf 2·130 bzw. 0·981,
und erreicht die Fläche die Kante des Kristallwürfels
[(5) bzw. (5′)], auf . . . . 2·182 bzw. 1·034.
Die höchsten Werte erhalten sie aber, wenn die
Fläche die Würfelecke erreicht hat [(3) bzw. (3′)] 2·498 bzw. 1·251.

Das Wachstum über die Würfelfläche ergibt sich demnach etwa folgendermassen: Über die vollständig ausgebildete äusserste Netzebene bilden sich nur unter verhältnismässig selten lokal zustande kommenden Übersättigungen einzelne zweidimensionale Kristallkeime welche, nachdem sie eine genügende Grösse erlangt und dadurch die Gefahr überstanden haben, von neuem abgelöst zu werden, spontan bis zum vollständigen Überdecken der Kristallfläche weiterwachsen. Es ist aber nicht nur die Bildung der Keime mit dem Zustandekommen einer lokalen Übersättigung verbunden, sondern die Bildung einer jeden neuen Ionenreihe an der wachsenden Netzebene erfordert ebenfalls eine, wenn auch nicht so grosse, Übersättigung. Man ersieht auch, dass ein Keim sich am leichtesten an einer Würfelecke bilden wird, schwerer an einer Kante und am schwersten über der Flächenmitte. Andererseits ist jedoch zu bedenken, dass die Zahlen der Plätze solcher Anlagerungsmöglichkeiten in umgekehrter Folge abnehmen. Erreicht der Keim die Ränder des Kristallwürfels, so ist sein Wachstum vollzogen und er dient noch höchstens seinerseits als Unterlage für die Ausbreitung der sich über ihn neubildenden Keime[1]).

Beim Auflösen geschieht der Abbau in umgekehrter Folge. Bei einem vollständig ausgebildeten Würfel sind verhältnismässig am schwächsten die Ionen bzw. Ionenpaare an einer Würfelecke gebunden, dann folgen diese an einer Kante und zuletzt die in der Flächenmitte (3, 2 und 1). Es ist also zu erwarten, dass beim Auflösen die Netzebenen von den Rändern gegen die Flächenmitte aufgerollt werden.

Eine besondere Bedeutung kommt der Lage 6 zu. Ist die wachsende Netzebene hinreichend gross, so werden alle anderen hier in Betracht kommenden Anlagerungen (8, 9 bzw. 17, 18) verschwindend selten im Verhältnis zu dieser vorkommen. Wollen wir hier den Anlagerungsvorgang als eine Art Adsorption betrachten, so ist das Adsorptionspotential durch (6) bzw. (6′) gegeben und wird demnach weitgehend konstant sein. Dieser Wert (6) bzw. (6′) muss genau dem Ener-

---

[1]) Die hier gegebene Darstellung des Wachstums über die (100)-Fläche des *NaCl* deckt sich weitgehend mit der Darstellung bei H. Brandes, Z. physikal. Chem. **126**, 198. 1927, welche auf einer Theorie von Volmer über das Kristallwachstum fusst. Während aber Volmer und Brandes von der Hypothese ausgehen, dass das Wachstum stets durch eine vorangehende Bildung von „zweidimensionalen Kristallkeimen“ vonstatten geht, wird diese Besonderheit hier für die (100)-Fläche hergeleitet. Der Unterschied zwischen dem hier vertretenen Standpunkt und dem von Volmer und Brandes ist jedoch prinzipiell und tritt besonders klar hervor bei der Betrachtung des Wachstums über gewisse andere Flächen, z. B. (110).

giebetrag gleich sein, welcher jedem einzelnen Ion bzw. Molekel durchschnittlich zugeführt werden muss, um das Gitter unendlich zu verdünnen, d. h. die Sättigungskonzentration wird durch diesen Wert bedingt sein.

Letzteres lässt sich auch kinetisch leicht auslegen. Es sei ein Kristall gegeben, an dessen Oberfläche alle möglichen Lagen vorhanden sind. Fassen wir von diesen nur eine bestimmte Lage ins Auge, und es soll allein an dieser Stelle ein Ion (Ionenkomplex) sich anlagern oder wegsublimieren können. Beobachten wir nun die Lage eine sehr lange Zeit hindurch und bilden den Bruch aus der Zeit, während welcher ein Ion angelagert gewesen ist, und der ganzen Zeit, so wollen wir die Umgebung übersättigt, gesättigt oder untersättigt in bezug auf diese Lage nennen, wenn der Bruch grösser, gleich oder kleiner als $\frac{1}{2}$ ist[1]).

Ist nun die Umgebung eines vollständig ausgebildeten *NaCl*-Würfels in diesem Sinne in bezug auf die Ionen (Molekeln) in der Lage 6 auch nur sehr wenig untersättigt, so dass sie in bezug auf die Ionen in der Lage 20 noch übersättigt ist und daher auch in bezug auf solche in den Lagen 5, 3, 4 und 1, so genügt nur das Zustandekommen einer zufälligen lokalen Untersättigung irgendwo in der Nähe der Kristalloberfläche, um eine verhältnismässig geringe Zahl der fester gebundenen Ionen abzulösen und die Lage 6 zu realisieren, damit von da ab die Auflösung solange spontan fortdauert, bis die Umgebung auch bezüglich dieser Lage gesättigt ist, oder bis die ganze angebrochene Netzebene in Lösung gegangen ist. Trifft letzteres zu, so wird sich der Vorgang noch so oft wiederholen können, bis die Umgebung auch in bezug auf die Lage 6 gesättigt ist, oder bis der ganze Kristall in Lösung gegangen ist. Auf ähnliche Weise gelangt man zum Ergebnis, dass, im Fall die Umgebung bezüglich der Ionen (Molekeln) in der Lage 6 übersättigt ist, der Kristall wachsen muss. Das Gleichgewicht zwischen Kristall und Umgebung wird also erst dann erreicht sein, wenn die Ionen (Molekeln) in Lage 6 in Gleichgewicht mit der Umgebung sind. Der Grund dafür liegt offenbar darin, dass sich beim Lösen oder Wachstum allein diese Lage beliebig oft wiederholen lässt. Gegenüber allen denjenigen Ionen, deren Abtrennungsarbeit grösser ist als

[1]) Vgl. A. Einstein, Ann. Phys. **33**, 1275. 1910.

die der sich in Lage 6 befindenden — solche sind die Ionen (Molekeln) in den Flächenmitten, Kanten und Ecken —, wird demnach die Gleichgewichtskonzentration übersättigt sein.

Rhombendodekaederfläche. Sollte eine vollständig ausgebildete Rhombendodekaederfläche vorliegen, so würden sich beim Wachstum nach den Ungleichungen

$$(22) > (21),\ (25) > (24) \text{ bzw. } (25') > (24')$$

zuerst nur solche Ionenreihen bilden, die möglichst weit voneinander entfernt sind. Darnach kann von einer Bildung von zweidimensionalen Kristallkeimen über eine solche Fläche nicht die Rede sein[1]). Aus denselben Ungleichungen folgt aber auch, dass eine vollständig ausgebildete (110)-Fläche überhaupt nicht dem Zustande mit minimaler Energie entspricht. Eine derartige Fläche würde sich, einmal zustande

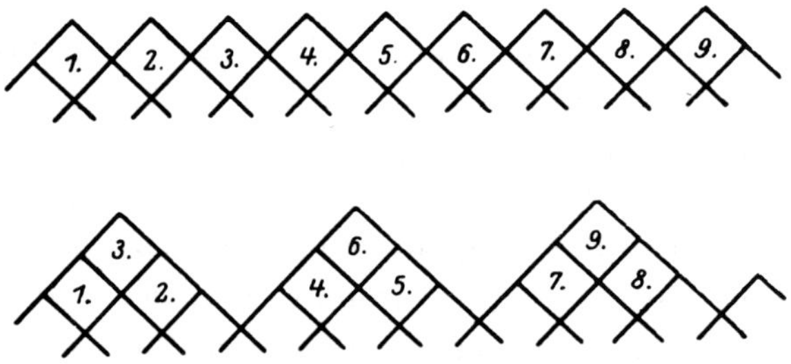

Fig. 6.

gekommen, weiter umlagern. Beispielsweise würde die Umänderung, bestehend in der Versetzung jeder dritten Ionenreihe (3., 6., 9., . . . in Fig. 6) in der Mitte über je zwei benachbarten unverändert gebliebenen Reihen (1. 2., 4. 5., . . .), mit einer beträchtlichen Energieabnahme begleitet sein[2]). Mit dieser Umänderung wird aber ein praktisch stabiler Zustand noch nicht erreicht sein. Der stabile Zustand wird theoretisch offenbar erst dann erreicht sein, wenn die (110)-Flächen auch als makroskopische Gebilde vollständig verschwinden und der Kristall nur noch von einem Minimum (6) an vollständig ausgebildeten Würfelflächen umgeben ist.

1) Derartige Kristallkeime spielen eine wesentliche Rolle in den Ausrechnungen von BRANDES, l. c., mit denen er die VOLMERsche Theorie zu stützen sucht.

2) Etwas mehr als $\frac{2\sqrt{2}\,[(2)-(23)]\,e^2}{3\cdot\delta^3} = 137$ erg $= 3{\cdot}3 \cdot 10^{-6}$ gcal pro cm^2 (110)-Fläche für $NaCl$.

In noch grösserem Masse instabil ist aber die

Oktaederfläche. Da (26) jedenfalls von einem sehr grossen negativen Betrag ist (vgl. auch das oben gesagte), so wird ein beträchtlicher Teil der Ionen einer vollständig ausgebildeten (111)-Fläche sogar spontan emitiert werden. Das Bestehen oder das Zustandekommen (wenigstens im Vakuum) einer ausgebildeten solchen Fläche ist demnach unmöglich.

Das bisher nur für drei der möglichen kristallographischen Flächen des *NaCl* dargelegte lässt sich beliebig über alle anderen Flächen erweitern. Wir werden uns hier mit dem Ergebnis begnügen: Die Kristalle des *NaCl* (im Vakuum) können nur von Würfelflächen umgeben sein. Jede Störung einer solchen Fläche führt zu Umänderungen, die zur Wiederherstellung der Würfelform führen.

Das, was man vom Wachstum der Kristalle vom *NaCl*-Typus weiss, stimmt gut mit dem oben dargelegten überein. Alle Alkalihaloide, welche im *NaCl*-Typus kristallisieren, geben normal nur Würfel ohne Kombinationen mit anderen Flächen. Dasselbe gilt auch für andere Salze, welche im gleichen Typus kristallisieren (z. B. *PbS*). Hierbei sei noch ganz besonders auf die experimentellen Ergebnisse hingewiesen, zu welchen F. Paneth und W. Thimann[1]) gelangt sind, als sie den Ionenaustausch an Kristalloberflächen mit Hilfe von radioaktiven Indikatoren erforschten.

Die Flächen (110) und (111), erhalten z. B. durch Anschleifen, können nach dem bisher dargelegten nur als makroskopische Gebilde betrachtet werden, bestehend aus einer grossen Anzahl einzelner Würfelflächen, die domen- bzw. pyramidenartig gruppiert sind. Theoretisch wird der Gleichgewichtszustand, wie schon erwähnt, erst dann erreicht, wenn der Kristall von 6 (100)-Flächen begrenzt ist. Praktisch ist er aber schon erreicht, wenn, wie nicht schwer gezeigt werden kann, die Länge der kleinsten Kante der einzelnen (100)-Flächen grössenordnungsmässig hundert Ionenabstände beträgt[2]). Will man die

[1]) F. Paneth und W. Thimann, Ber. Dtsch. Chem. Ges. **57**, 1218. 1924.

[2]) Es seien hier die Beziehungen ohne Herleitung angegeben, welche für das Sättigungskonzentrationsverhältnis gelten müssen, nämlich

$$\frac{C_a}{C_\infty} = e^{\frac{2 \cdot N \cdot \Delta\varphi}{a^2 \cdot R \cdot T}}$$

für die (110)-Fläche und

$$\frac{C_a}{C_\infty} = e^{\frac{2 \cdot N \cdot 3 \cdot \Delta\varphi}{a^2 \cdot R \cdot T}}$$

Wachstumsgeschwindigkeit der (100)-Fläche (nahe am Gleichgewichtszustand) mit diesen der (110)- und (111)-Fläche (geschliffen) vergleichen, so muss sie viel kleiner als diese ausfallen, denn die Wachstumsgeschwindigkeit von (100) ist dann aus der Wahrscheinlichkeit der Anlagerung 11 zu errechnen, die Wachstumsgeschwindigkeit von (110) aus der Anlagerung 12 und die Wachstumsgeschwindigkeit von (111) aus der Anlagerung 13. Für die Auflösungsgeschwindigkeiten kommen hingegen Abtrennungen 1, 2 und 3 in Betracht.

Es mögen am Schluss noch die möglichen Abweichungen zusammengestellt sein, welche zu erwarten sind, wenn der Kristall von andersartigen Molekeln (Lösungsmittel, Lösungsgenossen) umgeben ist. Geht der Kristall in vollständig dissoziiertem Zustande in Lösung, so kommen selbstverständlich nur die φ-Werte in Betracht, welche aber alle wesentlich verkleinert (letzteres kann man bekanntlich als eine Folge der grösseren Dielektrizitätskonstante des Lösungsmittels auffassen) und noch enger aneinander gruppiert sein werden, während sie jedoch auch hier im grossen und ganzen dieselbe Reihenfolge beibehalten. Die φ-Werte werden auch durch eine grössere Lösungskonzentration heruntergesetzt (am stärksten wird sich dieser Einfluss auswirken, wenn der Kristall von seiner Schmelze umgeben ist), wegen der Einwirkung der gelösten Ionen aufeinander, wodurch eine gitterähnliche Anordnung der Ionen auch im Lösungsmittel zu erwarten ist[1]). Die grössten Abweichungen werden aber eintreten, wenn die Molekeln des Lösungsmittels oder der Lösungsgenossen nur an bestimmten kristallographischen Flächen stark adsorbiert werden. Hier kann die Reihenfolge oft durchbrochen sein. VALETON[2]) erklärt auf diese Weise das Auskristallisieren des $NaCl$ in Oktaedern aus einer Lösung, welche $CO(NH_2)_2$ enthält; das an den (111)-Flächen adsorbierte $CO(NH_2)_2$ soll deren Wachstum hindern. Bei dieser Erklärung bleibt nun aber die Frage offen, ob das $CO(NH_2)_2$ die vollständig ausgebauten

---

für die (111)-Fläche. Mit C_a ist hier die Sättigungskonzentration einer (110)- oder (111)-Fläche bezeichnet, in welcher die Länge der Kante (der kürzigsten bei der Rhombendodekaederfläche) der einzelnen Domen- oder Pyramideu-(100)-Flächen a Ionenabstände beträgt. N ist die LOSCHMIDTsche Zahl, R die Gaskonstante und T die abs. Temperatur. Nach M. BORN und O. STERN (Sitzber. Preuss. Akad. Wiss. 919. 1919) ist für $\Delta\varphi$ der Wert $\frac{0{\cdot}095 \cdot e^2}{\delta}$ einzusetzen.

1) Vgl. P. DEBYE und E. HÜCKEL, Physikal. Ztschr. **24**, 185, 334. 1923. **25**, 97. 1924. **26**, 93. 1925. 2) J. J. P. VALETON, Physikal. Ztschr. **21**, 608. 1920.

(111)-Flächen genügend stabilisieren kann oder ob auch hier nur ein makroskopisches Gebilde vorliegt, indem die Oktaederflächen in Wirklichkeit aus einer grossen Anzahl sehr kleiner Würfelpyramiden bestehen, die durch an den Pyramidenspitzen anhaftenden $CO(NH_2)_2$-Molekeln stabilisiert sind.

Zusammenfassung.

Die vorliegende Arbeit ist auf folgende zwei Annahmen aufgebaut: erstens, dass die Oberfläche des Kristalls nur unwesentlich vom Bau im Kristallinnern abweicht, d. h., dass die Molekeln (Atome, Ionen) an der Oberfläche an bestimmten Ruhelagen gebunden sind, die weitgehend dem Gitter entsprechen, und zweitens, dass die Molekeln an der Oberfläche diejenigen Lagen einnehmen, welchen ein Energieminimum zukommt. Um also das Wachstum bzw. Auflösen eines Kristalls herleiten zu können, muss man über die Werte der Abtrennungsarbeit orientiert sein (das ist die Arbeit, welcher es bedarf, um eine Molekel von ihrem Platz an der Oberfläche bis ins Unendliche zu entfernen), welche den verschiedenen Lagen an der Oberfläche zukommt.

Dies wird einfachheitshalber an den Kristallen vom $NaCl$-Typus erprobt. Einige charakteristische Abtrennungsarbeiten sind in Tabelle 1 zusammengestellt. Die erste Spalte enthält die Ziffern, welche die Lagen der Ionen angeben, die aus den Fig. 2, 3 und 4 zu ersehen sind. Die zweite Spalte enthält den elektrostatischen Anteil der Abtrennungsarbeiten (φ_1), die dritte den der BORNschen Abstossung (φ_2), die vierte gibt die Summe beider an ($\varphi = \varphi_1 + \varphi_2$). In die fünfte Spalte sind schliesslich die Abtrennungsarbeiten für zweiionige Molekeln eingetragen, denn es wird gezeigt (vgl. Tabelle 2), dass das Minimum der Abtrennungsarbeiten von Ionenkomplexen, bestehend aus beliebig vielen Ionen, gerade den aus zwei Ionen bestehenden zufällt. Die Ausrechnungen der Abtrennungsarbeiten werden demnach so geführt, als wenn der Anteil der (Gitter- und Ionen-)Deformation durch die Deformierung der anderen Ionen, welche durch das Entfernen des betreffenden Ions entblösst werden, gerade kompensiert wird. Dies trifft aber (mit Ausnahme für die Lage 6, bei welcher diese Annahme streng erfüllt sein muss) nur näherungsweise zu.

Aus den Werten für die Abtrennungsarbeiten wird geschlossen, dass für Kristalle vom $NaCl$-Typus nur die Flächen (100) stabil sind; die Flächen (110) und (111) sind (im Vakuum) nur als makroskopische

Gebilde denkbar, d. h., dass sie in Wirklichkeit aus einer grossen Menge von Würfelflächen bestehen, welche domen- bzw. pyramidenartig gruppiert sind.

Beim Wachstum lagern sich am leichtesten Molekeln (Ionen) an einer Würfelecke, dann an einer Kante und am schwersten an der Flächenmitte an. Bei der Würfelfläche (nicht aber bei einer eventuell zustande gekommenen Rhombendodekaeder- oder Oktaederfläche) bilden sich beim Wachstum „zweidimensionale Kristallkeime". Die Auflösung geschieht in umgekehrter Folge. Damit werden auch die Wachstums- bzw. Auflösungsgeschwindigkeiten der Flächen (100), (110) und (111) in Zusammenhang gebracht.

CRYSTAL GROWTH AND SURFACE STRUCTURE

Part I

By W. K. Burton * and N. Cabrera

Received 15th February, 1949

Introduction. As a preliminary to the study of the rate of growth of crystals, we consider in Part I of this paper the influence of surface structure on the rate of advance of the growing surface. If, for the time being, we confine our attention to crystals with perfect lattices, it is found that crystal surfaces can be divided into two classes, (*a*) close-packed † surfaces and (*b*) non-close-packed or " stepped " surfaces, which possess essentially different properties. A surface is close-packed if, when it is as flat as possible, all the surface molecules are at the same distance from a plane parallel to it ; in all other cases the surface will present a stepped appearance, as in Fig. 1, the height of each step being of molecular dimensions. By way of illustration, in the simple cubic system (100) surfaces, (111) surfaces and (110) surfaces are close-packed, all other surfaces are stepped. In a stepped surface

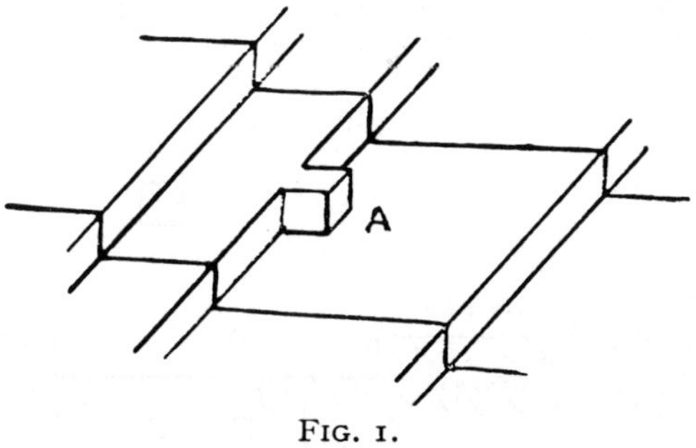

Fig. 1.

the terraces in Fig. 1 are pieces of close-packed surface. In the case of a (1*n*0) surface of a simple cubic crystal, the terraces will be (100) surfaces. This point of view is fruitful because it can be shown that for a stepped surface the portions between the steps play almost no part in growth phenomena at low supersaturations. In fact, deposition on a close-packed surface can only take place by surface nucleation : small " islands " of molecules collect on the surface and grow so as to produce a new layer, a process which is very slow at low supersaturations. On the other hand, deposition on the edge of a step A (Fig. 1) can take place without there being a linear nucleation process. Hence the growth problem for a stepped surface is essentially solved, once the corresponding problem for steps has been solved. If a crystal grows at all, some kind of steps must exist at some time in the surface. These steps may be of the kind already mentioned, or they may be boundaries of two-dimensional nuclei. Growth essentially depends on the existence of " kinks " in these steps. Easy growth is guaranteed if these

* Seconded from I.C.I., Ltd., Butterwick Research Laboratories, The Frythe, Welwyn, Herts.

† Note that our definition of " close-packed " differs somewhat from current usage.

kinks are always present, and this criterion can be reduced to the question of the existence of kinks, when the external concentration is the equilibrium value. For if kinks are present at equilibrium, then when the external concentration is raised there are already suitable deposition points available. If there are no kinks at equilibrium, then these must be created, and a large hindrance to growth appears. It can be shown that the concentration of kinks in a step in equilibrium is high, and that the concentration of kinks in a close-packed surface at equilibrium is negligible. This again speaks in favour of our classification of surfaces into stepped and close-packed surfaces.

In this paper we are concerned with the equilibrium structure and rate of growth of an infinite surface. It is, of course, clear that an infinite surface is in equilibrium with the same external concentration (e.g., vapour concentration) whatever the surface. A finite surface will not be in equilibrium in the same sense as in the case of an infinite surface, and consequently, in general, some change will tend to take place. But changes of orientation can take place only by means of processes which occur at the boundary of the surface, and hence for a surface of observable size the change will occur at an unobservably slow rate, the associated relaxation time tending to infinity with the size of the crystal. Therefore, if we confine ourselves to a region on a finite surface which is almost flat, then its structure will be the same as that in an infinite surface having the same orientation.

The two basic equilibrium problems are now (*a*) the equilibrium structure of an infinite step, and (*b*) the equilibrium structure of an infinite close-packed surface.

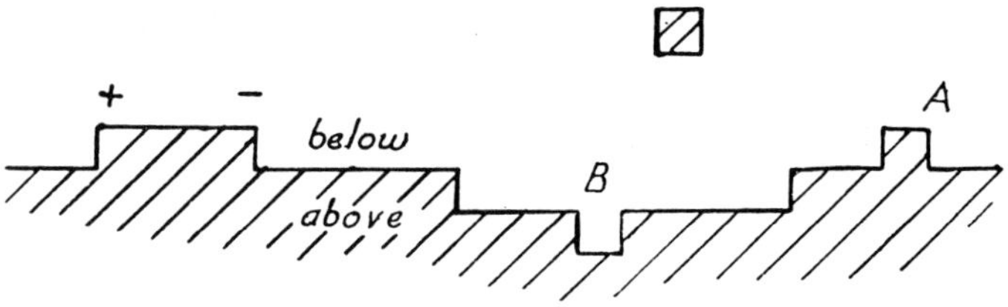

FIG. 2.

The Infinite Step. Consider then, a semi-infinite layer of molecules on an infinite close-packed plane crystal surface bounded by a connected line. This we call a step: it can have any mean direction. At $T = 0°$ K, the step will be perfectly straight, but as the temperature is increased it will consist of a number of " kinks," separated by certain distances as in Fig. 2, a certain number of adsorbed molecules (A) and a certain number of holes (B). We need to know only the concentration of kinks to form a picture of the mean structure of the step. This idea, introduced by Frenkel [1] simplifies the treatment of the problem very much: we call the kinks " Frenkel kinks " (F.k.). It is clear that the concentration of kinks in a step will depend on its orientation, and that there will be orientations for which the number of kinks is a minimum. For instance, for the (001) face of a simple cubic crystal, the (10) steps will have the smallest number of kinks. This minimum number will tend to zero with T. Accordingly, if we can show that a (10) step contains a large number of kinks at $T > 0$ under equilibrium conditions we know that steps of all orientations also contain a large number of kinks.

If we use a simple cubic model with nearest neighbour interactions (Kossel crystal) it is easy to find the equilibrium concentration of adsorbed molecules,

[1] Frenkel, *J. Physics, U.S.S.R.*, 1945, **9**, 392.

holes and kinks in a (10) step. Let the energy of interaction between neighbouring molecules be φ. Then the energy necessary to form an adsorbed atom in the step (Fig. 3) will be φ. The energy to form a hole is also φ, since an energy 2φ is required to form a hole and an adsorbed molecule. The energy to form a kink is, however, only $\frac{1}{2}\varphi$, since from Fig. 4 and Fig. 5 only an energy 2φ is required to form four kinks. There is no change in energy in going from Fig. 4 to Fig. 5. The numbers of positive and negative kinks (Fig. 2) are, of course, equal. We conclude that the probability for having a hole or an adsorbed molecule at a given place on the step are both given by

$$n = \exp(-\varphi/kT) \quad . \quad . \quad . \quad . \quad (1)$$

and that the probability for having a kink at a given place on the step is given by

$$n_+ = n_- = \exp(-\varphi/2kT) \quad . \quad . \quad . \quad . \quad (2)$$

If $T \sim 600°$ K and we take a typical value of φ as 0·2 eV, we find that there is a kink for every ten molecules in the step, and an adsorbed molecule or hole for every hundred molecules.

We have, of course, simplified the problem very much: there is a considerable probability for the existence of kinks of multiple height, particularly for steps which deviate a great deal from the [10] direction (in the simple cubic case). The complete theory has been developed elsewhere.[2]

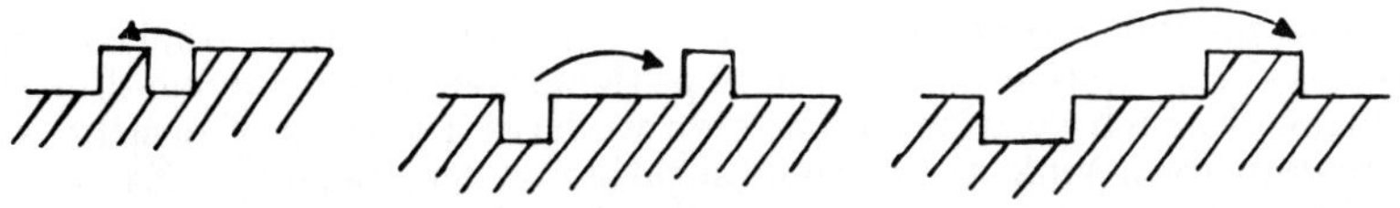

FIG. 3. FIG. 4. FIG. 5.

In view of the fact that steps of different orientations have different concentrations of kinks in them, the edge-free energy per unit length of a step varies with the orientation and is a minimum for the (10) step. It might be thought that steps other than (10) steps are not in real equilibrium and that there must be a tendency for these steps to change into (10) steps. If we are considering infinite steps, this conclusion would be erroneous, for it can be shown that steps of all orientations are in equilibrium with the same external concentration of molecules, despite the fact that the concentration of Frenkel kinks varies with the orientation.

Frenkel [1] has treated the kinetical problem of the transformation of any step into a (10) step, assuming on energy grounds that the others are not in equilibrium. He obtains in this way a time of relaxation independent of the length of the step. This result is incorrect because the "torque" which applies to the steps not in a [10] direction is evaluated by Frenkel by taking the derivative of the potential energy with respect to the orientation angle. But his formula contains only points corresponding to the equilibrium positions of the steps, and not the intermediate non-equilibrium positions through which the step would have to pass in order to change at all. In fact for an infinite step, each equilibrium position is surrounded by infinitely high potential barriers which cannot be surmounted.

For a finite step, the situation is different. Such a step can only be in equilibrium with a supersaturated or undersaturated external phase, and then the equilibrium is unstable and subject to stringent restrictions as regards shape. The sharper the corners of a finite step, the greater the

[2] Burton and Cabrera (to be published elsewhere).

rate of evaporation, and an arbitrarily oriented step tends to become a (10) step during the evaporation. The time required for this process to take place increases with the length of the step, because the processes which permit the transformation occur only at the corners.

It must not be thought, however, that all the considerations which apply to kinks in a step apply to steps in a surface. It is still true that surfaces of all orientations are in equilibrium with the same vapour concentration in the same sense as for steps, but the fact that for some surfaces the concentration of steps is large does not imply that double steps, treble steps, etc., will be frequent.* The difference between the energy of two single steps and one double step is proportional to the step length, and is very large if the interactions are not of the nearest neighbour type. Similarly, there is no question of steps being formed by thermal fluctuations,* as kinks are formed in a step, since the energy of formation of a step is proportional to its length and is enormous for long steps. Thus a stepped surface tends to become as flat as possible, and at equilibrium, only single steps will appear. It follows that the macroscopic steps which have been observed, e.g., on metals by Graf,[3] on growing crystals have nothing to do with equilibrium problems, but are essentially kinetic in origin. If a surface is produced with macroscopic steps in it, it is obvious that the rate of approach to macroscopic equilibrium is negligibly small and the structure is essentially frozen in.

Close-packed Surfaces. The circumstance which makes stepped surfaces so easy to treat is that the steps themselves present a one-dimensional problem. In each position on the step we have a variety of possible states: occupation by a kink of positive, negative or zero height. Each of these possible states can occur independently at each point, and hence the probability for the occurrence of a compound state affecting more than one position is the product of the probabilities for the individual states at each of the individual positions. We have assumed so far that those parts of the crystal surface between steps can be ignored, and this assumption is shown to be reasonable in the following discussion. However, if there are no steps in the surface, which is the normal case in a close-packed perfect crystal surface, then we are presented with an essentially different two-dimensional problem. We assume that in the close-packed surface of a crystal there can be differences of level, i.e., that " jumps " can occur in the surface. The presence of jumps provide suitable places for evaporation and condensation, provided that the jumps are not due merely to the presence of adsorbed molecules and holes. The problem is to estimate the number of jumps at equilibrium as a function of temperature.

In this case the jumps themselves cannot be assigned independently, since it is possible to have twice as many jumps in a surface as there are molecules. Fig. 6 shows a picture of part of a surface; the small squares represent molecules seen from above. The heights of these molecules above some arbitrary plane can, of course, be assigned independently, but the distribution of jumps across the full lines in the figure cannot. For suppose we start at the molecule A and follow any closed path such as ABCDEF, then although we can have any jump we choose between neighbouring molecules on this path, providing we do not close it, the necessity for finishing at A at the same level at which we started implies that the magnitude of any jump on a closed path must be fixed by the magnitude of the others.

[3] Graf, *Z. Elektrochem.*, 1942, **48**, 181.

* At least, if the interactions are all attractive.

So there are innumerable sets of relations, corresponding to all the closed paths on the crystal surface, between the jump probabilities. In fact, to specify the probability for the existence of a jump at a given point involves the knowledge of the state of the surface at every other point. So we are faced with a so-called co-operative phenomenon. This makes the Frenkel kink picture employed previously almost unworkable. We must therefore look for some other method.

We have made preliminary calculations on the basis of a model which is somewhat oversimplified: we suppose the levels in the crystal surface to be capable of two values only. The method employed is that due to Montroll,[4] Kramers and Wannier,[5] Onsager,[6] Onsager and Kaufman [7] and Wannier,[8] originally devised for the treatment of ferromagnetism, using the two-dimensional Ising model. Just as there is a transition or critical temperature associated with an infinite specific heat in the case of the two-dimensional ferromagnet, so there is in the case of this crystal surface model.

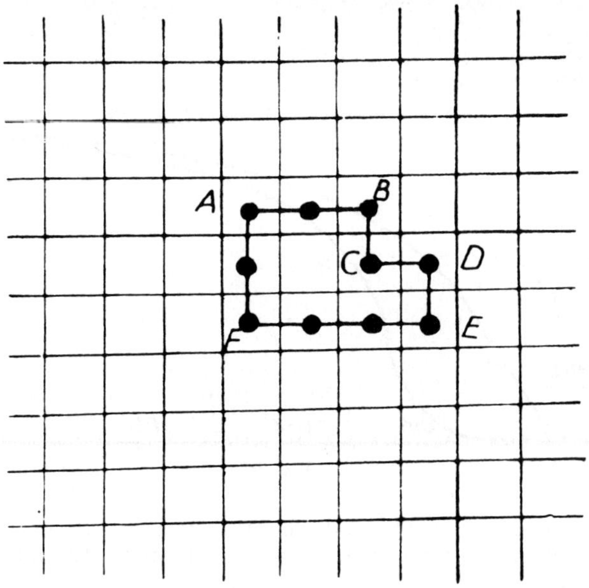

FIG. 6.

The problem is to find the increase in potential energy of the surface due to the presence of jumps in it. The mean number of jumps can then be found. If the surface of the crystal were perfectly flat we should say that the surface potential energy, for example, of the (100) surface of the Kossel crystal per molecule was $\varphi_1/2$ in the nearest neighbour model, corresponding to one unused " bond " per molecule, which we can imagine as sticking out perpendicular to the crystal surface. If, however, the surface is not flat, then there will be additional unused bonds sticking out parallel to the surface, and each of these bonds will contribute $\varphi_1/2$ to the potential energy

[4] Montroll, *J. Chem. Physics*, 1941, **9**, 706.
[5] Kramers and Wannier, *Physic. Rev.*, 1941, **60**, 252, 263.
[6] Onsager, *Physic. Rev.*, 1944, **65**, 117.
[7] Onsager and Kaufman, *Report Int. Conf. on Fund. Particles and Low Temperatures* (Cambridge, July, 1946), Vol. II. : Low Temperatures, Physical Society (1947).
[8] Wannier, *Rev. Mod. Physics*, 1945, **17**, 50.

of the surface. If we take our zero of energy to correspond to a flat surface, then if we evaluate the potential energy per molecule of the surface at equilibrium and divide it by $\varphi_1/2$ we get a figure for the number of unused bonds in the surface which are parallel to it. This figure, s, represents the " roughness " of the surface. This is the quantity we aim to evaluate as a function of temperature. We expect it to go from 0 to 1 as T goes from 0 to ∞.

The crystal surface model we are considering is equivalent to a square lattice of units which we call atoms capable of two states which we designate by $+1$ and -1. If two neighbouring atoms have the same state their interaction energy is zero, otherwise it is $\varphi_1/2$. The first possibility describes the two molecules in the crystal surface when they are at the same level, the second when their levels are different. For the sake of generality we assume, following Onsager, that the interactions can be different in the two directions [10] and [01]: in the case of the (100) surface we shall equate them.

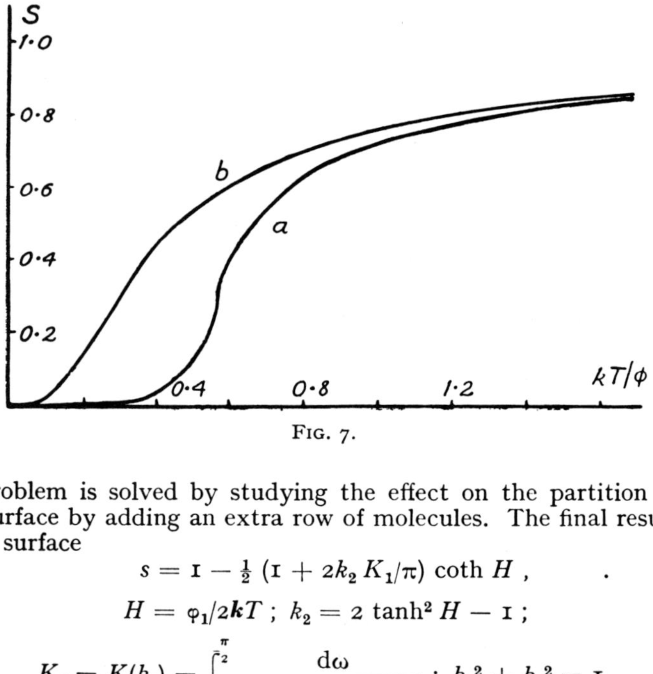

FIG. 7.

The problem is solved by studying the effect on the partition function for the surface by adding an extra row of molecules. The final result is, for the (100) surface

$$s = 1 - \tfrac{1}{2}(1 + 2k_2 K_1/\pi) \coth H , \qquad (3)$$

where $H = \varphi_1/2\boldsymbol{k}T$; $k_2 = 2 \tanh^2 H - 1$;

$$K_1 = K(k_1) = \int_0^{\frac{\pi}{2}} \frac{d\omega}{(1 - k_1^2 \sin^2\omega)^{1/2}} ; \; k_1^2 + k_2^2 = 1 \qquad (4)$$

K_1 is the complete elliptic integral of the first kind. A graph of s against T is shown in Fig. 7 (*a*). The curve possesses a vertical tangent at $T = T_c$ given by $k_1 = 1$ or $k_2 = 0$, i.e., by $\sinh H_c = 1$,

or

$$H_c = \varphi_1/2\boldsymbol{k}T_c = \ln \cot \frac{\pi}{8} \sim 0{\cdot}9 \qquad (5)$$

If we had assumed the jumps to be independent, the result would have been

$$s = \frac{2 \exp(-\varphi_1/2\boldsymbol{k}T)}{1 + \exp(-\varphi_1/2\boldsymbol{k}T)} , \qquad (6)$$

which gives rise to curve b in Fig. 7.

In the absence of square symmetry, Onsager [6] [7] has shown that that preceding condition becomes

$$\sinh H_c \sinh H_c' = 1 \ , \ (H_c' = \varphi_2/2kT_c) \ , \qquad (7)$$

so that we can apply our result to the (110) surface of our model. In the case of this surface we have a rectangular lattice with energy of interaction $\varphi_1/2$ in one direction and $\varphi_2/2$ in the other, where φ_2 is the strength of the second nearest neighbour interaction. Consequently, if the second nearest neighbour interactions are small enough, the critical temperature can be as low as we like.

The value of T_c has been worked out for all surfaces in the symmetrical case.[8] The result is

$$\text{gd}\ H_c = \pi/Z \ , \qquad (8)$$

where gd x is the Gudermannian function, and Z is the number of nearest neighbours in the surface, of a given molecule in the surface, when it is as flat as possible. There are three cases: (*a*) surface lattice triangular, $Z = 6$; (*b*) surface lattice square, $Z = 4$; (*c*) surface lattice hexagonal, $Z = 3$. For these cases we have respectively from (8),

$$\exp (2H_c) = 3 \ , \qquad (9)$$

$$\sinh H_c = 1 \ , \qquad (10)$$

$$\cosh H_c = 2 \ . \qquad (11)$$

Eqn. (9) enables us to give the critical temperature for the (111) face of a simple cubic crystal. The surface in this case has a triangular lattice and the nearest neighbour interactions in the surface are due to the second nearest neighbours in the crystal lattice. From (9) we get

$$2H_c' = \varphi_2/kT_c \sim 1{\cdot}1 \ .$$

In Table I we give T_c under the assumption that $\varphi_1 = 0{\cdot}2$ eV, $\varphi_1/\varphi_2 = 8$. If T is much below T_c, the concentration of jumps is almost entirely due to the presence of adsorbed molecules.

TABLE I

Lattice	Surface	T_c
Simple cubic . .	(100)	1000° C
	(110)	400° C
	(111)	−30° C
Face-centred cubic . .	(111)	1700° C

We see that the critical temperature gives the boundary separating the régime where the jump concentration is negligible and surface nucleation is required for growth, $T < T_c$, from that régime $T > T_c$, where the jump concentration is high, and no nucleation is required for growth. If $T > T_c$ the surface will grow rapidly and disappear leaving only the slow growing faces for which $T < T_c$. At ordinary temperatures then, the transition phenomena will only occur for non-habit faces.

Broadly speaking, we have shown that close-packed surfaces will not grow at low supersaturations (see Part II) because of the need for surface nucleation. However, we have assumed that the crystal lattice is perfect. It is clear that the structure of a close-packed surface at equilibrium is extremely sensitive to lattice imperfections, and as Frank [9] has pointed out the presence of a few dislocations terminating in the surface ensures the presence of suitable sites for condensation or evaporation. In fact, dislocations again produce a stepped surface. The perfect close-packed surface will rarely, if ever, occur in reality.

H. H. Wills Physical Laboratory,
University of Bristol.

[9] Burton, Cabrera and Frank, *Nature*, 1949, **163**, 398. Frank, This Discussion.

THE JOURNAL OF CHEMICAL PHYSICS VOLUME 21, NUMBER 11 NOVEMBER, 1953

The Distribution of Solute in Crystals Grown from the Melt. Part I. Theoretical

J. A. BURTON, R. C. PRIM, and W. P. SLICHTER
Bell Telephone Laboratories, Murray Hill, New Jersey
(Received May 18, 1953)

The incorporation of solute elements into single crystals of germanium grown from the melt is examined in terms of a simple model. The theory takes account of the contribution of solute transport in the melt, owing to diffusion and fluid motion, to the over-all process of impurity incorporation during steady-state crystallization. The analysis is extended to treat the transient inclusion of solute which results when the composition of the melt is abruptly changed.

HETEROGENEOUS chemical reactions are comprised of several processes. One of these is the chemical transformation itself, and associated with it the adsorption and desorption processes, occurring at the interface of the two phases. Elsewhere the transport of reactants or products to or from the interface may be a significant factor. Diffusion is a consideration in the transport process, particularly with solid-liquid reactions.

Nernst[1] postulated that the chemical change itself occurs almost instantaneously, and supposed the over-all rate of the reaction to be set by a diffusion-dominated transport process. This viewpoint has been endorsed by some workers, but others have argued for the importance of other processes, sometimes to the extent of denying that transport contributes to the reaction rate at all. It is now widely believed that the importance of a given process, such as transport, to the over-all rate depends critically upon the system under study, and for a given system may even depend upon the experimental conditions. The subject of heterogeneous reactions has been reviewed by Moelwyn-Hughes,[2] and by Bircumshaw and Riddiford[3] with special attention to transport processes.

The present paper treats theoretically the incorporation of impurity elements into single crystals of germanium grown from the melt.[4] The paper which follows describes some experimental studies of such crystals. The crystallization is viewed as a heterogeneous reaction. The chemical process consists of the incorporation of impurity at the solid-liquid interface. It depends strongly upon the impurity, and possibly upon some conditions of crystallization. The transport process is particularly sensitive to crystallization conditions, and is the chief subject of this discussion.

1. DISTRIBUTION COEFFICIENT

The incorporation of impurity in the crystal may be characterized by a distribution coefficient. In treating a binary solution having solid and liquid phases, one may define an equilibrium coefficient k_0 as the ratio of the concentration of solute in the solid C_S to that in the liquid C_L, when equilibrium exists between the two phases at a given temperature. When the solute composition of the system is decreased, so that the equilibrium temperature approaches the melting point of the pure solvent, k_0 converges to a constant value. With solutions in germanium, k_0 is ordinarily less than unity and depends markedly upon the impurity. When crystallization occurs very slowly, the solid forming at any moment from the melt has composition $C_S=k_0C_L$, provided one may assume diffusion in the solid to be negligible. As the crystallization proceeds, the rejection of solute by the solid enriches the melt, and so the solid formed in the later stages becomes progressively richer, in a manner which has been described by several authors.[5]

However, if crystallization does not proceed slowly, solute atoms are rejected by the advancing solid at a greater rate than they can diffuse into the bulk of the melt. A concentration gradient thus develops just ahead of the advancing crystal. It is this enriched region which directly determines the rate of solute incorporation into the solid. If C_L is the solute concentration in the bulk of the liquid, where stirring and convection currents keep the composition virtually uniform, one may define an effective distribution coefficient k as the ratio C_S/C_L at any moment.

The equilibrium value of the distribution coefficient, k_0, may of course be regarded as the ratio α/β, where α and β are rate constants, expressed in cm sec^{-1}, for two exchange processes occurring at the phase interface which have reached equilibrium. Here α describes the entrance of solute into the crystal and β describes the exit process into the melt. True equilibrium presumably occurs only if the crystallization speed is essentially zero. When crystallization occurs at measurable speed, doubtless the equilibrium at the interface will be disturbed at least to some degree. Thus the effective distribution coefficient k, which describes the over-all reaction of solute incorporation into the crystal at non-zero growth speed, may vary with the crystallization

[1] W. Nernst, Z. physik. Chem. 47, 52 (1904).
[2] E. A. Moelwyn-Hughes, *The Kinetics of Reactions in Solution* (Oxford University Press, London, 1947), second edition.
[3] L. L. Bircumshaw and A. C. Riddiford, Quart. Rev. Chem. Soc. (London), 6, 157 (1952). See also A. C. Riddiford, J. Phys. Chem. 56, 745 (1952).
[4] G. K. Teal and J. B. Little, Phys. Rev. 78, 647 (1950).
[5] E. Scheuer, Z. Metallkunde, 23, 237 (1931); A. Hayes and J. Chipman, Trans. Am. Inst. Mining Met. Engs. 135, 85 (1939); R. H. McFee, J. Chem. Phys. 15, 856 (1947); W. G. Pfann, J. Metals 4, 747 (1952).

rate due to two factors: (a) the contribution of transport processes in the melt, mentioned in the preceding paragraph; (b) the effect upon the exchange process at the interface, i.e., upon the chemical process itself.

The present paper will be devoted chiefly to (a), since transport of solute in the melt is found experimentally to be of major importance. Hall[6] has postulated a mechanism for the dependence of k upon growth rate which in effect ascribes the behavior to (b). He has taken (a) to be unimportant in practice, but this view is not in accord with our own experience.[7] Some mention will be made presently of the effect of nonzero growth rate upon the exchange process at the interface, but a detailed discussion will be reserved for later presentation.

2. ANALYSIS OF FLUID FLOW

For any type of fluid flow, whether laminar or turbulent, the fluid velocity tends toward zero with approach to the solid-liquid interface, except for the flow normal to the interface due to crystallization. There is thus some region of the melt, next to the crystal, in which the principal transport of solute away from the interface occurs by diffusion. Fluid motion dominates solute transport in more remote regions. Crystallization from the melt according to the method of Teal and Little[4] involves continual rotation of the crystal, the purpose being in part to yield symmetrical growth. This rotation tends to produce ordered, laminar flow in the melt. If turbulence and random convection currents are small enough in comparison, the fluid flow is essentially that due to the stirring. Experimentally, there is no superficial evidence of turbulence in the liquid, nor would turbulence be expected from general considerations[8] of the conditions of stirring. Hence, it is presumed that the fluid flow is laminar, and that it can be analyzed in the following way, which is similar to the treatment used by Levich[9] in his study of diffusion-limited electrode reactions.

The interface of a rotating crystal pulled from the melt is approximately a plane disk. As is well known, a disk rotating upon a liquid acts as a centrifugal fan, spinning fluid radially and tangentially, and hence drawing material toward the rotating surface from the body of the liquid. The fluid flow pattern produced by an infinite disk rotating upon a semi-infinite liquid has been calculated by Cochran,[10] solely in terms of the angular velocity of the disk and the kinematic viscosity of the liquid. In Cochran's example the flow velocity normal to the disk is independent of radial distance from the rotation axis, and falls off rapidly in proximity to the disk. Crystal and crucible dimensions are typically of the order of centimeters, whereas the diffusion-dominated region of present interest is probably only about 10^{-2} or 10^{-3} cm thick. Therefore Cochran's analysis should give a reasonable approximation for flow in the melt, provided the analysis is confined to regions of the melt which lie close to the crystal and separated from the edges of the crystal and crucible. Since the melt is not infinitely deep, an analysis like that made by Batchelor,[11] treating the flow between two parallel rotating disks with finite separation, should be more exact. However this last approach is more difficult than seems warranted.

Conservation of solute atoms in the melt is expressed by the continuity equation

$$\partial C/\partial t = -\nabla\cdot(C\mathbf{V} - D\nabla C), \tag{1}$$

where $\mathbf{V}$ is the vector fluid velocity, and D is the diffusion coefficient of the solute, assumed to be independent of concentration in the dilute solutions which are encountered. A one-dimensional treatment is appropriate, since the solid solute concentration is found experimentally to be virtually uniform in the radial direction, perpendicular to the growth direction. Then, since the fluid is incompressible, Eq. (1) reduces to the following in the steady state:

$$D\frac{d^2C}{dx^2} - V_x\frac{dC}{dx} = 0. \tag{2}$$

The coordinate system is fixed with respect to the solid-liquid interface, which is located at $x=0$, with the positive x direction extending into the melt. Velocity V_x is taken to be the sum of the normal fluid velocity W, and the growth velocity f. The latter is chosen to be positive for growth and negative for melting. The boundary conditions for steady-state growth are:

$$C \to C_L \quad \text{as} \quad x \to \infty, \tag{3}$$

$$(C_0 - C_s)f + D\frac{dC}{dx} = 0 \quad \text{at} \quad x = 0, \tag{4}$$

where as before C_L and C_0 are the melt concentrations in the bulk of the liquid and at the interface, respectively.

Relations (2)–(4) can be solved numerically, using Cochran's tables for W. For the small values of x which are of interest here, however, Cochran gives the following approximation,

$$W = 0.51\omega^{3/2}\nu^{-1/2}x^2 \quad \text{for} \quad x < \nu^{1/2}\omega^{-1/2}, \tag{5}$$

where ω is the angular velocity of crystal rotation and ν is the kinematic viscosity of the liquid. The following solution is obtained.*

$$\frac{C_0 - C_L}{C_0 - C_S} = \int_0^\infty e^{-(X + BX^3)}dX, \tag{6}$$

where $B = 0.17f^{-3}\omega^{3/2}D^2\nu^{-1/2}$ and $X = fx/D$.

[6] R. N. Hall, Phys. Rev. **88**, 139 (1952).
[7] See Part II, J. Chem. Phys. **21**, 1991 (1953).
[8] See *Modern Developments in Fluid Dynamics*, edited by S. Goldstein (Oxford University Press, London, 1938), pp. 113, 367.
[9] B. Levich, Acta Physicochim. U. R. S. S. **17**, 257 (1942).
[10] W. G. Cochran, Proc. Camb. Phil. Soc. **30**, 365 (1934).
[11] G. K. Batchelor, Quart. J. Mech. Appl. Math. **4**, 29 (1951).
* Strictly speaking, the integration may not be carried beyond $x = \sqrt{(\nu/\omega)}$, but practically the matter is unimportant, since with the physical constants of the present process there is virtually no contribution to the integral for $x > \sqrt{(\nu/\omega)}$.

For practical purposes it is more convenient, however, to make an approximation not unlike Nernst's approach. Thus, it is assumed that beyond a distance δ, from the growing interface the fluid flow keeps the concentration uniformly equal to C_L. Within δ the normal flow velocity is merely f, and here diffusion likewise contributes to the transport. Thus Eq. (3) becomes

$$D\frac{d^2C}{dx^2}+f\frac{dC}{dx}=0 \tag{7}$$

and (3) is replaced by

$$C=C_L \quad \text{at} \quad x=\delta. \tag{8}$$

The following solution results for the concentration at the interface.

$$\frac{C_0-C_S}{C_L-C_S}=e^{\Delta}, \tag{9}$$

where $\Delta=f\delta/D$. The somewhat arbitrary quantity δ may be characterized by defining it so that it yields the same dependence of the composition upon the growth parameters that is given by the more exact solution, (6). Thus, δ is required to vary in such a way that

$$e^{-\Delta}=1-J, \tag{10}$$

where J is the integral standing on the right in Eq. (6).

For small enough values of the growth rate, δ depends simply upon the rotation rate and certain physical properties of the liquid phase.

$$\delta=1.6D^{1/3}\nu^{1/6}\omega^{-1/2}. \tag{11}$$

Thus it is seen that if the growth rate is small enough, Δ varies linearly with f and with $\omega^{-\frac{1}{2}}$. The variation of Δ with $B^{-\frac{1}{2}}$, i.e., its dependence upon the term $f\omega^{-\frac{1}{2}}$, is shown in Fig. 1.

The foregoing treatment has described steady-state solute transport in the fluid for both crystal growth and for melting. In the case of growth there exists an additional relation between C_S and C_0, which is given in its simplest form by the equilibrium distribution coefficient

$$C_S/C_0=k_0. \tag{12}$$

The relation is described more generally as depending upon f, and possibly also upon other quantities such as acceleration:

$$C_S/C_0=k^*(f, \partial f/\partial t, \cdots). \tag{13}$$

As has been stated, no attempt will be made here to explore the manner in which k^* depends upon these factors. Suffice it to say that one would expect the behavior to be qualitatively similar to that postulated by Hall,[6] in that the process at the interface should shift toward an enhanced tendency for solute incorporation at higher growth rates.

In any case, whatever the form of k^*, Eqs. (9) and (13) lead to the following expression for the effective distribution coefficient in the steady state:

$$k=\frac{k^*}{k^*+(1-k^*)e^{-\Delta}}. \tag{14}$$

For the important case in which equilibrium prevails at the interface virtually independently of growth rate,

$$k=\frac{k_0}{k_0+(1-k_0)e^{-\Delta}}. \tag{15}$$

The variation of k with growth rate is shown in Fig. 2 for two rates of crystal rotation, and for three values of k_0. Reasonable values have been assumed here for D and ν: $D=5\times10^{-5}$ cm^2 sec^{-1} and $\nu=2.5\times10^{-3}$ cgs units. The variation described by Eq. (15), for equilibrium at the interface, is given in each case. If this equilibrium were disturbed by the use of nonzero growth rate, the steady-state variation described by Eq. (14) would of course cause the curves to stand above those in Fig. 2.

3. TRANSIENT ANALYSIS

Transient behavior in the melt will now be examined for the case of rapid exchange at the interface, i.e., $k^*=k_0$. The transient case to be considered is that in which the solute concentration in the bulk of the melt is abruptly increased. Because of the linearity of the problem, one may deal solely with the case in which this concentration jumps from zero to a final value at $t=0$.

Retaining the concept of diffusion-dominated region of thickness δ, beyond which the melt composition is uniform, the partial differential equation and boundary

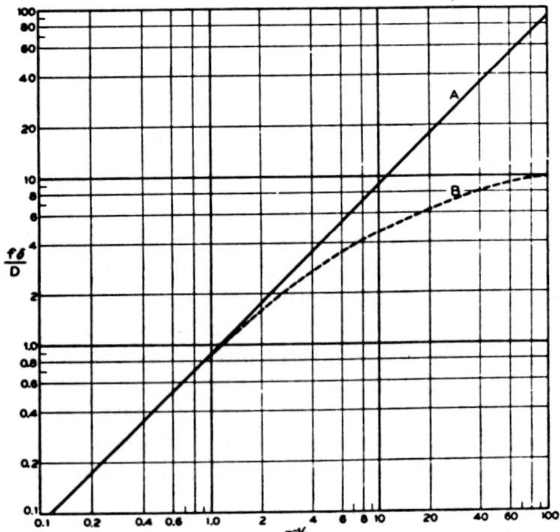

FIG. 1. Variation of $f\delta/D$ with $B^{-\frac{1}{2}}$, i.e., with $f\omega^{-\frac{1}{2}}$. Curve A neglects the dependence of δ upon f. Curve B gives the exact variation.

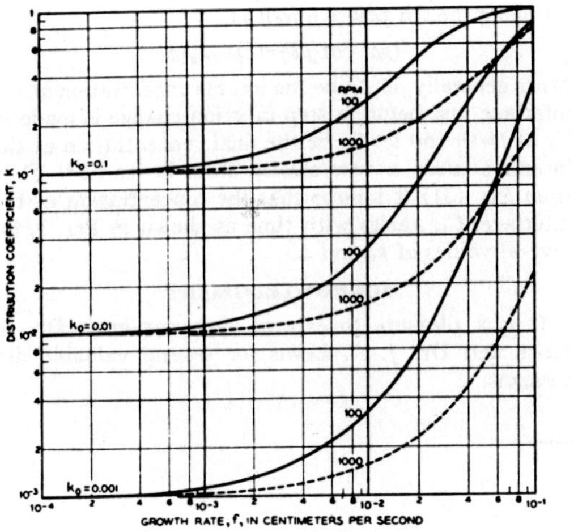

FIG. 2. Dependence of the effective distribution coefficient upon growth rate and rotation rate, for several values of equilibrium distribution coefficient.

conditions for $0\leq x\leq\delta$ become

$$D\frac{\partial^2 C}{\partial x^2}+f\frac{\partial C}{\partial x}=\frac{\partial C}{\partial t}, \tag{16}$$

$$-D\frac{\partial C}{\partial x}=(1-k_0)fC_0 \quad \text{at} \quad x=0, \tag{17}$$

$$C=0 \quad \text{for} \quad 0<x<\delta, \quad t=0, \tag{18}$$

$$C=C_L \quad \text{for} \quad x=\delta, \quad t=0. \tag{19}$$

It is convenient to change to variables $\tilde{C}$ and y:

$$\tilde{C}\equiv C-C_{SS} \tag{20}$$

$$y\equiv\delta-x, \tag{21}$$

where C_{SS} is the steady-state result obtained from solving Eq. (7). Accordingly, Eqs. (16)–(19) become

$$D\frac{\partial^2\tilde{C}}{\partial y^2}-f\frac{\partial\tilde{C}}{\partial y}=\frac{\partial\tilde{C}}{\partial t} \tag{22}$$

$$D\frac{\partial\tilde{C}}{\partial y}=(1-k_0)f\tilde{C} \quad \text{at} \quad y=\delta \tag{23}$$

$$\tilde{C}=-C_{SS}(y) \quad \text{for} \quad y>0, \quad t=0 \tag{24}$$

$$\tilde{C}=0 \quad \text{for} \quad y=0, \quad t\geq 0, \tag{25}$$

where

$$C_{SS}=C_L\frac{k_0+(1-k_0)e^{-\Delta}e^{-fy/D}}{k_0+(1-k_0)e^{-\Delta}},$$

and again $\Delta=f\delta/D$. The following set of solutions to Eq. (22) satisfies relation (25) and has the property that $\tilde{C}\rightarrow 0$ as $t\rightarrow\infty$.

$$\tilde{C}_\mu=e^{fy/2D}\sin\mu y\cdot\exp\left\{-\left[\left(\frac{f}{2D}\right)^2+\mu^2\right]Dt\right\}. \tag{26}$$

Here the μ's are positive numbers which, in order for condition (23) to be obeyed, must be the roots of the equation

$$(\mu\delta)\cot(\mu\delta)=(\tfrac{1}{2}-k_0)\Delta. \tag{27}$$

Let $\mu_i\delta(i=1, 2, 3, \cdots)$ denote the ith positive root of (27). Condition (24) is obeyed by proper choice of multipliers B_i in a series of terms from the solution set (26).

$$e^{fy/2D}\sum_{i=1}^{\infty}B_i\sin\mu_i y=-C_{SS}(y) \quad \text{for} \quad 0<y\leq\delta. \tag{28}$$

Since the solutions $\tilde{C}_{\mu_i}$ are orthogonal over the interval

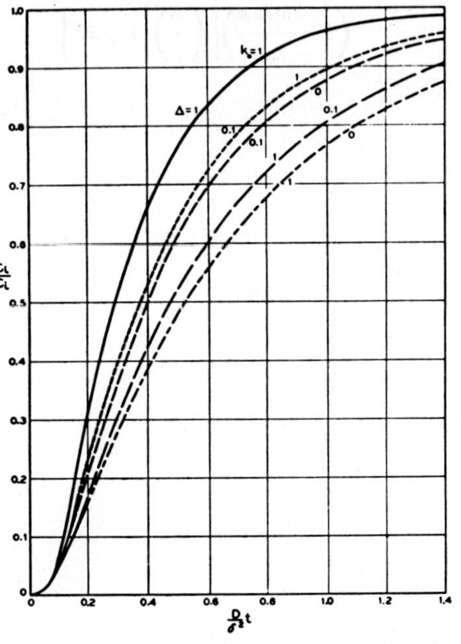

FIG. 3. Concentration at a crystal interface as a function of time following a step-function change in solute concentration in the melt.

$0\leq x\leq\delta$, the B_i's are given by

$$B_i=\frac{\int_0^\delta -\exp\left(-\frac{fy}{2D}\right)\cdot C_{SS}(y)\sin\mu_i y dy}{\int_0^\delta \sin^2\mu_i y dy}. \tag{29}$$

From this one can compute

$$\frac{\tilde{C}}{C_L}=-2e^{fy/2D}\times\sum_{i=1}^{\infty}\frac{\mu_i\delta\sin\mu_i y\cdot\exp\left\{-\left[\left(\frac{\Delta}{2}\right)^2+(\mu_i\delta)^2\right]\frac{Dt}{\delta^2}\right\}}{\left(1-\frac{\sin 2\mu_i\delta}{2\mu_i\delta}\right)\left[\left(\frac{\Delta}{2}\right)^2+(\mu_i\delta)^2\right]}. \tag{30}$$

Then the concentration of solute in the melt next to the interface is found to be

$$\frac{C_0(t)}{C_L}=\frac{1}{k_0+(1-k_0)e^{-\Delta}}-2e^{\Delta/2}\times\sum_{i=1}^{\infty}\frac{\mu_i\delta\sin\mu_i\delta\cdot\exp\left\{-\left[\left(\frac{\Delta}{2}\right)^2+(\mu_i\delta)^2\right]\frac{Dt}{\delta^2}\right\}}{\left(1-\frac{\sin 2\mu_i\delta}{2\mu_i\delta}\right)\left[\left(\frac{\Delta}{2}\right)^2+(\mu_i\delta)^2\right]}, \quad (31)$$

$\mu_i\delta$ being the ith positive root of

$$(\mu\delta)\cot(\mu\delta)=(\tfrac{1}{2}-k_0)\Delta.$$

More generally, let C_i be the initial concentration at the interface just before a step-function change is made in C_L at $t=0$, and let C_f be the final concentration at the interface after a new steady state is reached. Then from Eq. (31) it follows that the concentration at the interface, C_0, varies with time as shown in Fig. 3, for several values of k_0 and Δ.

ACKNOWLEDGMENT

It is a pleasure to express appreciation to Dr. H. Reiss and Dr. J. A. Lewis for several valuable discussions.

Acta Cryst. (1955). **8**, 49

On the Relations Between Structure and Morphology of Crystals. I

By P. Hartman and W. G. Perdok

Kristallografisch Instituut der Rijksuniversiteit, Melkweg 1, Groningen, Netherlands

(*Received 4 October 1954*)

An attempt is made to find relations between crystal structure and crystal morphology on an energy basis. It is concluded that the morphology of a crystal is governed by chains of strong bonds running through the structure. The effective period of such a chain of strong bonds is called a periodic bond chain vector (P.B.C. vector). The faces of a crystal are divided into three classes: (*a*) flat faces or *F*-faces, each of which is parallel to at least two P.B.C. vectors; (*b*) stepped or *S*-faces, each of which is parallel to at least one P.B.C. vector; (*c*) kinked faces or *K*-faces which are not parallel to any P.B.C. vector. *F*-faces are the most important faces; *S*-faces are of medium importance and *K*-faces are very rare or do not occur at all. Two examples are given, concerning the morphology of diamond and urotropine respectively.

Introduction

As soon as crystals became the subject of thorough investigation, attempts were made to correlate morphological development with internal structure. Up to now only geometrical characteristics of the structure had been taken into account (Bravais, Friedel, Fedorov, Niggli, Donnay), but, as crystal growth is a physical process, energy quantities will probably play a more important role than geometrical quantities like row densities and mesh areas.

Criticism of this kind has already been made by Wells (1946*a*, *b*, *c*) and by Buerger (1947), but these authors did not give a method by which the influence of energy factors could be taken into account in a practical way.

In this paper we present some theoretical considerations, which make it possible to correlate crystal morphology and crystal structure, starting from qualitative considerations on bond energies (see also Hartman & Perdok (1952) for a preliminary note and Hartman (1953) for details).

Outline of the main ideas

(*a*) The influence of strong bonds in the structure on the shape of a crystal is strikingly demonstrated by fibrous crystals like asbestos, where chains of strong bonds run parallel to the fibre axis. Niggli (1923), however, showed that even in crystals lacking such extreme properties, a main zone axis is parallel to a *Hauptbindungsrichtung* in the structure, as far as external influences can be excluded. It will be shown, however, that these *Hauptbindungsrichtungen* have to be replaced by the directions of chains of strong bonds.

(*b*) Gibbs (1906) showed thermodynamically that in the case of a crystal in equilibrium with its surroundings the condition that $\Sigma\sigma_i F_i$ is a minimum applies. Here σ_i is the specific surface free energy of the *i*th face and F_i the area of this face.

Wulff (1901), later Liebmann (1914) and more recently von Laue (1943) showed the Gibbs condition to be equivalent to the statement that a point can be located in the crystal (the Wulff point) from which the distances to the different crystal faces are proportional to the specific surface free energies, or, in other words, that the surface area of a crystal face —and consequently its morphological importance— decreases in general with increasing surface free energy.

The Gibbs condition, however, has never been applied to practical morphological problems because, apart from the fact that crystal growth is not a reversible process, no method is known by which the surface free energies of an actual crystal can be measured or calculated. Therefore we have to find an energy quantity associated with the crystal faces that is more accessible.

A considerable simplification of the problem is obtained by replacing the surface free energies by the surface energies, as defined by Born (1923) in his lattice theory; this means that only bond energies are taken into account.

Instead of this surface energy, however, we take the 'attachment energy', which is defined as the bond energy released when one building unit is attached to the surface of a crystal face. Now we assume that the time needed for the formation of a bond decreases with increasing bond energy. Therefore, the displacement velocity of a crystal face increases with increasing attachment energy; consequently the attachment energy will be representative for its morphological importance because a crystal face will disappear the sooner during crystal growth the faster it moves away from the growth centre. Though our assumption cannot be supported by strict thermodynamical and kinetical evidence, we found that the attachment energies, provided that these can be calculated, represent the morphological importance much better than the mesh areas (see Part II to appear later).

(*c*) Consider a two-dimensional crystal bounded by (10) and (01), each unit cell of which contains one building unit (Fig. 1(*a*)). Suppose there are two types

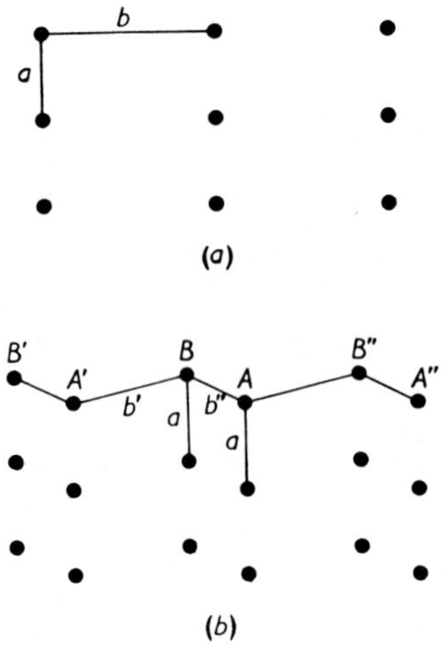

Fig. 1. (*a*) Two-dimensional crystal in which bond *a* is stronger than bond *b*. The crystal will be elongated in the direction of bond *a*.

(*b*) Two-dimensional crystal in which bonds *a* and *b''* are of the same strength, while bond *b'* is much weaker. The strong bond *b''* has no influence on the shape of the crystal, because it is the stronger bond in the chain -*b'*-*b''*-*b'*-*b''*-. The shape of the crystal is determined by the bonds *a* and *b'*. The crystal will be elongated in the direction of bond *a*.

of bonds: *a* in the direction [10] and *b* in the direction [01]; the bond energy of *a* is larger than that of *b*. Now the attachment energy on (10) is *a*, that on (01) is *b*, so that (10) has a greater displacement velocity than (01). Consequently the crystal will be elongated into the direction [10], i.e. the direction of the stronger bond.

Suppose now, that in a second case each cell has two building units, *A* and *B* (Fig. 1(*b*)), and that they are bound by a strong bond, the bond between *A* and *B''* being weak. We denote this weak bond by *b'* and the strong bond between *A* and *B* by *b''*; the bonds *a* between like building units *A* and like building units *B* in the [10] direction are assumed to have both the same strength as *b''*.

The growth in the direction [01] is now governed by two bonds *b'* and *b''*, of which the weaker determines the displacement velocity, so that the crystal will have smaller dimensions in the [01] than in the [10] direction. This means that the influence of the strong bond *b''* is reduced by its combination with *b'*.

From these examples three conclusions can be drawn:

(1) For a crystal to grow in the direction of a strong bond, these bonds must form an uninterrupted chain through the structure.
(2) If a bond chain contains bonds of different type, its influence on the shape of the crystal is determined by the weakest bond present in the chain.
(3) Important zone directions must be parallel to bond chains containing strong bonds only.

Obviously these chains are periodical in pattern: each period connects a building unit to a structurally equivalent one. In complicated structures each period may consist of several links or 'partial bond vectors' (representing the distance between centres of building units in length and direction). In general, the effective zone direction can be found as the direction of the sum vector of all the partial bond vectors; hence it is parallel to the translation relating two equivalent building units. This sum vector we call a *periodic bond chain vector* (P.B.C. vector). Sometimes the length of a P.B.C. vector is a submultiple of the translation distance, owing to pseudo-halvings, pseudo-thirdings etc.

Our working hypothesis is, then, that the P.B.C. *vectors give the clue to the understanding of the morphological development of a crystal*; important zones are parallel to P.B.C. vectors, and correspond to chains that contain only strong bonds. As soon as a chain of otherwise strong bonds contains one weak bond, it loses its morphological importance. Prominent faces are parallel to at least two high-energy bond chains.

(*d*) The use of the term 'strong bond' needs some further explanation. In general a strong bond is understood as a bond requiring a large amount of energy to be broken, or releasing a large amount of energy when it is formed. But we must be aware of the fact that not every strong bond in a crystal structure has necessarily released its energy in the crystallization process. This is quite obvious in the case of molecular structures; the strong, generally covalent, bonds between the atoms in the molecule have been formed before crystallization could take place and consequently do not have any influence on the morphology of the crystal. A similar effect may be observed in other types of structures: sometimes certain strong bonds may already have been formed in the liquid phase (precondensation), causing a difference in morphological development according to whether the crystal has grown from the melt or from the vapour. A strong bond can also lose its significance through the influence of the solvent. Molecules of the solvent may be adsorbed at the surface of a crystal face so that the formation of a new bond in the structure must be preceded by the breaking of the 'adsorption bond'. In this way the net amount of energy released in the crystallization process may be lowered to such an extent that the effect is discernible in the morphological development.

Therefore, it may be emphasized that we have to define a strong bond as a bond releasing a high amount of energy *in the crystallization process*.

(*e*) To obtain a general morphological picture of a crystal species we have to divide the crystal faces into three classes depending on their positions with respect to the P.B.C. vectors: *class F, or flat faces*, containing two or more coplanar P.B.C. vectors, *class S, or stepped faces*, containing one P.B.C. vector and *class K, or kinked faces*, containing no P.B.C. vector (for the terminology cf. Burton & Cabrera (1949); the name 'flat face' does not imply that all building units should be exactly coplanar: the coplanarity refers only to the P.B.C. vectors).

A glance at Fig. 2 will explain the difference be-

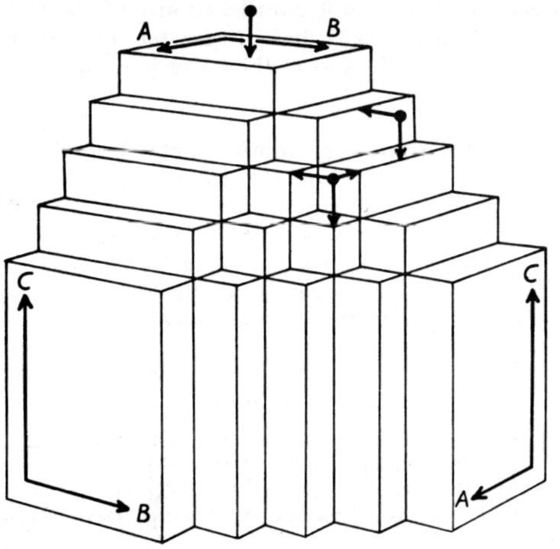

Fig. 2. Hypothetical crystal with three P. B. C. vectors: $A||[100]$, $B||[010]$ and $C||[001]$. The figure shows the *F*-faces (100), (010) and (001); the *S*-faces (110), (101) and (011); and the *K*-face (111).

tween these classes. Suppose there are three P.B.C. vectors: vector $A||[100]$, vector $B||[010]$, and vector $C||[001]$. These P.B.C. vectors define six *F*-faces, namely (001) and (00$\bar{1}$) defined by A and B; (010) and (0$\bar{1}$0) defined by A and C; (100) and ($\bar{1}$00) defined by B and C. Any face parallel to only one of the vectors A, B or C is an *S*-face. In Fig. 2 three of these are shown: (011), (101) and (110). Faces which are not parallel to any of the vectors are *K*-faces, one of which, namely (111), is shown in Fig. 2.

Another feature can be read off from the figure: the attachment of a building unit to the surface of an *F*-face involves the release of only a relatively small amount of energy, namely the bond energy in forming bonds of those P.B.C. vectors which do not lie in this *F*-face. The attachment of a building unit to the edge of a step of an *S*-face involves the formation of at least one strong bond more than in the case of an *F*-face. The attachment of a building unit into a kink involves the formation of at least one strong bond more than in the case of an *S*-face.

Hence the displacement velocities of *K*-faces are greater than those of *S*-faces, and the displacement velocities of the *F*-faces are the smallest. *Consequently the F-faces will become the larger (final growth) faces, and the K-faces are often not observed or belong to the very rare forms. All the other faces are S-faces.*

(*f*) Up to now we have considered only the morphological importance in connexion with the chance of disappearance of the crystal faces in the growth process. But it can be shown that a chance of appearance has also to be taken into account. For that purpose the very beginning of the crystallization process has to be considered.

When crystal growth is starting from a small germ there is in general a notable degree of supersaturation. The supply of material is then so abundant that any building unit, once attached to the surface of the germ, is already overgrown by a subsequent layer before it can diffuse back into the disordered phase. In this stage all kinds of zones with the directions $mp+nq+$ etc. (p, q, etc. being P.B.C. vectors) grow out with about the same velocity—the attachment energy is not yet the determining factor—so that the germ develops into a 'seed' with an approach to an isometric shape. As time proceeds and the external conditions come closer to 'equilibrium' conditions, the attachment energy begins to direct the growth process; the seed will develop more and more, so that its 'faces' (which might be represented by only one mesh) become real crystal faces with a noticeable extension.

If from now on the conditions of growth remain constant, no new faces can be formed which were not present originally on the seed. It is obvious that a higher index face cannot appear at all, as long as the diameter of the 'seed' is so small that there is no room for one mesh on its surface. Therefore, the greater the dimensions of the mesh corresponding to a crystal face, the smaller is the chance that it will appear, and consequently the less is its morphological importance. At this point the geometry of the lattice enters also into our considerations, which are otherwise confined to energy. The chance of appearance is of interest in comparing the relative importance of *S*-faces within one zone and will be treated more fully in Part II of this paper.

(*g*) Statistical methods sometimes enable us to arrange the crystal forms according to their importance (see, for example, Niggli (1923) and Parker (1923)). In agreement with the conclusions given above, the forms found in the beginning of such a list prove to be *F*-forms, the rest being *S*-forms, while *K*-forms close the list or do not occur at all. This general picture of the morphology was found to be correct in all cases examined so far. In Part II we will treat some minerals in greater detail and show that the theoretical morphological aspect, obtained by calculating the attachment energies, is in very good agreement with the experimental data.

Examples

(1) *Significance of periodic bond chains, illustrated in the case of diamond*

The three minerals diamond, arsenolite and senarmontite crystallize in the same type of structure. In diamond the building units are atoms, linked together by covalent bonds. The building units of the other minerals are molecules and the bonds between them are mainly of the van der Waals type. Both types of bonds decrease very rapidly in strength with increasing distance. Hence only the bond between building units at (0, 0, 0) and ($\frac{1}{4}$, $\frac{1}{4}$, $\frac{1}{4}$), and structural equivalents, need to be considered. Two of these bonds form the P.B.C. vector [$\frac{1}{2}$, $\frac{1}{2}$, 0]. The most prominent form of the three minerals is the octahedron. The faces of this form are, indeed, parallel to three P.B.C. vectors.

Niggli (1941) showed that the explanation on the basis of structure geometry encounters difficulties. Indeed here Niggli's conception of 'row density' cannot be used as a criterion for the importance of a zone. Some rows are covered with matter in such a way that a relatively short distance is followed by a distance three times as long. The question arises whether the shortest distance or the mean distance is determinative for the importance of a zone. According to the first criterion (shortest distance) the zone [111] would be more important than [110] (and presumably the dodecahedron more important than the octahedron). The second criterion (mean distance) indicates the zone [110] as more important than [111], in agreement with observations. These difficulties arise because the bonds between the atoms are not considered. The row [111] contains the shortest distance which corresponds at the same time to the strongest bond, but the three-times longer distance does not correspond to any bond at all.

(2) *Relative importance of F-, S- and K-faces, illustrated in the case of urotropine*

Urotropine crystallizes in a molecular structure in which the centres of the molecules lie in the nodes of a cubic body-centred structure. Two bonds can be distinguished: bond *a* between atoms in (0, 0, 0) and ($\frac{1}{2}$, $\frac{1}{2}$, $\frac{1}{2}$) and bond *b* between atoms in (0, 0, 0) and (1, 0, 0). The latter bond is slightly longer so that it will be less strong than bond *a*. Every bond constitutes a P.B.C. vector and hence only the P.B.C. vectors [$\frac{1}{2}$, $\frac{1}{2}$, $\frac{1}{2}$] and [1, 0, 0], and their symmetrical equivalents, have to be taken into account. The faces of the forms {110} and {100} are parallel to three and two, respectively, of these P.B.C. vectors, and hence these are *F*-faces. Experiments on the growth of urotropine crystals from their vapour (Stranski & Honigmann, 1950) proved the growth form to be {110}. The equilibrium forms, obtained by tempering at room temperature, are {110}, {100} and {211}, the latter two forms being rather small. According to the theory of Stranski {111} should also be present, when {211} is present. In our terms the observations can be understood because {211} is an *S*-form, whereas {111} is a *K*-form as it is not parallel to any of the P.B.C. vectors. Hence {111} has a greater displacement velocity than {211} and is therefore more apt to disappear.

The authors are very much indebted to Prof. Dr P. Terpstra, head of the Crystallographic Institute, for his encouraging interest and criticism, to Prof. Dr J. D. H. Donnay and Dr G. Donnay for stimulating discussions during the first stage of the work, and to Prof. Dr E. H. Wiebenga for his critical remarks on some thermodynamical questions.

References

Born, M. (1923). *Atomtheorie des festen Zustandes*, 2nd ed., p. 538. Leipzig; Berlin: Teubner.
Buerger, M. J. (1947). *Amer. Min.* **32**, 593.
Burton, W. K. & Cabrera, N. (1949). *Disc. Faraday Soc.* No. 5, 33.
Gibbs, J. W. (1906). *Scientific Papers*, vol. 1.
Hartman, P. (1953). Thesis, Groningen.
Hartman, P. & Perdok, W. G. (1952). *Proc. K. Ned. Akad. Wet.* B, **55**, 134.
Laue, M. von (1943). *Z. Kristallogr.* **105**, 124.
Liebmann, H. (1914). *Z. Kristallogr.* **53**, 171.
Niggli, P. (1923). *Z. Kristallogr.* **58**, 490.
Niggli, P. (1941). *Lehrbuch der Mineralogie und Kristallchemie*, 3rd ed., part 1, p. 355. Berlin: Borntraeger.
Parker, R. L. (1923). *Z. Kristallogr.* **59**, 1.
Stranski, I. N. & Honigmann, B. (1950). *Z. Phys. Chem.* **194**, 180.
Wells, A. F. (1946*a*). *Phil. Mag.* (7), **37**, 184.
Wells, A. F. (1946*b*). *Phil. Mag.* (7), **37**, 217.
Wells, A. F. (1946*c*). *Phil. Mag.* (7), **37**, 605.
Wulff, G. (1901). *Z. Kristallogr.* **34**, 449.

THE INFLUENCE OF DISLOCATIONS ON CRYSTAL GROWTH

By F. C. Frank

Received 16th February, 1949

The kinetic theory of the nucleation of new phases, developed especially by Volmer,[1] by Farkas,[2] by Kaischew and Stranski [3] and by Becker and Döring,[4] indicates that under typical conditions * the self-nucleation from vapour of new crystals, new liquid drops and fresh two-dimensional monolayers of molecules on a "saturated" crystal face require respectively supersaturations of the vapour by factors of typically 10, 5 and 1·5 respectively in order to proceed at appreciable rates. Experimentally, the first two of these figures are apparently correct: but the third is much larger than the actual supersaturation required to cause further growth of a crystal already formed. In fact, the existence of a critical finite supersaturation for further growth has only been established for a few materials, and then for individual faces of individual crystals, being different from case to case; at the most it is about 1 %. Volmer and Schultze,[5] who found a critical supersaturation of 0·8 % for the growth of an iodine crystal from the vapour, interpreted this as the critical supersaturation for two-dimensional nucleation: but the quantitative discrepancy is far too great (for details of the growth rate formulæ, see the contributions of Burton and Cabrera to this Discussion).

However, this discrepancy is not in the least surprising. One ought not to expect that any visible crystal will exhibit a completed perfect face needing fresh two-dimensional nucleation in order to grow. Investigation of the mechanical properties of solids shows that no macroscopic specimen ever exhibits the theoretical strength of the perfect crystal; and this enormous discrepancy (a factor of 100, say, and *more* for "good"

1 Volmer and Weber, *Z. physik. Chem.*, 1926, **119**, 277. Volmer, *Kinetik der Phasenbildung* (Leipzig, 1939).
2 Farkas, *Z. physik. Chem.*, 1927, **125**, 236.
3 Kaischew and Stranski, *Z. physik. Chem. B*, 1934, **26**, 317; *Physik. Z.*, 1935, **36**, 393.
4 Becker and Döring, *Ann. Physik*, 1935, **24**, 719.
5 Volmer and Schultze, *Z. physik. Chem. A*, 1931, **156**, 1.

* Typical conditions may be taken as such that the vapour pressure lies within a few powers of 10 of 1 mm. Hg: or the temperature between about 0·5 and 0·8 times T_b, the boiling point in °K.

crystals) is attributed to the presence of dislocations. In the early stages of the development of dislocation theory by Polanyi,[6] Orowan [7] and Taylor,[8] only one aspect of the dislocation was recognized, in which the displacement direction was normal to the dislocation line. In 1939 Burgers [9] drew attention to the "screw" form assumed by the dislocation when the displacement is parallel to the dislocation line, and the developments of dislocation theory by Mott and Nabarro,[10] Frank [11] and others emphasize the fact that dislocation lines can be curved and exhibit any orientation. Fig. 1 shows (*a*) as a continuous deformation of a plane, (*b*) in a block model, the form of a simple cubic crystal when a screw dislocation emerges normally at the

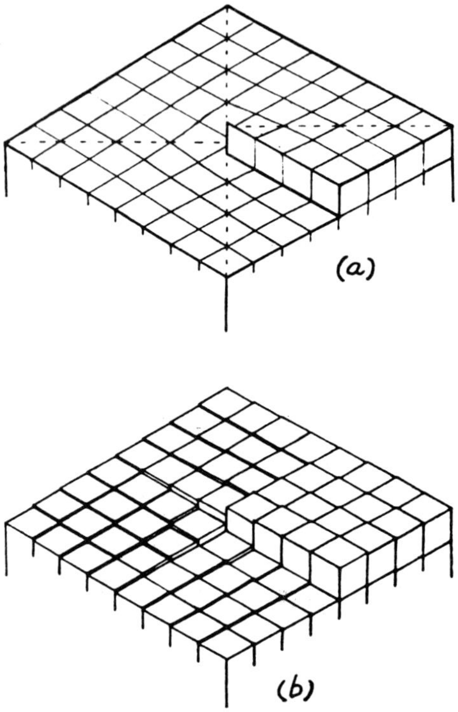

FIG. 1.—The end of a screw dislocation.

cube-face. It is clear that when dislocations of this type are present, the crystal face always has exposed molecular terraces on which growth can continue, and the need for fresh two-dimensional nucleation never arises. If just one dislocation of this type emerges at the centre of the face, that crystal face can grow perpetually "up a spiral staircase." If there are two, respectively right- and left-handed, we can show that the terrace connecting them will grow indefinitely if the supersaturation is raised to such a value that the diameter, l_0, of the critical two-dimensional nucleus is less than the distance between them. More precisely, since the critical nucleus is not

[6] Polanyi, *Z. Physik*, 1934, **89**, 660.
[7] Orowan, *Z. Physik*, 1934, **89**, 634.
[8] Taylor, *Proc. Roy. Soc. A*, 1934, **145**, 362.
[9] Burgers, *Proc. Kon. Ned. Akad. Wet.*, 1939, **42**, 293.
[10] Mott and Nabarro, *The Strength of Solids* (Physical Society, London), 1948, p. 1.
[11] Frank, *ibid.*, p. 46.

circular, we should say that growth occurs when the critical nucleus, correctly oriented, will pass between two points in the positions of the two dislocations. Likewise when a single dislocation is close to the boundary of the face, growth occurs if the critical nucleus will pass between the dislocation and the boundary. If it will not pass, the terrace rests in a position corresponding to a portion of the boundary of the critical nucleus (Fig. 2). For rough calculations we may approximate the boundary as a circle of radius $\frac{1}{2}l_o$, and we have a close analogy to the equilibrium (or non-equilibrium) of a bubble at an orifice.

Measuring in molecular spacings, we have

$$l_o = \varphi/\boldsymbol{k}T \ln \alpha,$$

where α is the saturation ratio: since the supersaturation is small, $(\alpha - 1)$ may be written in place of $\ln \alpha$. φ is the neighbour-neighbour binding energy of the crystal. For a rule of thumb we may use Trouton's rule and take $\varphi/\boldsymbol{k}T$ as $3{\cdot}5\ T_b/T$. Thus at an absolute temperature of 0·6 of the boiling point of the material, and a supersaturation of 1 %, l_o is about 600 molecular spacings: or 6000 at 0·1 %.

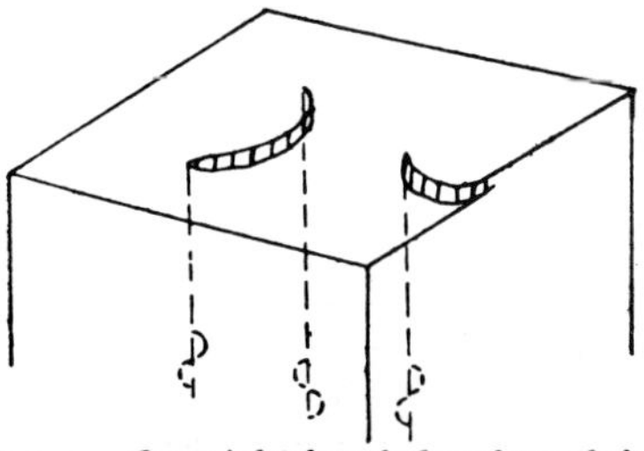

FIG. 2.—One right-handed and two left-handed screw dislocations ending in a crystal face.

In the theory of mechanical deformation, it is commonly estimated that in an annealed metal crystal there are about 10^8 dislocation lines intersecting each square centimetre. This appears to be the limiting perfection attainable in metals, and would be classed, indeed, as high perfection from the point of view of X-ray diffraction. (This limit may well be connected with the impurity content.) This is only an order-of-magnitude estimate, and does not necessarily apply to other materials than metals: but it serves as a guide, and suggests that critical supersaturations of the order of a fraction of 1 % are reasonably to be expected.

We are perforce limited for quantitative discussion to the case of growth from the vapour of homopolar crystals, since the classical nucleation rate theory has not been quantitatively developed for any other case. But experimental indications, and such theoretical guesswork as we can make, suggest that the conditions governing the growth from solution of crystals, including ionic crystals, are substantially similar. It is possible, but less certain, that the same is true of growth from the melt. Perhaps the most distinctively different case is that of the growth, either from vapour or solution, of crystals of highly non-equiaxed organic molecules. There are indications that in such cases growth proceeds through the formation of adsorption films, dense, but differing in molecular orientation from the bulk crystal (e.g., liquid, or liquid-crystalline) within which subsequent rearrangement occurs.

The general importance of dislocations for crystal growth accounts immediately for many observations, such as the individual behaviour of each crystal face, particularly on the microscopic scale, leading sometimes to such unexpected results as the formation of lath-shaped crystals for a lattice of cubic symmetry.

Under steady uniform supersaturation the terrace attached to an isolated growth-promoting dislocation in a crystal otherwise perfect in its neighbourhood will grow outwards in a spiral of which the spacing between turns, and the rate of their advance, will be uniform at a considerable distance from the centre. Near the centre the rate of advance must be less, since the radius of curvature of the spiral terrace-line must remain less than $\frac{1}{2}l_0$. At given supersaturation and distance from other terrace-lines, the rate of advance, v, is an increasing function of the radius of curvature, being 0 when it is $\frac{1}{2}l_0$ and, say, v_∞ when the terrace becomes straight. Supposing it increased very steeply to v_∞ for a very small increase of the radius of curvature above $\frac{1}{2}l_0$, the inner portion of the spiral would be an arc of a circle of this radius, and the spiral would make $v_\infty/\pi l_0$ turns per second. The spacing of turns in the outer region of the spiral would then be πl_0. Actually v will not increase infinitely steeply to v_∞, so that the number of turns per second will be less, and the spacing greater, but still of the same order of magnitude: let us guess $2\pi l_0$. Macroscopically this spirally terraced hill would appear to be a flat cone, with its sides inclined at an angle of $\frac{1}{2}\pi l_0$ radians to the true lattice surface—say, 1 min. for a supersaturation of 1 %, and in other cases pro-

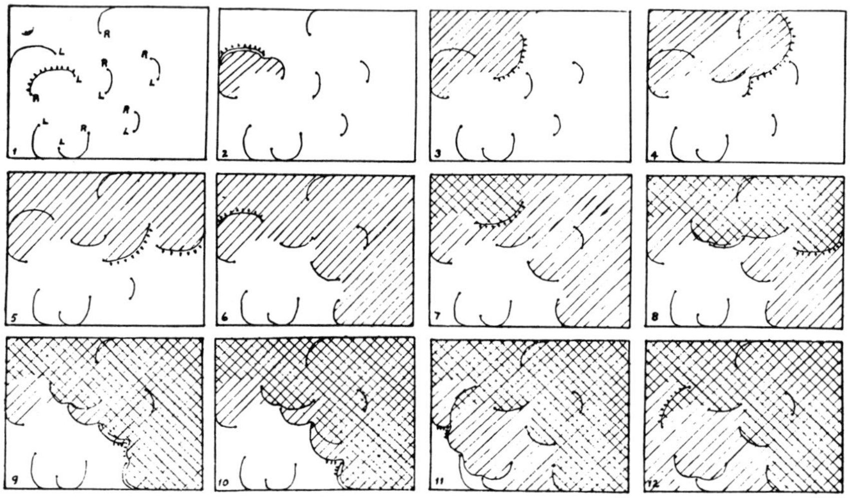

FIG. 3.—The influence of random dislocations on crystal growth.

portional to the supersaturation. We have so far neglected the dependence of the rate of advance of the terrace on its direction. On this account, instead of a flat cone, we shall have a more or less sharply defined flat pyramid having the symmetry appropriate to the crystal face.

When growth spreads from an isolated pair of dislocations, respectively right- and left-handed, the observable result will be practically the same provided that the supersaturation suffices to make l_0 less than their separation. If it is not, no growth occurs at all. If it is, the terrace-line connecting them repeatedly spreads out on one side, wraps round, and meets itself on the other side: thus forming a short connecting terrace-line again, and an outward-growing closed loop. The rate of formation of such loops will be the same in order of magnitude as the rate of formation of turns of the spiral from a single dislocation. The result will be a flat cone or pyramid indistinguishable from the previous case.

In the case that there is a random distribution of dislocations a variety of phenomena occur, exhibited pictorially in Fig. 3 (*1* to *12*). In these pictures there is supposed to be positive supersaturation, so that each terrace makes a curve convex on its cliff side, running from one dislocation to another of opposite sense, or to the boundary of the crystal face. The supersaturation is supposed to be low, and fluctuating, so that in general only one terrace-line—normally the longest—moves at a time. In each picture the terrace due to move next is specially marked. Shading indicates the area covered by fresh growth after picture *1*. Among points to be specially noticed are :

(i) the holding up of one terrace-line behind another (pictures *2*, *8*, *9*, *10*) or at a dislocation connected to another terrace (*9*, *10*, *11*, *12*) ;

(ii) the way in which a close pair of dislocations connecting a terrace facing the advancing terrace break it and so impede its passage (many examples, especially pictures *4*, *5*, *6*). In these two ways, a dislocation pair holding a terrace facing *either* way is an obstruction to the passage of an advancing terrace ;

(iii) the way in which the obstructions of type (i) are broken down (*10*, *11*, *4*) ;

(iv) the relatively impregnable region in the bottom left-hand corner. In *6* growth into this region has ceased by obstruction of type (ii) : a new advancing terrace is held up again (at *9*) by obstruction of type (i) : but this obstruction is more easily broken down, and by *12* all but a small portion of the crystal face has increased in thickness by at least one monolayer. A third advancing terrace, now commencing, will finally overrun this strong-point : however, a continuous line of closely spaced dislocations could be totally impenetrable below a critical supersaturation.

Obstruction of type (i) requires a little more consideration. One way in which type (i) obstruction can break down is the following. Each " pinned " terrace-line holds its equilibrium form by small statistical fluctuations back and forth. When two terraces lie together, the lower cannot fluctuate back under, nor the upper fluctuate forward over the other. Thus they exert a small effective repulsion on each other, and the lower one may be pushed beyond the critical curvature when the upper one arrives. Secondly, there is only a small region of seriously deformed crystal structure and hence of seriously reduced binding energy for new molecules, in the immediate neighbourhood of the dislocation. When the two terraces at such a point of obstruction face each other at an acute angle, as in pictures *9*, *10*, *11*, only a small number of molecules need condense in these unfavourable positions to enable the terrace to link across and pass on. If the obstruction arises from a straight row of dislocations spaced l_1 apart, this angle becomes smaller as l_0 decreases, diminishing rapidly from 120° when l_0 becomes less than $2l_1$. The obstruction will be ineffective when l_0 is significantly smaller than this value. Even when it is greater, a comparatively small number of molecules (say, 6 to 10) in unfavourable positions suffice to overcome the obstruction, so that statistical fluctuations (negligible with regard to obstruction of type (ii)) can be effective. Thus obstruction of type (i) probably only imposes a delay rather than a total prohibition of growth.

In view of this, one might suppose it a particularly important question whether the numbers of right-handed and left-handed dislocation-ends in a face are equal or not : the surplus of one kind might have very long terrace-lines linking them to the boundary. This is not the case for reasonably uniformly or randomly distributed dislocations, unless the relative numbers are very different. If, in an area A, n dislocations of one kind and m of another are formed randomly, like head and tail throws of a coin, the probable excess of one kind, $n - m$, is $1{\cdot}35\ (n + m)^{1/2} \approx 1{\cdot}9\, n^{1/2}$: but if it does not exceed $\pi n^{1/2}$ (where $n > m$) the dislocations linked to the boundary can all be close to it, and the longest necessary terrace inappreciably longer than in the case $n = m$, i.e., still of the order of magnitude $(A/n)^{1/2}$. In a systematically deformed crystal it is possible to have $n \gg m$, and then there is always a terrace-line at least as long as the $(m + 1)$th furthest dislocation of the n from the boundary.

The most important aspect of the type (i) obstruction by a fence of dislocations all of the same kind is that every boundary between two crystal blocks inclined at a small angle to each other constitutes such a fence (see Fig. 4, and Fig. 12 in ref. 9). The distance between the dislocations in the fence, measured in molecular spacings, is equal to the reciprocal angle of rotation between the two blocks, whether for " tilt," " twist " or more general boundaries, so long as the angle is small. A possible cause of the *visible* growth terraces sometimes seen advancing over a crystal face is that a number of molecular terraces have accumulated behind such a fence, and then been set free by a rise in supersaturation: but it is possible to think of alternative causes which can bring about the same " bunching " of molecular growth terraces into visible ones.

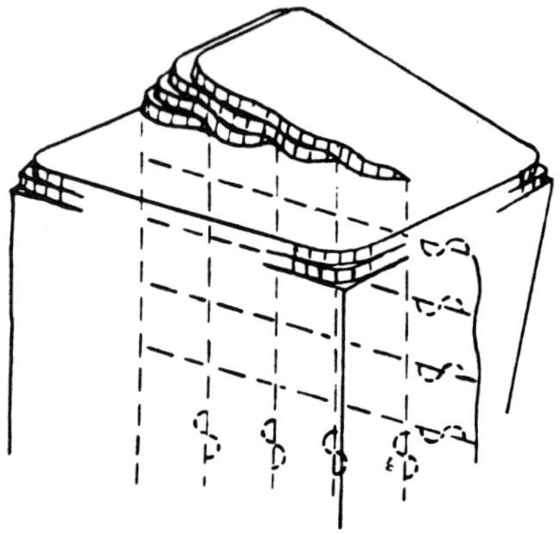

FIG. 4.—" Twist " boundary—a crossed grid of screw dislocations.

It remains to elaborate the concept of dislocations somewhat, to free it from the simplifications introduced by considering only simple cubic crystals, with cube faces. In the general case the important property of a dislocation is its displacement vector (or Burgers vector). If this vector has a component normal to the crystal face on which the dislocation line ends, there will be an associated molecular terrace in the face, promoting crystal growth. But there is also an important distinction between perfect dislocations, whose displacement vectors are lattice vectors, and imperfect dislocations whose displacement vectors lead in general from a lattice position to a twin-lattice position. Such is the dislocation with displacement vector $\left(-\frac{1}{3}, -\frac{1}{3}, -\frac{1}{3}\right)$, produced in the close-packed cubic crystal by omission of part of a (111) close-packed plane of atoms. This dislocation cannot glide,[12] but must lie in its (111) plane: ending in a $(11\bar{1})$ or similar surface, it attaches a molecular growth terrace in the usual way—but every time this growth terrace reaches the trace in the surface of the missing plane of atoms, the terrace must pause unless there is a definite supersaturation. At this boundary the lattice is not continuous but has a translation-twin relationship. Instead of the usual 6 contacts per added atom, characteristic of cubic close-packing, one row of atoms added at this boundary make 7 contacts each, and the next row only 5. The latter loosely bound row will only be formed at a definite supersaturation, or by statistical fluctuation after delay.

[12] Frank, *Proc. Physic. Soc. A*, 1949, **62**, 202.

We must give a brief account of the origin of the dislocations which, it is suggested, dominate crystal growth. The chief origins which have been thought of so far are :

(i) Surface nucleation of layers in improper (e.g., twin) positions and proper positions simultaneously on the same face. Where these meet there is a dislocation. It must be remembered that the initial nucleation of the crystal always takes place at high supersaturation, much more than adequate for the Becker-Döring condition for surface nucleation on a perfect face.

(ii) Formation of one-dimensional dislocations in the edge row of the growing terrace (cf., van der Merwe's contribution to this Discussion). Such one-dimensional dislocations have an energy similar to the latent heat of evaporation of a molecule, and consequently exist in thermal equilibrium. During rapid growth at high supersaturation they can be trapped in an edge row, developing into two-dimensional and thence into three-dimensional dislocations.

(iii) The development of curvature in the growing crystal owing to the presence of impurities (a subject to be treated at length elsewhere). This ultimately leads to stress in the surface which demands a certain supersaturation for further growth, which can then continue if, and only if, dislocations are formed.

(iv) When *systems* of dislocations are present (particularly sub-grain boundaries) it is probable that the stress they would cause in perfect crystal compels the formation of further members of the system in growth : i.e., sub-grain *boundaries* are propagated in lineage structure.

(v) Aggregation of molecular vacancies into flat collapsed cavities (the edges of which are dislocation loops) whenever the temperature of a crystal is lowered. This is very likely the process responsible for the intensification of X-ray reflection (the so-called establishment of mosaic structure) when an organic crystal is plunged in liquid air.

(vi) Plastic yield under mechanical stress : this is believed not to create dislocations *ab initio* but to multiply those already present.[11]

These various considerations indicate that the initial dislocations necessary for growth are formed inevitably in the conditions needed for nucleation : and that to secure the best attainable perfection thereafter we must ensure small supersaturation (this involves good stirring, or there will be large supersaturation at the corners when it is small at the centre of a face), high purity of materials, steady temperature and absence of mechanical stresses.

The effect which dislocations have upon crystal growth produces a rather odd natural selection both of imperfection and perfection in crystals. The nucleation stage with high supersaturation makes a population of initial nuclei of varied, mostly rather great, imperfection. If growth is now carried out at low supersaturation, only a few of these seeds, in which dislocations are relatively far apart, will grow. The lower the supersaturation at this stage, the fewer and the more perfect the seeds which will actually grow. But the completely perfect crystal will not grow in any circumstances : the conditions which could cause it to grow would also soon make it imperfect.

H. H. Wills Physical Laboratory,
Royal Fort,
Bristol 8.

MECHANISM OF GROWTH

By Kenneth A. Jackson

A CRYSTAL grows when atoms are added to it. The way in which atoms are added to the solid determines the morphology of the solid and the number and distribution of imperfections in the solid.

A crystalline solid can grow from its liquid, from its vapor, from a solution, or from another solid. The character of the crystallization will depend on the phase into which the crystal is growing, and on other conditions such as the temperature, pressure, concentration, etc. These conditions determine the atom movements by which the growth of a crystal takes place.

The atom movements cannot be observed directly. In the present paper we will discuss two manifestations of the atom movements; namely, the rates of growth of crystals, and the morphology of the crystal surfaces. These manifestations will be discussed in terms of atom movement, and related to the conditions of growth.

Rates of Growth

Some of the atomistic mechanisms which have been used to predict the rate of crystal growth will be outlined below. The predictions made by these mechanisms can be compared with rates of growth measured at various amounts of supersaturation or supercooling. The details of these mechanisms will be omitted below. We will emphasize the assumptions involved in each of these models in order to clearly define the applicability of each mechanism.

Surface Nucleation

The basic premise of a surface nucleation theory is that there is difficulty associated with starting a new layer of atoms on a low index surface. A disk of atoms on a low index surface has a free energy given by:

$$\Delta F_D = ar\sigma_E - br^2\Delta F_v \qquad \text{Equation 1}$$

where σ_E is the surface free energy per atom and ar the number of atoms on the periphery of the disk; ΔF_v is the free energy per atom associated with the transformation and $br^2 = n$, the number of atoms in the disk. Such a disk will be stable if the disk is larger than a certain critical size defined by the critical radius r^*:

$$r^* = \sigma_E a/2b\Delta F_v \qquad \text{Equation 2}$$

The author, Kenneth A. Jackson, is associated with the Division of Engineering and Applied Physics, Harvard University, Cambridge, Massachusetts.

In order to calculate the growth rate of the crystal, it is necessary to calculate the rate at which disks of size r* develop. The simplest assumptions upon which such a calculation can be based are:

1. Most of the atoms on the surface are not part of a disk. This implies that the number of atoms on the surface, N_o say, is such that $N_o >> n^*$, the number of atoms in a disk of critical size.
2. Atoms join or leave the disks singly. This assumption requires that the probability of one disk impinging upon another be small, and therefore that most of the N atom sites on the surface are vacant, i.e., $N >> N_o$.

These two assumptions permit the use of Boltzmann statistics.

The frequency of formation of disks containing n atoms can be written as:†

$$I = I_o \exp(-\Delta F_D/kT) \qquad \text{Equation 3}$$

where I_o depends on the rates at which atoms join and leave the solid, and on the amount of time an individual atom will adhere to the surface.

I*, the rate of formation of disks of radius r*, defines the growth rate. I* increases as the temperature decreases, or as the supersaturation increases. I* changes from a value that is essentially zero to a finite rate in a very small temperature (supersaturation) range. This small temperature range defines the minimum amount of supercooling that is necessary for measurable growth to take place. This minimum amount of supercooling is usually several centigrade degrees.

Surface nucleation theory predicts that no growth should occur unless the supercooling (supersaturation) is greater than a critical amount. However, growth has been observed at very small amounts of supercooling (4).

Imperfections

A crystal can grow at an arbitrarily small amount of supercooling if it is not necessary to form new layers. This is the case for growth with the aid of a screw dislocation as proposed by Frank (5). The step generated by the dislocation moves up one plane each time it sweeps around the dislocation. Many observations (6) of spirals resulting from growth and of spirals during growth show that the screw dislocation plays an important role in the growth of crystals. It should be emphasized that an imperfection is necessary for growth only on certain planes. Growth on other than a few close-packed planes presents no difficulty. The rate of growth on the close-packed planes is so slow that it determines the rate of growth of the crystal.

† For a detailed development of these equations see Volmer (1)[1], Becker and Döring (2), Hollomon and Turnbull (3).

[1] The figures appearing in parentheses pertain to the references appended to this paper.

In order to calculate the rate of growth of a crystal due to screw dislocations, Burton, Cabrera and Frank (7) divided the growth process into two stages. The first stage is the arrival of atoms at the surface. The rate of arrival can be calculated with the aid of the kinetic theory of gases. The second stage is the movement of the atom along the surface to a position at the growth step. The fraction of the atoms that reach a stable growth position determines the rate of growth. This fraction depends on the time an atom is likely to remain on the surface, the distance between steps and the number of kinks (growth sites) in the steps. This treatment provides a valid description of growth from the vapor.

Growth from a Liquid

Hillig and Turnbull (8) have calculated the rate of growth at screw dislocations for the growth of a crystal from its liquid. This calculation was made as follows:

According to a simple kinetic model (9) a crystal grows from its liquid at a velocity v_o given by

$$v_o = D\,\Delta S\,\Delta T\,(lRT)^{-1} \qquad \text{Equation 4}$$

where D the diffusion coefficient, ΔS the entropy difference between solid and liquid, l the jump distance, T the absolute temperature, R the gas constant and ΔT the supercooling. If atoms can be added to the crystal only at a growth step, the growth velocity v_o will be reduced by a factor a, the fraction of surface sites which are growth steps. Let us assume that a growth step is an Archimedes spiral generated by a screw dislocation. The minimum radius of the spiral must be the critical nucleus size. This defines the pitch of the spiral and hence:

$$a = l\,\Delta S\,\Delta T\,(4\pi\sigma V_m)^{-1} \qquad \text{Equation 5}$$

where σ is the surface free energy per unit area, and V_m is the molecular volume.

Finally, the growth velocity v is given by $v = av_o$
or:

$$v = 3\,(\Delta S)^2 D(\Delta T)^2/4\,\pi\,V_m\,RT\,\sigma \qquad \text{Equation 6}$$

Measured Growth Rates for Growth from Liquids

The rate of growth has been measured as a function of supercooling for five liquids: Tin by Rosenberg and Winegard (10), water by Hillig and D. Turnbull (8) and by S. Lindenmeyer et al (11); Salol by Neumann and Micas (12) and by H. Pollatschek (13), Glycerol by Volmer and Marder (14) and phosphorus by Powell, Gillman and Hildebrande (15). All of these measurements can be described by an equation of the form $v = A\Delta T^{\eta}$. Experimentally η lies between 1.7 to 2.3 for the various materials. Equation 6 predicts $\eta = 2$. Hillig and Turnbull predict a value of A for Salol and Glycerol that is in excellent agreement with experiment. For water, tin and phosphorus, however, the predicted value of A is from one to three orders of magnitude too small.

When Salol and Glycerol grow into their supercooled liquids, the crystals of solid are bounded by well defined, geometrically plane surfaces. The rate of growth of these crystals is slow on an absolute scale. Water, tin and phosphorus, however, grow dendritically into their supercooled liquids. The rate of growth is much more rapid—three to five orders of magnitude faster for equivalent supercooling than Salol or Glycerol. The rate of growth of tin, water and phosphorus is much faster than predicted by Equation 6. Equation 6 correctly predicts the rate of growth of Salol and Glycerol.

Ottomar Jäntsch (16) has developed an equation for the rate of growth of a crystal into a liquid. In the derivation of this equation, growth is assumed to occur without nucleation at "repeatable step" sites on the surface. The growth at these preferred growth sites takes place at a rate given by an equation that is essentially similar to Equation 4. The rate of atom movement, however, is introduced through the viscosity η, instead of the diffusion coefficient, O. Jäntsch has measured the viscosity of supercooled liquid Salol from its melting point down to a temperature where the viscosity is essentially infinite. To this rate of growth at preferred growth sites is added the rate of growth due to surface nucleation as predicted by Becker and Döring (2). Unfortunately, the resultant equation contains three parameters which are not known, so that no absolute prediction of a growth rate is possible. Jäntsch estimates these parameters by fitting his equation to the experimental curves. Excellent fit of the experimental curve for growth rate as a function of supercooling is obtained for Salol. The experimental curve for Glycerol cannot be fitted exactly. Unfortunately, the values of the parameters which are required to obtain the best fit do not agree with other estimates of these parameters.

One point is particularly noteworthy. The measured viscosity for Salol increases sharply in the same temperature range in which the growth rate of Salol crystals decreases. This occurs as liquid Salol approaches a "glassy" state at low temperatures. The viscosity measurements in this region correlate very well with the measured decrease in growth rate.

The Measurement of Growth Rates

There is an interesting discrepancy between the growth rate for water reported by Hillig and Turnbull (8) and Lindenmeyer et al (11). The measurements reported by Hillig and Turnbull were for water freezing in small bore glass tubes. Lindenmeyer studied the freezing of water in a much larger container. He observed that growth was more rapid along the walls of his (glass) container than down the center. Growth was also faster along a glass rod placed in the water than through free water. Growth was still faster along a piece of brass placed in the water. The reason for this is not resolved. It is believed to be a result of the glass acting as a heat sink because it is not a heat source as the ice-water interface is. The effect may, however, be due to surface energy. The rate at which the ice grew along the outside of the glass rod corresponds to the rate of growth measured by Hillig and Turnbull in glass tubes. The rate of growth in free water was slower than this. This observation indicates that the existing measurements on water are influenced by heat flow or surface energy, (or something else) in such a way that these results cannot be explained in terms of atomistic growth mechanisms alone. The influence of the unknown factor or factors (e.g. heat flow) must be understood before these measurements can be compared with the type of theory which has been discussed above.

Rate of Dendritic Growth

Dendritic growth in a pure material occurs because a plane interface cannot dissipate the latent heat it generates rapidly enough for existing conditions. (See Wienberg and Chalmers (17).) Growth can occur much more rapidly if the latent heat is generated at a small tip and spreads into the cooler liquid ahead of the tip. In considering the rate at which dendritic growth occurs, the evolution and dissipation of latent heat at the dendrite tip must be considered. Clifton and Eyring (18) have attempted to calculate the rate of dendrite growth on this basis. They considered the dendrite tip to be a circular heat source moving along an axis, tracing a cylinder. The heat flow analysis is then combined with an equation similar to Equation 4 and compared with experimental measurements. An alternate way of handling the problem is due to Fisher (19). At normal growth rates, heat flow is much faster than the rate of movement of the dendrite, so that the heat flow problem is solved as a steady state problem. Neither of these treatments predict an absolute growth rate, but both consider heat flow and the kinetics of atomic movement simultaneously.

Surface Structure

From the discussion above, it is evident that the growth of crystals from the vapor or from a solution is fairly well understood in principle. Growth from liquids, is in a more confused state. Some substances, such as Salol and Glycerol, solidify in a manner similar to the way in which most vapors condense. Other liquids, such as water and tin solidify in a completely different manner.

The reason for this difference has been suggested by Burton, Cabrera and Frank (7). They stated that some crystal surfaces are rough and some tend to be atomically smooth. Nucleation is required on smooth surfaces, but not on rough surfaces.

To determine whether a surface is rough or smooth, let us examine how the free energy of a surface changes if atoms are added to an atomically smooth surface.

Assuming the atoms are added randomly, the change in surface free energy due to the addition of these atoms may be written:

$$\Delta F_s = -\Delta E_o - \Delta E_1 + T\Delta S_o - T\Delta S_1 - P\Delta V \qquad \text{Equation 7}$$

The zero of ΔF_s will be taken as the free energy of an atomically plane interface.

ΔE_0 is the energy gained by adding N_A single atoms to the interface from the liquid or vapor.

ΔE_1 is the average energy gained by the N_A atoms due to the presence of other atoms on the surface.

ΔS_0 is the difference in entropy between the solid and the liquid or vapor.

ΔS_1 is the entropy due to the possible randomness of the atoms on the surface.

$P\Delta V$ is the term arising from the change in volume during condensation. This term is negligible for the solid-liquid transition.

We shall consider the case where atoms may be added only to one plane immediately above the base plane. Let us further assume that the energy of an atom on the solid is $2L_0\eta/v$ where L_0 is the change in internal energy on freezing or condensation (not the normal latent heat which is the change in enthalpy.) η is the number of nearest neighbors, and v is the total possible number of nearest neighbors. This assumption is likely to be in error by as much as a factor of two for the solid-vapor case, but is probably much better for a liquid-solid interface.

Then $$\Delta E_o = 2L_o\,(\eta_o/v)\,N_A \qquad \text{Equation 8}$$

where N_A is the number of atoms on the surface, and η_0 is the number of nearest neighbors of a single atom on the plane surface.

On the average each of the N_A atoms has a fraction N_A/N of its nearest neighbor sites filled. If an atom can have a total of η_1 such nearest neighbors, then

$$\Delta E_1 = (L_o\,\eta_1/v)\,(N_A^2/N) \qquad \text{Equation 9}$$

We have also

$$\Delta S_o = (L/T_E)\,N_A \qquad \text{Equation 10}$$

Where L is the latent heat of fusion or vaporization.

There are N_A atoms to arrange on sites of the surface. The probability of any such arrangement $W = N!/N_A!\,(N-N_A)!$

Using Stirlings approximation, and the Boltzmann relationship, we obtain

$$\Delta S_1 = k \ln W = k N \ln [N/(N - N_A)] + k N_A \ln [(N - N_A)/N_A] \quad \text{Equation 11}$$

Assuming that the vapor is an ideal gas, and that the volume of the solid is very small compared to the volume of the vapor, we obtain

$$P\Delta V = N_A k T \quad \text{Equation 12}$$

Finally; using

$$L = L_o + k T_E \quad \text{Equation 13}$$

$$\Delta F_s/NkT_E = -(L_o/kT_E)(N_A/N)[\eta_1/v)(N_A/N) + 2\eta_o/v] + (T/T_E)(L_o/kT_E)(N_A/N) - (T/T_E) \ln [N/(N - N_A)] - (T/T_E)(N_A/N) \ln [(N - N_A)/N_A] \quad \text{Equation 14}$$

For $T = T_E$, Equation 14 reduces to

$$\Delta F_s/NkT_E = a N_A (1 - N_A)/N^2 - \ln [N/(N - N_A)] - (N_A/N) \ln [(N - N_A)/N_A] \quad \text{Equation 15}$$

Where

$$a = (L_o/kT_E)(\eta_1/v) \quad \text{Equation 16}$$

Equation 15 is plotted in Fig. 1 for various values of a. a is made up of two factors: the first is $L_o/kT_E \approx \Delta S/R$ which depends on the material and the phase from which the crystal is growing; the second factor, η_1/v, depends on the crystal face under consideration. η_1/v is the fraction of the total number of nearest neighbours in a plane parallel to the face under consideration. a is large if the entropy difference between the crystal and the condensing phase is large, and is largest for the closest packed planes of the crystal.

There are two distinct types of crystal faces represented by the curves of Fig. 1. These are typified by the curves labelled (1) and (3) for which $a = 1$ and $a = 10$ respectively.

Let us consider first a surface typified by curve (1). In this case the lowest free energy occurs when half the available surface sites are filled. (i.e. $N_A/N = 0.5$) This is a "rough" surface. Such an interface certainly does not satisfy the second assumption on which Equation 3 depends. Such a surface would not require nucleation of new layers in the normal sense.

The problem of calculating a nucleation frequency in this case is a problem of calculating the largest cluster which will exist on a densely populated surface. Very large clusters will occur on such a surface by chance. There are too many atoms on the surface for them not to form clusters. The problem of nucleation is resolved if the surface of the substrate is large enough, since a critical nucleus will exist on it purely by chance. A new layer forms whenever the base plane grows large enough. From examining configurations, one would estimate that

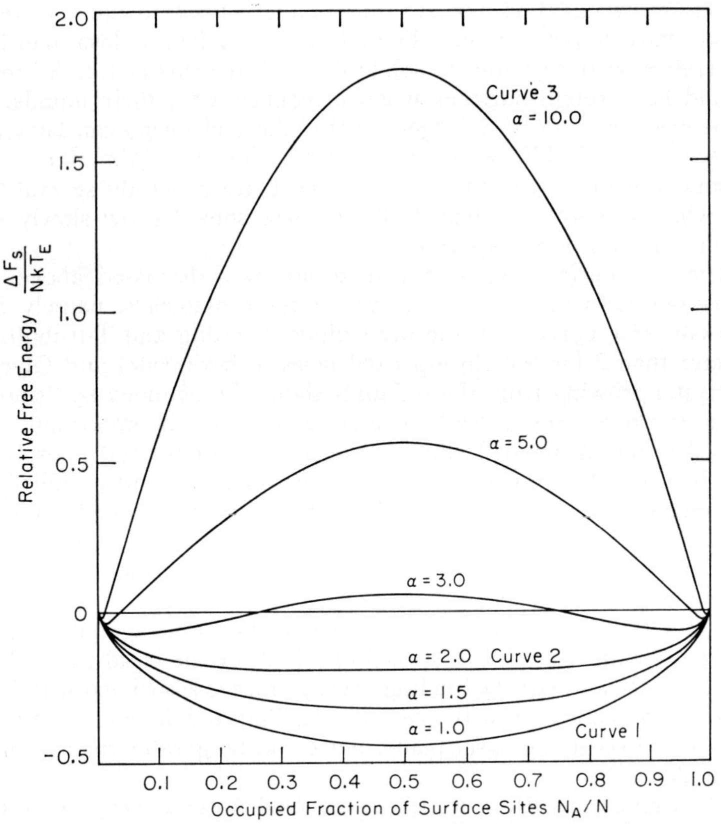

Fig. 1—Relative Surface Free Energy as a Function of the Fraction of Surface Sites Which are Occupied. α depends on the crystal face, the type of crystal, and the phase from which the crystal is growing.

"large enough" for the base plane is about ten to one hundred times the critical radius.

Once a coherent disk on a new layer has formed, the next layer can start immediately. The surface need never pass through the high free energy $N_A = N$ configuration.

Curve (3) in Fig. 1 corresponds to a surface whose free energy is lowest when there are a few extra atoms on the plane and a few atoms missing from the plane below. This is a "smooth" surface. Surface nucleation will be necessary to form new layers on such a surface: the assumptions of surface nucleation theory are valid in this case.

The borderline between the rough surface and the smooth surface is represented by curve (2) of Fig. 1. For this case $\alpha = 2$. If α is less than 2, the surface will be rough. If α is greater than 2, new layers will form with difficulty.

Let us now examine typical values of α to determine which materials should have rough surfaces. For all metals, L/kT_E is less than 2 for the transition from liquid to solid: the typical value is 1.2. All metals should have rough surfaces when in contact with their liquids. For some elements L/kT_E is larger, so that these elements can have $\alpha > 2$ for some faces. $L/kT_E \approx \Delta S/R$ is about 20 for the sublimation of most vapors. For growth from the vapor, there are generally several faces for which α is greater than 2. These faces should grow slowly since surface nucleation is required.

The rate of freezing of five materials was discussed above. The measured rates of growth for two of these materials, namely Salol and Glycerol, agree with the predictions of Hillig and Turnbull. α is greater than 2 for the close-packed faces of both Salol and Glycerol. A crystal growing from these liquids should be bounded by "smooth" faces. In these cases, growth at imperfections will be important as assumed in the theory of Hillig and Turnbull. For tin and phosphorus, α is less than two for all faces. These crystals have little difficulty in forming new atomic layers during growth from the melt. Tin and phosphorus should be able to freeze much more rapidly, in principle, than materials with smooth surfaces where the formation of a new layer presents a problem.

Water is a borderline case. Ordinary ice has a hexagonal structure. If the c/a ratio were ideal, α would be 1.97 for the basal plane. However, slightly more of the binding energy of ice is associated with bonds in the basal plane than with other bonds. Thus α will be less than 2 for all planes except the basal plane, but could be greater than 2 for the basal plane.

The rate of growth of ice in supercooled water is very different in and perpendicular to the basal plane. Ice grows dendritically in the basal plane. The ice dendrite develops as a sheet. The growth rate normal to the basal plane is very slow. However, the growth rates which have been measured (9,12) are those in the basal plane. These measured rates of growth for water should therefore be grouped with those for tin and phosphorus. Measurements of the rate of growth of ice along the c-axis should agree with the predictions of Hillig and Turnbull.

Growth Forms

The various growth forms which are observed can be rationalized in terms of the factor or factors which control the growth. The two most important factors which can limit the rate of crystallization are:

1) the rate at which new layers of the solid can be formed
2) the concentration of heat or of impurities at the crystal surface.

It is the balance between these factors which determines the

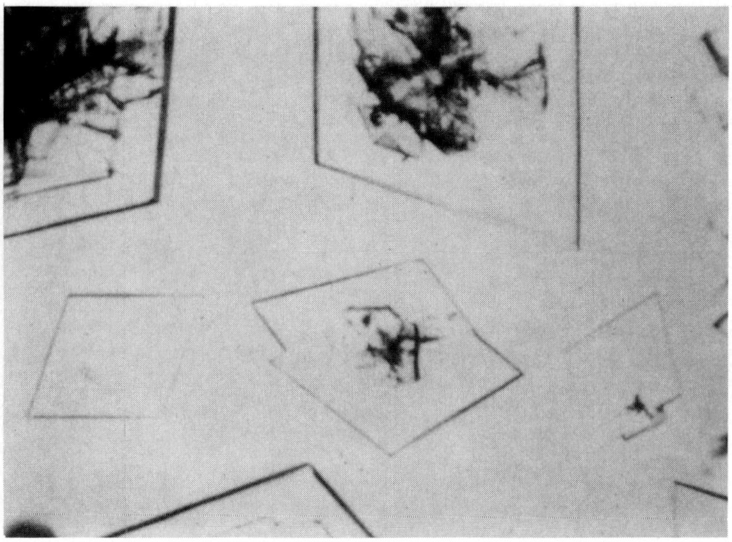

Fig. 2—Salol Crystals Growing in Liquid Salol at Room Temperature. (i.e. with 20 centigrade degrees supercooling). (× 5).

growth form. If any one part of the crystallization process is much slower than the others, that part of the process will control the rate of crystallization and the growth form.

In terms of the controlling factors, all modes of crystal growth can be classified in terms of one or more of three basic growth forms. These three basic growth forms are: dendritic growth, faceted growth, and diffusion controlled growth.

Diffusion Controlled Growth

As the name implies, diffusion controlled growth is limited by the rate at which latent heat or alloying elements which are rejected at the interface can be removed from the region of the interface. A familiar example of this type of growth occurs when the interface is an isotherm. In this case, the rate of extraction of latent heat determines the growth rate. The interface can be completely independent of crystallography. For this type of growth to occur, the atoms must be able to join the solid rapidly enough so that they do not limit the process.

Faceted Growth

This form of growth is distinguished by large and well-developed crystal facets. Although faceted growth is typical of growth from a vapor or from a dilute solution, this form of growth can also occur in

Fig. 3—Ice Dendrites Growing into Water at —2 °C. (Actual Size).

liquids: for example, Salol solidifies in this way. Fig. 2 is a photograph of Salol crystals growing in liquid Salol at room temperature.

Faceted growth occurs because growth on some crystal faces is extremely slow. The slow growing faces are those which are "smooth" under the existing conditions, and can therefore grow only by surface nucleation or with the aid of imperfections. The criterion established above predicts whether or not a crystal face is smooth under given conditions, and therefore whether that face should develop a facet.

Dendritic Growth

Dendritic growth occurs only when there is supercooled material into which the solid can grow. Fig. 3 is a photograph of an ice dendrite growing into supercooled water. All metals and many other substances can grow dendritically into supercooled melts. Some substances grow dendritically into a supercooled vapor (e.g. some snowflakes).

Two conditions are necessary for dendritic growth to occur:

1) the growth must not be limited by slow-growing "smooth" crystal faces,

2) the growth must not be limited by the rate of removal of heat from the system. Dendritic growth is thus, in a sense, uncontrolled growth. The latent heat from the freezing dendrite is dissipated by heating the unfrozen liquid. The rate of dendritic growth is the result of a balance between the rate of dissipation of latent heat and the rate at which atoms can be added to the solid.

Dendritic growth develops a crystallographic form because of slight differences in growth rate along some crystallographic directions. If part of the solid gets ahead of the rest, it will tend to get further ahead because it will heat the liquid near it with its latent heat. The tip of a protuberance is nearest the supercooled liquid. This effect magnifies the slight differences in growth rate in some crystallographic directions.

Intermediate Growth Forms

The three growth forms which have been enumerated above are ideal growth forms. Often growth occurs which is intermediate between these forms. For instance, ice dendrites growing in supercooled water develop facets on the basal plane: there is little growth normal to the basal plane; while the growth in the basal plane is very rapid and dendritic. In this case the growth is faceted or dendritic depending only on the crystallographic direction.

Dendrites can also grow into a constitutionally supercooled liquid. In this case, the average interface is controlled by heat flow and is an isotherm. The geometry of the supercooled zone is controlled by long range diffusion away from the mean interface. The rate of growth of dendrites into a constitutionally supercooled region can be controlled partly or entirely by local diffusion of an impurity or second component away from the dendrite tips.

The "platelet" substructure which has been observed by many authors (see Elbaum and Chalmers (20), Rosenberg and Tiller (21)) is a type of faceted growth which occurs at an interface which is an isotherm. The platelet substructure is the result of small differences in growth rate along various crystallographic directions. The result is that small segments of low index planes are exposed to the liquid. The difference in rate for the various directions cannot be very large however, or the structure would become faceted, with large regions of low index planes exposed.

Conclusion

Crystal surfaces can be divided into two classes: those on which surface nucleation is required, and those on which it is not. All crystals have some planes of the latter type; not all crystals have some of the former. When surface nucleation is required, it is likely to be a bottleneck in the growth process, so that the growth rate depends on the rate of nucleation. The theories of growth (2,7) that have been developed for growth from the vapor, and for growth from the melt (9,17) apply to the cases in which nucleation of a new layer is difficult. Reasonable agreement has been obtained between theory and experiment for these cases.

For the cases where no surface nucleation is required, the process is not controlled solely by the rate at which atoms can be added to the surface. The growth rate is determined by some other factor or by a compromise between a number of different factors of which the rate of addition of atoms is one. For these cases, the effects of these other factors must be eliminated experimentally, or treated theoretically before an adequate theoretical description of the growth process can be found.

References

1. M. Volmer and A. Weber, *Zeitschrift für physikalische Chemie,* Vol. 119, 1926, p. 277; M. Volmer, *Zeitschrift für Elektrochemie,* Vol. 35, 1929, p. 555; M. Volmer, *Kinetic der Phasenbildung,* 1939. Steinkopf, Dresden und Leipzig.
2. R. Becker and W. Döring, *Annalen der Physik,* Vol. 24, 1935, p. 719.
3. J. H. Hollomon and D. Turnbull, "Nucleation", *Progress in Metal Physics,* Vol. IV, 1953, p. 333. Interscience Publishers, Inc. New York.
4. M. Volmer and W. Schultze, *Zeitschrift für physikalische Chemie,* Vol. 156A, 1932, p. 1.
5. F. C. Frank, *Discussions of the Faraday Society,* No. 5, 1949, p. 48 and 67; *Philosophical Magazine,* Vol. 41, 1950, p. 200; *Philosophical Magazine,* Supplement, Vol. 1, 1952, p. 91.
6. L. J. Griffin, *Philosophical Magazine,* Vol. 41, Ser. 7, 1950, p. 196; I. M. Dawson and V. Vand, *Nature,* Vol. 167, 1951, p. 476 and *Proceedings of the Royal Society,* Vol. 206A, 1951, p. 555; A. R. Verma, *Nature,* Vol. 167, 1951, p. 939 and *Philosophical Magazine,* Vol. 42, Ser. 7, 1951, p. 1005; S. Amelinckx, *Nature,* Vol. 167, 1951, p. 939.
7. W. K. Burton, N. Cabrera and F. C. Frank, *Philosophical Transactions of the Royal Society of London,* Vol. 243A, 1951, p. 299.
8. W. B. Hillig and D. Turnbull, *Journal of Chemical Physics,* Vol. 24, 1956, p. 914.
9. H. A. Wilson, *Philosophical Magazine,* Vol. 50, 1900, p. 238; J. Frenkel, *Physikalische Zeitschrift der Sowjetunion,* Vol. 1, 1932, p. 498.
10. A. Rosenberg and W. C. Winegard, "The Rate of Growth of Dendrites in Supercooled Tin", *Acta Metallurgica,* Vol. 2, No. 2, March 1954, p. 342.
11. C. S. Lindenmeyer, G. T. Orrok, K. A. Jackson and B. Chalmers, *Journal of Chemical Physics,* Vol. 27, 1957, p. 822.
12. K. Neumann and G. Micas, *Zeitschrift für physikalische Chemie (Frankfurt),* Vol. 2, 1954, p. 25.
13. H. Pollatschek, *Zeitschrift für physikalische Chemie,* Vol. 142, 1929, p. 289.
14. M. Volmer and M. Marder, *Zeitschrift für physikalische Chemie,* Vol. 154A, 1931, p. 97.
15. R. E. Powell, T. S. Gilman and J. H. Hildebrande, *Journal,* American Chemical Society, Vol. 73, 1951, p. 2525.
16. O. Jäntsch, *Zeitschrift für Kristallographie,* Vol. 108, Nos. 3–4, 1956, p. 185.
17. F. Weinberg and B. Chalmers, *Canadian Journal of Physics,* Vol. 29, 1951, p. 382.
18. D. F. Clifton and H. Eyring, Fourth International Congress of Crystallography, Montreal, 1957. (Abstract: *Acta Crystallographica,* Vol. 10, 1957, p. 830.)
19. J. C. Fisher, private communication.
20. C. Elbaum and B. Chalmers, "The Topography of Solid-Liquid Interfaces of Metal Crystals Growing From the Melt", *Canadian Journal of Physics,* Vol. 33, May 1955, p. 196.
21. A. Rosenberg and W. A. Tiller, *Acta Metallurgica,* Vol. 5, 1957, p. 565.

KINETICS OF GROWTH OF A CRYSTAL NEEDLE IN A SUPERCOOLED BINARY MELT

D. E. Temkin

Institute of Metal Studies and Physics of Metals, I. P. Bardin Central Scientific Research Institute of Ferrous Metallurgy
Translated from Kristallografiya, Vol. 7, No. 3, pp. 446-450, May-June, 1962
Original article submitted July 20, 1961

The question of the steady growth of a crystal needle having the form of a paraboloid of revolution in a binary supercooled melt is examined. It is considered that the surface of the needle is nonisothermal, due to the varying curvature along it and the normal growth velocity. For a given content C_0 of the second component in the melt, the needle becomes thinner with increase in supercooling, and its growth velocity increases. For given supercooling, with increase in C_0 the needle becomes thicker and its growth is retarded. Parameters characterizing the kinetics of growth of a needle are calculated for the Sn–Pb system.

In the article [1], the question of the growth velocity of a crystal needle having the form of a paraboloid of revolution in a supercooled one-component melt was examined. In that article, in contrast to [2], allowance was made for the nonisothermal character of the surface of the growing crystal, due to the different values of curvature and growth velocity at different points of the interface. The influence of the first factor (curvature of the interface) results in a reduction of the equilibrium temperature T_c of the crystal with the melt

$$T_c = T_{c,\infty} - 2\sigma T_{c,\infty}/\gamma_1 Qr, \qquad (1)$$

where $T_{c,\infty}$ is the equilibrium temperature for a plane interface; σ is the specific surface energy of the crystal–melt interface; γ_1 is the density of the crystal; Q is the heat of crystallization; and $1/r$ is the mean curvature of the interface at the given point.

Due to the influence of the second factor (growth velocity) at different points of the needle surface, supercooling relative to the temperature T_c is different. In [1], the connection between normal growth velocity v_n and supercooling $(T_c - T_s)$ was assumed to be linear: $v_n = K(T_c - T_s)$, where T_s is the temperature at the given point on the crystal surface and K is a coefficient determining the mechanism of growth of the crystal. Taking (1) into account, we get

$$T_s = T_{c,\infty} - (2\sigma T_{c,\infty}/\gamma_1 Qr) - v_n/K. \qquad (2)$$

Analysis of the internal and external temperature fields of the parabolic needle, taking the above-mentioned circumstances into account, led to the following equations, connecting the maximum rate of advance of the needle v_m and the radius of curvature ρ_0 of the tip of a needle growing with the velocity v_m with supercooling of the melt $(T_{c,\infty} - T_0)$:

$$\left(2 + \frac{L_1}{K\rho_0}\right)^n = \frac{2\alpha a_2}{(\gamma_1/\gamma_2)(2n-1)L_2\sigma} \times \left[\frac{(2n-1)}{n}\frac{(T_{c,\infty} - T_0)c_2}{Q}\right]^n \times \left[\rho_0 - (n-1)\frac{L_1}{K}\right], \qquad (3)$$

$$v_m = (2n-1)L_2\sigma/\rho_0\,[\rho_0 - (n-1)L_1/K]. \qquad (4)$$

Here, the following notation is adopted: T_0, temperature of the melt at a point infinitely remote from the crystal surface; $L = \lambda_2[1.33 + 0.60\lambda_1/\lambda_2]/\gamma_1 Q$; $L_2 = [3.86 + 2.08\lambda_1/\lambda_2]\lambda_2 T_{c,\infty}/(\gamma_1 Q)^2$; λ_1, λ_2, thermal conductivity of the solid and liquid phases, respectively; c_2, a_2, specific heat and thermal conductivity of the melt. In Eqs. (3)-(4), which are true for slight supercooling, $[(T_{c,\infty} - T_0)c_2/Q \ll 1]$, $\alpha = 0.457$ and $n = 1.21$ for $(v_m\rho_0/2a_2) \leq 0.003$.

We shall now consider the growth conditions of a needle in a supercooled binary melt, the state of which at infinity is characterized by the figurative point $A(T_0, C_0)$ situated below the liquidus (Fig. 1). As shown by Ivantsov [3], the concentration field around a needle-shaped crystal having the form of a paraboloid of revolution [equation of needle surface $z = (\rho_0/2) -$

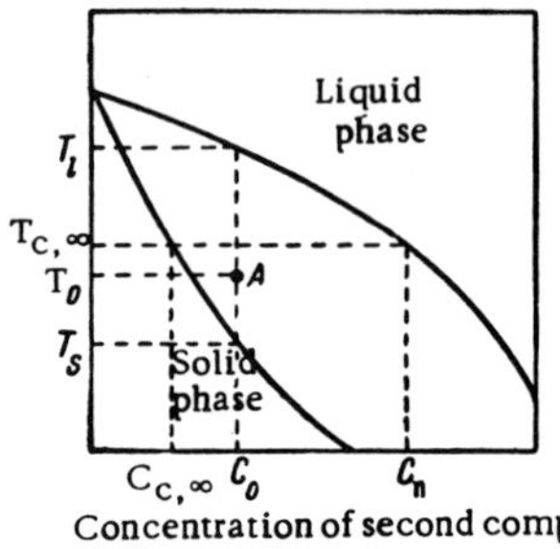

Fig. 1. Scheme of part of the equilibrium diagram of a binary alloy.

$(x^2 + y^2)/2\rho_0]$ and moving with a certain velocity v_m in the direction of the $\underline{z}$ axis is described by the equation

$$C(x, y, z) = C_0 + (C_s - C_0)\, Ei\left[-\frac{v_m\rho_0}{2D}\left(\frac{z}{\rho_0} + \sqrt{\frac{x^2+y^2+z^2}{\rho_0^2}}\right)\right] \Big/ Ei\left(-\frac{v_m\rho_0}{2D}\right), \quad (5)$$

where D is the coefficient of diffusion of the second component (impurity) in the melt. From the condition of balance of the impurity on the crystal-melt interface

$$D\frac{\partial C}{\partial n}\Big|_{z=(\rho_0/2)-(x^2+y^2)/2\rho_0} = (C_c - C_s)\, v_n \quad (6)$$

we get the equation

$$-(v_m\rho_0/2D)\exp(v_m\rho_0/2D)\, Ei(-v_m\rho_0/2D)$$

$$= (C_s - C_0)/(C_s - C_c). \quad (7)$$

Here C_s is the concentration of the impurity in the melt at the needle surface, C_c is the concentration inside the needle. Thus, according to (5) and (7), in the growth of a parabolic needle, the concentration C_s along the surface of the crystal and C_c inside the crystal are constant.

In equilibrium conditions with a plane interface, the concentration in the solid phase C_c, in agreement with the equilibrium diagram, is connected simply with C_s and the temperature $T_{c,\infty}$ (Fig. 1). A simple thermodynamic analysis shows that for not very small values of $\underline{r}$ (when the deivations from equilibrium characterized by the constitutional diagram are not large, since in the expansion of the chemical potentials according to temperature and concentration we can confine ourselves only to the first terms of the expansion) the following relationships occur:

$$C_{c,\infty} - C_s = (2\sigma/r)\,[V_1q_2 - V_2q_1] \Big/ \left[q_2\frac{\partial\mu_1}{\partial C} - q_1\frac{\partial\mu_2}{\partial C}\right], \quad (8)$$

$$T_{c,\infty} - T_c = (2\sigma T_{c,\infty}/rq_1)\left\{V_1 - \frac{\partial\mu_1}{\partial C}[V_1q_2 - V_2q_1] \Big/ \left[q_2\frac{\partial\mu_2}{\partial C} - q_1\frac{\partial\mu_2}{\partial C}\right]\right\}. \quad (9)$$

Here μ_i is the chemical potential in the solid phase; V_i is the partial molar volume in the solid phase; q_i is the heat of transition of the component from the solid to the liquid phase, referred to 1 mole ($i = 1,2$; the index 1 relates to the solvent, and 2 to the impurity). In expressions (8) and (9), the derivatives are taken at the point ($T_{c,\infty}$; $C_{c,\infty}$). For ideal solutions [4], $\partial\mu_1/\partial C = -RT$ and $\partial\mu_2/\partial C = RT/C$, so that

$$C_{c,\infty} - C_c = -\frac{2\sigma C_{c,\infty}}{rRT_{c,\infty}}\,\frac{(V_1q_2 - V_2q_1)}{(C_{c,\infty}q_2 + q_1)},$$

$$T_{c,\infty} - T_c = \frac{2\sigma T_{c,\infty}V_1}{rq_1}\left\{1 - \frac{C_{c,\infty}(q_2 - V_2q_1/V_1)}{C_{c,\infty}q_2 + q_1}\right\}.$$

These relationships show that for not very small values of $\underline{r}$ ($r > 10^{-5}$ cm) and low concentrations $C_{c,\infty}$ we can consider that $C_c \simeq C_{c,\infty}$, and that the value of ($T_{c,\infty} - T_c$) can be calculated from formula (1), just as for a one-component system. This circumstance makes it possible to use Eqs. (3)-(4) for describing the thermal phenomena and Eq. (7) for describing diffusion phenomena. The temperature $T_{c,\infty}$ appearing in Eqs. (3) and (4), equal to the temperature at points on the needle surface infinitely remote from the tip, is connected with the concentration on the surface C_s by the equilibrium diagram. Thus, Eqs. (3), (4), and (7), together with the equation for the liquidus, characterizing the dependence of $T_{c,\infty}$ on C_s, fully describe the kinetics of growth of a needle having the form of a paraboloid of revolution. In these equations, four unknowns: v_m, ρ_0, C_s, and T_c, have to be determined.

The above-mentioned system of equations can be transformed somewhat. We put $(C_s - C_0)/(C_s - C_{c,\infty}) = \theta$ and write Eq. (7) in the form

$$v_m\rho_0/2D = f(\theta). \quad (10)$$

Figure 2 shows plots of the dependence of $v_m\rho_0/2D$ on θ. The value of θ varies from 0 [for $T_l - T_0 = 0$, T_l is the liquidus temperature (Fig. 1)] to 1 (for $T_l - T_0 \to \infty$). With variation of θ in these limits, $f(\theta)$ varies from 0 to ∞. For $\theta \ll 1$, the function $f(\theta)$ may be represented in the form $f(\theta) \simeq \alpha'\theta^{n'}$, where α' and n' assume different values according to the range of variations of θ (see table). For θ close to 1, $f(\theta) \simeq 1/(1-\theta)$. On the basis of Eqs. (4) and (10), we can write

$$\rho_0 = (n-1)L_1/K + (2n-1)L_2\sigma/2Df(\theta), \quad (11)$$

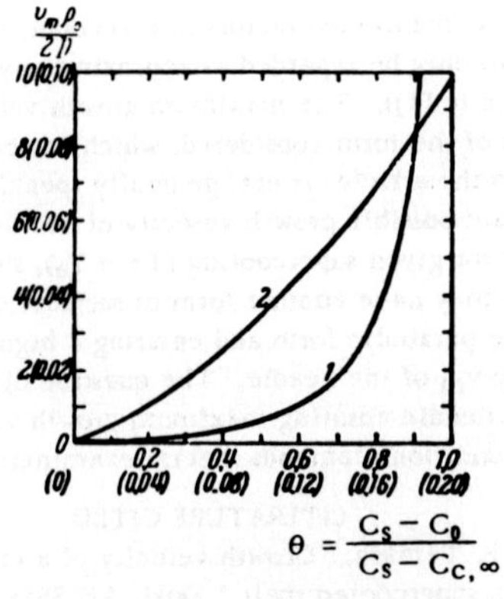

Fig. 2. Plot of the function $\theta = -(v_m\rho_0/2D)\exp(v_m\rho_0/2D) \times \mathrm{Ei}(-v_m\rho_0/2D)$. The numbers in brackets indicate the scale for curve 2.

$$v_m = 2Df(\theta)/\{[(n-1)L_1/K] + (2n-1)L_2\sigma/2Df(\theta)\}, \tag{12}$$

$$\frac{(T_{C,\infty} - T_0)c_2}{Q} = \frac{n}{2n-1} \times \left(2 + \frac{L_1}{K\rho_0}\right)\left(\frac{\gamma_1}{\gamma_2}\frac{D}{a_2}\frac{f(\theta)}{\alpha}\right)^{1/n} \tag{13}$$

In cases where the liquidus temperature varies linearly with the concentration C_0, $T_l = T_{C,0} - mC_0$ ($T_{C,0}$ is the melting point of the pure solvent), and the distribution coefficient $g = C_{C,\infty}/C_s$ does not depend on the composition, we have

$$\theta = (T_l - T_{C,\infty})/(T_l - T_{C,\infty} + mC_0)(1 - g). \tag{14}$$

By way of example, from Eqs. (11)-(14) we calculated v_m, ρ_0, $T_{C,\infty} - T_0$ and the composition of the crystal as a function of the supercooling of the melt ($T_l - T_0$) for tin with additions of lead. In the calculation, the values adopted for the physical parameters of the alloy were the same as in [1] for pure tin: Q = 14 cal/g; γ_1 = 7.3 g/cm^3; γ_2 = 6.98 g/cm^3; λ_1 = 0.140 cal per cm · sec°C; λ_2 = 0.082 cal/cm · sec°C; C_2 = 0.060 cal per g°C; σ = 36 erg/cm^2; K = 32 cm/sec°C; D = $2\cdot10^{-5}$ cm^2/sec. In addition, it was assumed that the liquidus and solidus of the Sn–Pb alloy are described by the equations T (°K) = 505 − 2.1C (wt.%) and T_s = 505 − 16.2C, so that the distribution coefficient g = 0.13.

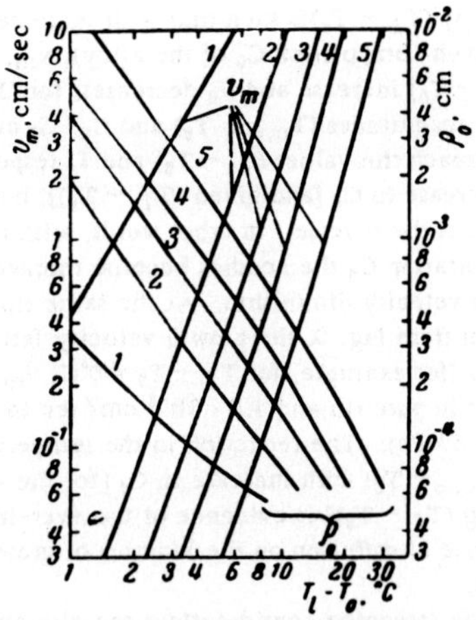

Fig. 3. Dependence of maximum growth velocity of parabolic needle (v_m) and radius of curvature of the tip of such a needle (ρ_0) on the initial supercooling $T_l - T_0$ of the binary alloy Sn–Pb. 1) 0; 2) 0.5; 3) 1.0; 4) 1.5; 5) 2.5 wt.% Pb.

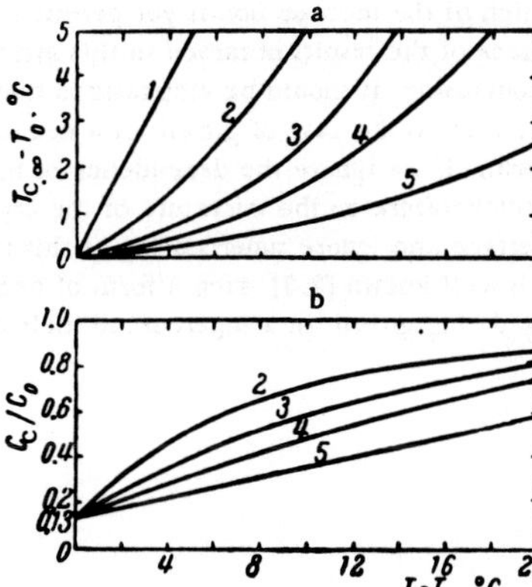

Fig. 4. Surface temperature of needle remote from the tip (a) and composition of the solid phase (b) as a function of the initial supercooling of Sn–Pb melt. 1) 0; 2) 0.5; 3) 1.0; 4) 1.5; 5) 2.5 wt.% Pb.

Figures 3 and 4 show the results of the calculations for pure tin and alloys with 0.5, 1.0, 1.5, and 2.5 wt.% Pb.

As will be readily seen, the qualitative dependence of the magnitudes of interest to us on supercooling of

Range of θ	0–0.016	0.016–0.024	0.024–0.040	0.040–0.070	0.070–0.150
α′	0.457	0.518	0.588	0.760	0.927
n′	1.21	1.24	1.27	1.35	1.43

the alloy $(T_l - T_0)$ is such that with increase in $(T_l - T_0)$ (for given composition C_0 of the alloy), v_m, C_c/C_0, and $(T_{c,\infty} - T_0)$ increase and ρ_0 decreases; for $(T_l - T_0) \to \infty$, the magnitudes $(T_{c,\infty} - T_0)$ and C_c/C_0 asymptotically approach the values $(T_s - T_0)$ and 1, respectively. For increase in C_0 [and given $(T_l - T_0)$], however, the picture is the reverse. In other words, with increase in concentration C_0 the needles become thicker and their growth velocity diminishes. At the same time, as will be seen from Fig. 3, the growth velocity falls off quite steeply (for example, for $T_l - T_0 = 6°C$, $v_m = 10$ cm per sec in pure tin and $4.5 \cdot 10^{-2}$ cm/sec in the alloy Sn + 2.5% Pb). The reduction in the temperature gradient $(T_{c,\infty} - T_0)$ with increase in C_0 [for the same supercooling $(T_l - T_0)$] is evidence of the ever-increasing influence of diffusion on the kinetics of growth of the needle.

The foregoing considerations are also applicable to the analysis of the growth kinetics of a needle of parabolic form in a supersaturated solution in the case where the normal growth may be regarded as being proportional to the first degree of supersaturation at the crystal-solution interface.

The absence of experimental data relating to the growth velocity of needle crystals on supercooling and composition of the melt do not as yet permit a quantitative check of the results obtained in this article.

In conclusion, it should be emphasized that the discussion relates to the case of growth of a needle of paraboloid form. If we ignore the dependence of the equilibrium temperature on the curvature of the crystal-melt interface and ignore supercooling at this interface, then, as is well known [2,3], such a form of needle will be steady during growth in a supercooled melt (taking the above-mentioned factors into account, the parabolic form can only be regarded as approximately steady, as was done in [1]). The maximum growth velocity v_m of needles of the form considered, which has been investigated in the article, is not, generally speaking, the maximum possible growth velocity of needle-shaped crystals for given supercooling $(T_l - T_0)$, since such crystals may have another form of surface, differing from the parabolic form and ensuring a higher growth velocity v_m of the needle. The question of the optimum form of needle ensuring maximum growth velocity in given conditions demands special examination.

LITERATURE CITED

1. D. E. Temkin, "Growth velocity of a crystal needle in a supercooled melt," Dokl. AN SSSR 132, 6, 1307-1310 (1960).
2. G. P. Ivantsov, "Temperature field around spherical, cylindrical, and needle-shaped crystals growing in a supercooled melt," Dokl. AN SSSR 58, 4, 567-569 (1947).
3. G. P. Ivantsov, "Growth of spherical and needle-shaped crystals of a binary alloy," Dokl. AN SSSR 83, 4, 573-576 (1952).
4. L. Landau and E. Lifshits, Statistical Physics [in Russian] (Gostekhizdat, Moscow, 1951), p. 284.

All abbreviations of periodicals in the above bibliography are letter-by-letter transliterations of the abbreviations as given in the original Russian journal. *Some or all of this periodical literature may well be available in English translation.* A complete list of the cover-to-cover English translations appears at the back of this issue.

Stability of a Planar Interface During Solidification of a Dilute Binary Alloy

W. W. MULLINS
Department of Metallurgical Engineering, Carnegie Institute of Technology, Pittsburgh, Pennsylvania
AND
R. F. SEKERKA
Physics Department, Harvard University, Cambridge, Massachusetts

(Received 15 July 1963; in final form 9 September 1963)

The stability of the shape of a moving planar liquid–solid interface during the unidirectional freezing of a dilute binary alloy is theoretically investigated by calculating the time dependence of the amplitude of a sinusoidal perturbation of infinitesimal amplitude introduced into the planar shape. The calculation is accomplished by using gradients of the steady-state thermal and diffusion fields satisfying the perturbed boundary conditions (capillarity included) to determine the velocity of each element of interface, a procedure justified in some detail. Instability occurs if any Fourier component of an arbitrary perturbation grows; stability occurs if all components decay. A stability criterion expressed in terms of growth parameters and system characteristics is thereby deduced and is compared with the currently used stability criterion of constitutional supercooling; some very marked differences are discussed.

INTRODUCTION

IN their original experimental study of the breakdown of a planar liquid–solid interface into cellular undulations during the unidirectional freezing of a dilute binary alloy, Rutter and Chalmers[1] proposed a criterion which predicted instability of the planar interface shape whenever growth conditions produced an adjacent layer of constitutionally supercooled liquid. The conditions under which constitutional supercooling (hereafter referred to as CS) occurs were subsequently placed on a quantitative basis by Tiller, Rutter, Jackson, and Chalmers.[2] Although the resulting quantitative CS criterion has successfully predicted the dependence of the breakdown conditions observed in a number of experiments[3] on such growth parameters as the growth rate and the temperature gradient in the liquid, the theoretical status of the CS criterion has remained somewhat uncertain, since it was originally deduced by the application of equilibrium arguments concerning supercooling to the interfacial region which comprises an open system in a steady or quasisteady state.

An approach more closely related to that of the present paper has been made by Temkin[4] who attempted to analyze the stability of a planar interface by comparing the velocity of the tip of a hemispherical boss, superimposed on the plane and projecting into the liquid, with the velocity of the interface far from the boss. The velocities were calculated from the fluxes of heat and solute obtained in turn from an approximate solution to the steady-state boundary value problem corresponding to the assumed interface shape with capillarity included in the boundary conditions. His treatment, however, has the following drawbacks: (1) In place of actually obtaining the unique solution of the boundary value problem he formulates, the author, without giving any justification, imposes a guessed form for the concentration at the interface. The approximate nature of this guess introduces an over determination which, as he points out, prevents certain boundary conditions from being everywhere satisfied; for example, the velocity near the equator of the boss is not uniquely determined, having one value when calculated from solute diffusion and a second value when calculated from heat flow (the latter actually giving an infinite value). In view of the arbitrary character of the approximate solution (never actually exhibited) and of the inconsistencies to which it leads, it is difficult to assess the reliability of the author's conclusions. (2) Even if the preceding boundary value problem were rigorously solved, the results would not afford a true criterion of stability since the latter must be based on whether or not an *arbitrary* infinitesimal perturbation of the planar shape grows with time. The hemispherical perturbation not only has a very special shape but it also gives the stability problem the specious appearance of a nucleation problem since the hemisphere, whose amplitude (radius) and wavelength or lateral extent (diameter) are necessarily proportional, must always exceed some critical size in order to grow owing to the dominance of capillarity for sufficiently small sphere radii; by contrast, we see below that instability prevails if and only if there are perturbations of arbitrarily small amplitude which grow.

The purpose of this paper is to develop a rigorous theory of the stability of the planar interface by calculating the time dependence of the amplitude of a sinusoidal perturbation of infinitesimal initial amplitude introduced into the shape of the plane; since an arbitrary infinitesimal perturbation in the plane may be analyzed into infinitesimal sinusoidal Fourier components, and since all the relevant equations are linear, the development of the perturbation is simply a super-

[1] J. W. Rutter and B. Chalmers, Can J. Phys. 31, 15 (1953).
[2] W. A. Tiller, J. W. Rutter, K. A. Jackson, and B. Chalmers, Acta Met. 1, 428 (1953).
[3] W. A. Tiller and J. W. Rutter, Can. J. Phys. 34, 729 (1956).
[4] D. E. Temkin, Dokl. Akad. Nauk. SSSR, 133, 174 (1960) [English transl.: Soviet Phys.—Doklady 5, 609 (1960)].

position of the development of its components. Therefore, the interface is unstable if any sinusoidal wave grows and is stable if none grow.

The principal physical assumptions of the present analysis are those of isotropy of bulk and surface parameters, and of local equilibrium at the interface. The critical mathematical simplification is the use of steady-state values (independent of time in the frame attached to the interface) for the thermal and diffusion fields. The justification for doing this is that the experiments are usually arranged so that the interface moves with a constant velocity; if the interface shape were also fixed, the use of steady-state values would be rigorously correct. We are, however, interested in cases in which the shape of the interface is changing due to the growth (or decay) of a perturbation in its planar shape. Clearly the steady-state field calculation gives valid results only for those perturbations whose shape changes sufficiently slowly.[5] Nevertheless, stability criteria based on slowly changing perturbations as distinguished from the accurate calculation of the behavior of every perturbation should be reliable for the following reason: when our calculations predict instability, there is always a sinusoidal perturbation of some wavelength λ_0, above which waves grow, below which waves decay, and at which a wave must have a constant amplitude (Fig. 1). There is then a range of sinusoidal perturbations, having wavelengths slightly greater than λ_0, which grow sufficiently slowly to be accompanied by steady-state fields and hence to be correctly described by the calculations[5]; therefore, instability is rigorously predicted. When, on the other hand, the calculations predict stability (for all wavelengths) it means that no wave can grow if accompanied by a steady-state diffusion field. (The thermal field is always in the steady state for all practical cases.) But it is all the more certain not to grow if the field lags behind the steady-state values for it is the lateral redistribution of solute which permits the wave to grow at all; that is, all waves decay if the solute is inhibited from moving parallel to the interface (see Sec. II). Therefore, the predictions concerning stability and instability based on the steady-state solutions should be reliable.

In the case that capillarity can be neglected (for certain ranges of the physical parameters), the results lead to a modified CS criterion [Eq. (32)] in fairly good agreement with the original one; otherwise they lead to a substantially different stability criterion. In the latter case, for example, we find a critical velocity, dependent on the liquid–solid interfacial tension [Eq. (27)] above which instability is impossible regardless of the values of the gradients or the degree of CS.

[5] The fractional change of amplitude should be small in a time equal to the relaxation time of the diffusion field (assumed larger than that of the thermal field) i.e., $|(\dot{\delta}/\delta)(\lambda^2/D)|\ll 1$, where λ is the wavelength of the sinusoidal perturbation and D is the solute diffusion coefficient in the liquid.

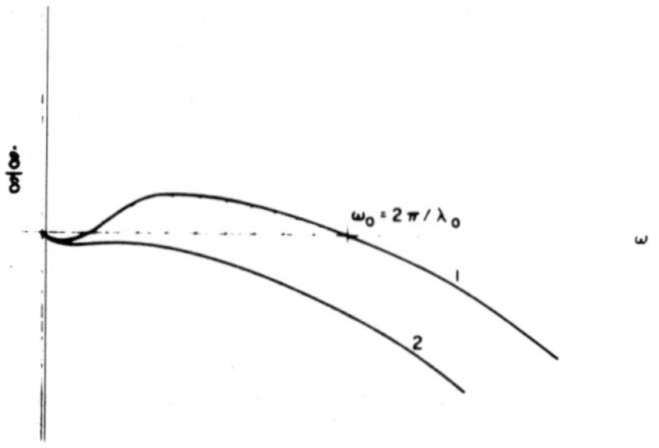

FIG. 1. $\dot{\delta}/\delta$ as a function of frequency for two cases: curve 1 unstable, curve 2 stable.

Even in the former case, the difference between the original and our modified CS should be experimentally demonstrable under the appropriate conditions [Eq. (34)]; in particular there are instances in which one can have instability without CS as well as CS without instability.

I. CALCULATION OF THE TIME DERIVATIVE $\dot{\delta}$ OF THE AMPLITUDE OF A FOURIER PERTURBATION

Let us consider a co-ordinate system attached to the planar interface moving with the constant velocity V with respect to the phases on either side[6]; let the z axis point toward the liquid and the plane $z=0$ coincide with the interface. Suppose a sinusoidal ripple, of infinitesimal amplitude, described by the equation

$$z=\phi(x,t)=\delta(t)\sin\omega x \quad (1)$$

is introduced into the planar interface between liquid and solid.[7] We wish to obtain an expression for $\dot{\delta}\equiv d\delta/dt$ in order to see whether the ripple grows or decays. Since this requires the calculation of the velocity $v(x)$ of each element of interface, as a function of its position x, in terms of the values of the local thermal and diffusion gradients we turn first to the determination of the thermal and diffusion fields which satisfy the required boundary conditions.

We seek expressions for the thermal and diffusion fields which:

(i) satisfy the appropriate steady-state equations in a frame moving at the constant velocity V, namely, for the liquid

$$\nabla^2 c+(V/D)(\partial c/\partial z)=0, \text{ (no convection)} \quad (2a)$$

$$\nabla^2 T+(V/D_{th})(\partial T/\partial z)=0, \quad (2b)$$

and for the solid

$$\nabla^2 T'+(V/D_{th}')(\partial T'/\partial z)=0, \quad (2c)$$

[6] Changes of density upon solidification are ignored in this treatment.

[7] For the rippled interface, the plane $z=0$ may be rigorously identified as the plane coinciding with the average position (in the z direction) of the interface and, therefore, traveling with the average velocity V (in the z direction) of the interface. The experimental conditions required to assure that V is indeed constant are discussed immediately after Eqs. (13) and (14).

where V = constant mean velocity of the interface with respect to either phase, c = concentration of solute in the liquid, T = temperature in the liquid, T' = temperature in the solid, D = diffusion coefficient of solute in the liquid, $D_{th}=\kappa_L/C_L$ = thermal diffusivity of the liquid, $D_{th}'=\kappa_S/C_S$ = thermal diffusivity of the solid, κ_L = conductivity of liquid, κ_S = conductivity of solid, C_L = specific heat of the liquid/unit volume, and C_S = specific heat of the solid/unit volume.

(ii) Satisfy the correct boundary conditions at infinity, i.e., c, T and T' should agree with the fields due to the unperturbed interface ($\delta=0$) several wavelengths from the interface.

(iii) Satisfy the following two boundary conditions at the interface $z=\phi$: first, according to the phase diagram and our assumption of local interface equilibrium the condition

$$T_\phi = mc_\phi + T_N \tag{3a}$$

must hold on the interface, where m is the slope (including sign) of the liquidus line on the phase diagram and T_N, the temperature (degrees Kelvin) in the absence of solute, is related to the melting temperature T_M (degrees Kelvin) of a flat interface by the capillary formula

$$T_N = T_M + T_M\Gamma K = T_M - T_M\Gamma\delta\omega^2 \sin\omega x. \tag{3b}$$

Here K is the average curvature at a point of the interface[8] (positive when concave toward the liquid) and $\Gamma=\gamma/L$ is a capillary constant in which γ is the specific liquid–solid interfacial free energy, assumed independent of composition, and L is the latent heat of the solvent per unit volume[8]; typically $\Gamma\simeq 10^{-8}$ cm (assuming $\gamma\simeq 30$ ergs/cm^2).

The second condition that must be satisfied at the interface is that the velocity $v(x)$ at each element of interface calculated from heat flow considerations must agree with the velocity calculated from diffusion considerations,[9] i.e.,

$$v(x)=\frac{1}{L}\left[K_S\left(\frac{\partial T'}{\partial z}\right)_\phi - K_L\left(\frac{\partial T}{\partial z}\right)_\phi\right]=\frac{D}{c_\phi(k-1)}\left(\frac{\partial c}{\partial z}\right)_\phi, \tag{4}$$

where k is the partition coefficient given by the ratio of the equilibrium concentration of solute on the solid side of the interface to that on the liquid side of the interface, and where the denominator $c_\phi(k-1)$ gives the difference in concentration between the solid and liquid sides of the interface.

The preceding conditions (i)–(iii) are most conveniently met in two stages. To this end we write for the temperature T_ϕ and concentration c_ϕ (liquid side) at the interface the expressions

$$T_\phi = T_0 + a\delta \sin\omega x = T_0 + a\phi, \tag{5a}$$

$$c_\phi = c_0 + b\delta \sin\omega x = c_0 + b\phi, \tag{5b}$$

where T_0 and c_0 are the values for a flat interface and the second terms are the first-order corrections corresponding to the infinitesimal ripple [the form of Eqs. (5) may be regarded as justified by the self-consistent values to be obtained for the coefficients a and b]. The two stages consist in first obtaining expressions for T, T' and c that satisfy conditions (i) and (ii) and that reduce to Eq. (5) on the interface and then secondly imposing condition (iii) comprising the two interface boundary conditions [Eqs. (3) and (4)] on these solutions thereby fixing a and b and yielding the complete solution.

The required expressions satisfying conditions (i) and (ii) and reducing to Eq. (5) on the interface $z=\phi$ (not $z=0$!) are the following: on the liquid side

$$c(x,z)-c_0=(G_cD/V)(1-e^{-(V/D)z})+\delta(b-G_c)\times\sin\omega x e^{-\omega^* z}, \tag{6}$$

$$T(x,z)-T_0=(GD_{th}/V)(1-e^{-(V/D_{th})z})+\delta(a-G)\times\sin\omega x e^{-\omega_{th} z}, \tag{7}$$

and on the solid side (primes denoting the solid)

$$T'(x,z)-T_0=(G'D_{th}'/V)(1-e^{-(V/D_{th}')z})+\delta(a-G')\times\sin\omega x e^{-\omega_{th}' z}, \tag{8}$$

where G and G' are the thermal gradients at the unperturbed flat interface ($\delta=0$) in the liquid and solid, respectively, G_c is the concentration gradient in the liquid at the unperturbed flat interface, and where

$$\omega^*=(V/2D)+[(V/2D)^2+\omega^2]^{\frac{1}{2}}, \tag{9a}$$

$$\omega_{th}=(V/2D_{th})+[(V/2D_{th})^2+\omega^2]^{\frac{1}{2}}, \tag{9b}$$

$$\omega_{th}'=(V/2D_{th}')-[(V/2D_{th}')^2+\omega^2]^{\frac{1}{2}}. \tag{9c}$$

It is easily verified by substitution that these expressions do indeed satisfy Eqs. (2a), (2b), and (2c), respectively, and that to first order[10] in δ Eq. (6) reduces to Eq. (5b), and Eqs. (7) and (8) to Eq. (5a) on the interface. Before proceeding to determine the constants a and b, we make several points concerning these solutions.

When $|z|\gg\lambda=2\pi/\omega$ the only terms in Eqs. (6)–(8) remaining are the leading ones; they describe the unperturbed fields. Whenever $\omega\gg V/2D$, $V/2D_{th}$, or $V/2D_{th}'$, respectively, Eqs. (6)–(9) show that the field in question obeys Laplace's equation for a stationary frame within a distance of several $\lambda=2\pi/\omega$ of the interface; as discussed farther on, this condition holds in all practical cases for the thermal fields.

The gradients of the thermal and diffusion fields at

[8] W. W. Mullins and R. F. Sekerka, J. Appl. Phys. 34, 323 (1963).

[9] Allowing for the influence of curvature on the partition coefficient k of solute between the two phases and on the slope m leads to results which are the same as those obtained here within the approximation of dilute solution theory.

[10] Equation (4) may be viewed as the simultaneous expression of heat balance and mass balance on a differential scale at the interface; diffusion in the solid is ignored.

the interface calculated from Eqs. (6)–(8) to the first order in δ are

$$(\partial c/\partial z)_\phi = -\omega^*(b-G_c)\delta \sin\omega x + G_c[1-(V/D)\delta \sin\omega x],$$
$$= -\omega^*\{b-G_c[1-(V/\omega^* D)]\}\delta \sin\omega x + G_c \quad (10)$$

$$(\partial T/\partial z)_\phi = -\omega_{th}\{a-G[1-(V/\omega_{th}D_{th})]\}\delta \sin\omega x + G,$$
$$\simeq -\omega(a-G)\delta \sin\omega x + G, \quad (11)$$

$$(\partial T'/\partial z)_\phi = +\omega_{th}'\{a-G'[1-(V/\omega_{th}'D_{th}')]\}\delta \sin\omega x + G'$$
$$\simeq +\omega(a-G')\delta \sin\omega x + G'. \quad (12)$$

The second form for the temperature gradients originates from the fact that for all cases of practical interest $\lambda = 2\pi/\omega \ll D_{th}/V \simeq 10^2$ cm (typical value for a metallic system); thus $V/\omega_{th}D_{th} \simeq V/\omega D_{th} \ll 1$ and the factor multiplying G in brackets is essentially unity; the same comment applies to the solid (D_{th}'). If Eqs. (10)–(12) for the gradients are substituted into the flux boundary condition Eq. (4) [using Eq. (5b) for c_ϕ in the denominator of Eq. (4)] and then an integration with respect to x over an interval of one wavelength is performed, all the sine terms drop out and we obtain

$$\frac{1}{\lambda}\int_0^\lambda v(x)dx \equiv V = \frac{1}{L}(\kappa_s G' - \kappa_L G), \quad (13)$$

and

$$\frac{1}{\lambda}\int_0^\lambda v(x)dx \equiv V = \frac{D}{c_0(k-1)}G_c = \frac{Dk}{c_\infty(k-1)}G_c, \quad (14)$$

where the last step in Eq. (14) is required by our assumed steady-state condition which demands c_∞ (liquid) = $\langle$conc.$\rangle_{av}$ (solid) = kc_0 (liquid). Equation (13), the average heat balance condition, together with Eqs. (7) and (8) (for $z \gg \lambda$) determine the temperatures that must be maintained by a pair of furnaces traveling at the constant velocity V in order that the average plane $z=0$ of the interface may assume a fixed relative position between the furnaces and see a thermal gradient G in the liquid. Alternatively, by changing to the co-ordinate system $z' = z + Vt$, one can obtain from the same equations the temperature as a function of time that must be produced by two fixed furnaces to temporarily achieve the same result; this corresponds to the thermal value technique described by Tiller and Rutter.[3] Equation (14) originally derived by Tiller[2] *et al.* for a flat interface ($\delta=0$), gives G_c in terms of directly measurable quantities.

Proceeding now to the second stage of the determination of the steady-state fields we substitute Eqs. (6)–(8) into Eqs. (3) and (4) [with the aid of Eqs. (10)–(12)] in order to determine a and b. Equating coefficients of like Fourier components, we obtain to first order in δ, after straightforward but tedious algebra, the expressions

$$b = \frac{2G_c T_M \Gamma \omega^3 + \omega G_c(\mathcal{G}+\mathcal{G}') + G_c[\omega^* - (V/D)](\mathcal{G}'-\mathcal{G})}{\omega^*(\mathcal{G}'-\mathcal{G}) + 2\omega m G_c - (\bar{\kappa} p/DL)(\mathcal{G}'-\mathcal{G})^2},$$
$$= \frac{2G_c T_M \Gamma \omega^3 + \omega G_c(\mathcal{G}'+\mathcal{G}) + G_c[\omega^* - (V/D)](\mathcal{G}'-\mathcal{G})}{2\omega m G_c + (\mathcal{G}'-\mathcal{G})[\omega^* - (V/D)p]}, \quad (15)$$

and

$$a = mb - T_M \Gamma \omega^2, \quad (16)$$

where we have introduced the following new symbols: $\bar{\kappa} = \frac{1}{2}(\kappa_s + \kappa_L)$, $\mathcal{G} = (\kappa_L/\bar{\kappa})G$, $\mathcal{G}' = (\kappa_s/\bar{\kappa})G'$, and $p = 1-k$. The script $\mathcal{G}$'s are thus the thermal gradients adjusted by a suitable conductivity ratio.

To determine $\dot{\delta}$, we substitute Eqs. (7) and (8) into Eq. (4) to obtain

$$v(x) = V + \dot{\delta}\sin\omega x = (\bar{\kappa}/L)(\mathcal{G}'-\mathcal{G}) + (\bar{\kappa}/L)\omega \times \{2a - (\mathcal{G}'+\mathcal{G})\}\delta \sin\omega x. \quad (17)$$

Equating like Fourier components we have

$$V = (\bar{\kappa}/L)(\mathcal{G}'-\mathcal{G}) \quad (18)$$
$$\dot{\delta} = (2\bar{\kappa}/L)\omega[a - \tfrac{1}{2}(\mathcal{G}'+\mathcal{G})]\delta. \quad (19)$$

Equation (18) is equivalent to Eq. (13). Substituting for a in Eq. (19) by using Eqs. (15) and (16), we obtain our central result

$$\frac{\dot{\delta}}{\delta} = \frac{V\omega\{-2T_M\Gamma\omega^2[\omega^* - (V/D)p] - (\mathcal{G}'+\mathcal{G})[\omega^* - (V/D)p] + 2mG_c[\omega^* - (V/D)]\}}{(\mathcal{G}'-\mathcal{G})[\omega^* - (V/D)p] + 2\omega m G_c}. \quad (20)$$

II. ANALYSIS OF THE STABILITY OF THE PLANAR INTERFACE

Stability of the interface with respect to an undulation, within the framework of our approximations, depends on the sign of $\dot{\delta}/\delta$; a positive value for any ω means growth of some undulations and hence instability of the original flat interface whereas a negative sign for all ω means decay of all undulations and hence stability.

The discussion in the introduction gave a rigorous justification for basing the prediction of instability on the steady-state solutions. It also implied that the justification for the prediction of stability on the same basis depends on the validity of the contention that a wave which is stable when accompanied by a steady-state diffusion field is even more stable (larger $|\dot{\delta}|$) if the solute has insufficient time to attain the steady-state distribution. This contention may now be supported by the preceding results. Equation (19) shows that steady-state instability can occur only if a exceeds the quantity $\frac{1}{2}(\mathcal{G}+\mathcal{G}')$ (assumed positive) and, therefore, according to Eq. (16) only if b and m have the same sign. Inspection of Eq. (5b) then shows that the concomitant alteration of concentration c_ϕ at the growing perturbation is just the opposite of that which would occur if a finite sine wave were suddenly introduced into the interface without permitting appreciable lateral diffusion of solute to occur. For example, if m were negative corresponding to $k<1$ [Eq. (28)], a growing perturbation would have a negative b and hence from Eq. (5b), a reduced concentration at the maxima and an increased concentration at the minima of the sine wave compared with values obtaining at the unperturbed interface. But these changes are the opposite of the initial changes that would occur for a finite wave suddenly introduced since in that case the rejection of solute by the freezing maxima and the liberation of solvent by the melting minima would cause the concentration to increase at the maxima and decrease at the minima; these changes taken alone would cause the temperature of the minima to exceed those of the maxima [Eq. (3a)] thereby giving rise to a flow of heat from minima to maxima favoring the disappearance of the wave. A similar argument applies to the case $m>0$. Therefore, we confirm the contention that if a wave cannot grow when accompanied by a steady-state diffusion field it is certainly not able to grow if the field lags behind by some transient component.

Proceeding with the analysis of Eq. (20) we note that the sign $\dot{\delta}/\delta$ depends only on the sign of the numerator since both terms in the denominator are always positive. This is true for the first term since $\mathcal{G}'>\mathcal{G}$ from Eq. (18), and since we have $\omega^*>V/D>(V/D)p$ from the definition of ω^* [Eq. (9a)] and from the fact that $p=1-k\leq 1$. The second term of the denominator is also positive since m and G_c always have the same sign [Eqs. (14) and (28)]. We, therefore, may expect instability or stability depending on whether or not the numerator ever becomes positive.

The numerator consists of three terms: the first term arises from capillarity (it vanishes if $\gamma=0$), is always negative and, therefore, favors decay of any harmonic; the second term arises from thermal gradients, is negative on our present assumption that $\mathcal{G}'$, $\mathcal{G}\geq 0$ and thus also favors decay[11]; the third term, representing the effect of solute on the equilibrium melting temperature, is always positive by the same arguments applied to the denominator and, therefore, always favors growth. Instability occurs if there is any frequency for which the magnitude of the third term exceeds that of the sum of the first two terms; otherwise stability prevails.

The frequency dependence of the terms comes about in essentially two ways: first there is an increasing dominance of the capillary effect with decreasing wavelength as evidenced by the factor ω^2 in the capillary term of the numerator; this causes stability to always prevail for sufficiently short wavelengths. The second basic frequency dependence which causes stability to prevail for sufficiently long wavelengths arises formally from the fact that for small ω the bracket (ω^*-V/D) multiplying the third term becomes approximately $(D/V)\omega^2$ [Eq. (9a)] and, therefore, small compared with the bracket $[\omega^*-(V/D)p]$ multiplying the first two terms which becomes approximately $(D/V)\omega^2+k(V/D)$. Some physical insight into this long wavelength case is provided by the observation that for sufficiently small ω, Eq. (15) combined with (18) shows that b goes to zero linearly in ω. It follows from Eq. (16) that a likewise goes to zero linearly in ω so that according to Eqs. (5) the interface tends toward a condition of constant temperature and concentration. Roughly speaking, this means that the solute redistribution becomes insignificant when the wavelength of the perturbation is sufficiently large. Equation (19) then shows, with $a\simeq 0$, that the pure thermal effect prevails and causes the perturbation to decay (we assume the wavelength is still short compared with the very large characteristic thermal distance). From the foregoing we conclude that if instability is present it must occur for a range of intermediate wavelengths. Figure 1 shows a schematic plot of $\dot{\delta}/\delta$ as a function of frequency for two cases; the curve possessing a maximum and becoming positive for a range of frequencies corresponds to an unstable interface; the other curve which is always nonpositive corresponds to a stable interface.

To study the sign of the numerator of Eq. (20) as a function of frequency, it is convenient to split out the frequency-independent terms that correspond to a modified CS criterion. For this purpose we factor out of the numerator bracket of Eq. (20) the positive quantity $2[\omega^*-p(V/D)]$ and write the remaining part upon whose sign stability depends as

$$\begin{aligned} S(\omega) &= -T_M\Gamma\omega^2-\tfrac{1}{2}(\mathcal{G}'+\mathcal{G}) \\ &\quad +mG_c\{[\omega^*-(V/D)]/[\omega^*-(V/D)p]\} \\ &= -T_M\Gamma\omega^2+mG_cg(\omega)-\tfrac{1}{2}(\mathcal{G}'+\mathcal{G})+mG_c \qquad (21) \\ &= f(\omega)-\tfrac{1}{2}(\mathcal{G}'+\mathcal{G})+mG_c, \end{aligned}$$

where

$$\begin{aligned} g(\omega) &= \frac{\omega^*-V/D}{\omega^*-(V/D)p}-1=\frac{-2k}{[1+(2\omega D/V)^2]^{\frac{1}{2}}-1+2k} \qquad (22) \\ &= -1+(D^2/V^2k)\omega^2+\cdots, \end{aligned}$$

and where

$$\begin{aligned} f(\omega) &= -T_M\Gamma\omega^2+mG_cg(\omega), \\ &= -mG_c+[(D^2mG_c/V^2k)-T_M\Gamma]\omega^2+\cdots. \qquad (23) \end{aligned}$$

The characteristics of $f(\omega)$ [and $g(\omega)$] that are important for our purposes are the following:

(i) $f(\omega)<0[g(\omega)<0]$,
(ii) $f(0)=-mG_c[g(0)=-1]$,
(iii) $f(\omega)$ either decreases monatonically as ω increases from zero or it has one maximum for some positive value

[11] In verifying the boundary conditions expressed by Eqs. (5), the exponentials in Eqs. (6)–(8) may be expanded and all resulting terms in powers of δ higher than the first may be discarded; e.g., $\exp[-(V/D)z]_{z=\phi}=\exp[-(V/D)\delta\sin\omega x]\sim 1-(V/D)\delta\sin\omega x$.

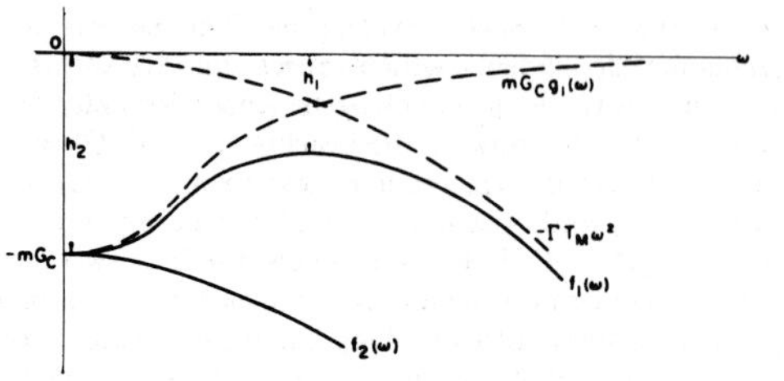

FIG. 2. Frequency-dependent part $f(\omega)$ of the stability function $S(\omega)$ for two cases; dotted curves show component terms of $f_1(\omega)$.

of ω; the first case holds when $A \equiv kT_M\Gamma V^2/mG_cD^2 \geqslant 1$ [negative or zero coefficient of ω^2 in the expansion of Eq. (23)], the second when $A<1$ (positive coefficient).

(iv) $f(\infty)=-\infty\,[g(\infty)=0]$.

Properties (ii) and (iv) follow immediately from the definitions given by Eqs. (22) and (23) as does property (i) when the inequality $p=1-k<1$ is taken into account; property (iii) is established in the Appendix. Figure 2 presents a schematic plot of the frequency-dependent term $f(\omega)$ with the separate contributions of the capillary term $-T_M\Gamma\omega^2$ and the term $mG_cg(\omega)$ shown as dotted curves.

The negativity of $f(\omega)$ [property (i)] means that it always favors stability; evidently it poses the least barrier to instability at the frequency for which it attains its largest value (value of smallest magnitude). Let us define h to be the magnitude of this maximum value, i.e.,

$$h=|\max f(\omega)|\,; \tag{24}$$

it follows immediately from properties (i) and (ii) that

$$0<h\leqslant mG_c. \tag{25}$$

The quantity h is shown on the graph of Fig. 2. With the preceding definition our fundamental stability criterion becomes

$$-\tfrac{1}{2}(\mathcal{G}'+\mathcal{G})+mG_c \begin{matrix} >h & \text{unstable} \\ <h & \text{stable.} \end{matrix} \tag{26}$$

In principle the value of h corresponding to a maximum of $f(\omega)$ can of course be determined by differentiation. The resulting equation that must be solved for ω, however, is essentially cubic.[13] A general formula for h will, therefore, not be given as it is easier in practice to simply plot $f(\omega)$ for the particular system under study, to determine h from the plot (Eq. 24) and then to apply the stability criterion given by Eq. (26). We confine the remaining discussion of this section to some qualitative remarks and to a discussion of certain special cases.

A striking new feature of the present treatment occurs for the case in which $f(\omega)$ decreases monatonically as ω increases from zero so that $|\max f|=|f(0)|=mG_c$. Since Eq. (21) then shows that $S(\omega)$ is always negative, there can be no instability under this condition. We call this case absolute stability. According to the results of the Appendix quoted above as property (iii), this absolute stability occurs when

$$A=kT_M\Gamma V^2/mG_cD^2=k^2T_M\Gamma V/[(k-1)mc_\infty D]\geqslant 1, \tag{27}$$

where Eq. (14) is used in the last step. Absolute stability may be thought of as arising when the capillary effect completely dominates the solute effect, a situation favored by the reduced scale of transport accompanying high velocities; in line with this interpretation we note that A would vanish if Γ were zero (no capillarity). Using the Van't Hoff (4) relation for dilute solutions, namely

$$k-1=(L/DT_M^2)m, \tag{28}$$

where m must be expressed in degrees per mole fraction in this formula, we obtain an alternate formula for A and another version of condition (27), namely,

$$A\simeq[k/(k-1)]^2\cdot(L/RT_M)\cdot\Gamma\cdot(V/D)\cdot(1/c_\infty)\geqslant 1, \tag{29}$$

where the approximation sign reflects the approximate character of the Van't Hoff relation and where c_∞ must be expressed in mole fractions in this particular formula. If we take as values $RT_M/L\simeq 1$, $\Gamma\simeq 10^{-8}$ cm, and $D/V\simeq 5\times 10^{-4}$ cm, then we must have $[k/(k-1)]^2\cdot(1/c_\infty)\gtrsim 5\times 10^4$ for absolute stability; this condition should be attainable in practice (values of $c_\infty\leqslant 10^{-4}$ are common and k need not be small).[14]

If capillarity is left out of the treatment, γ and Γ are zero so that $f(\omega)=mG_cg(\omega)$; since $g(\infty)=0$, [property (iv)], this means that $h=\max|f(\omega)|=mG_c\max|g(\omega)|=0$ and that stability depends only on the sign of the frequency-independent terms $-\tfrac{1}{2}(\mathcal{G}'+\mathcal{G})+mG_c$ according to Eq. (25). Although the inclusion of capillarity requires in principle that some finite h always appear in the condition determining stability [Eq. (26)], it is sufficient in practice to take $h=0$ if it is small compared with the difference between the two terms $\tfrac{1}{2}(\mathcal{G}+\mathcal{G}')$ and mG_c; it is probably often safe to neglect h even if it is small compared with either term as the terms often differ by an appreciable percentage in a cell growht experiment. To form a rough estimate of the conditions under which the latter relation holds (e.g., $h<mG_c$), we require that the capillary term in $f(\omega)$ be small compared with mG_c at a frequency ω for which $g(\omega)$ is small in magnitude compared with 1; in other words, referring to Fig. 2, we are seeking the condition under which the dotted curve $mG_cg(\omega)$ has risen nearly to

[12] If the liquid is supercooled, $G<0$ and $\mathcal{G}+\mathcal{G}'$ may be negative leading to a thermal gradient instability. This case has been previously discussed by Mullins and Sekerka.[8]

[13] It is cubic in the variable $\{1+[2V\omega/D]^2\}^{\frac{1}{2}}$.

[14] The condition that the old CS criterion predict instability in conflict with our prediction of absolute stability is that $G<mG_c$ and $A>1$ simultaneously hold; from Eq. (27) this is equivalent to the condition $G<mG_c<k(V/D)^2T_M\Gamma\simeq 20°$K/cm assuming the same values as above and $T_M\sim 400°$C.

zero before the capillary curve $T_M \Gamma \omega^2$ has had a chance to fall by an appreciable fraction of mG_c; this will assure that the maximum h will be small compared with mG_c.

The value ω^+ of ω required to cause $g(\omega)$ to equal a small fraction α is found by equating the denominator of $g(\omega)$ [Eq. (22)] to $\alpha^{-1}(2k)$ and solving for ω; neglecting unity in comparison with α^{-1}, the result is

$$\omega^+ = \frac{V}{D}[(k/\alpha)^2 + (k/\alpha)]^{\frac{1}{2}}. \qquad (30)$$

Substituting this value into the capillary term and requiring it to be less than $\alpha m G_c$, we obtain upon rearrangement and in the same approximation

$$\alpha \frac{T_M \Gamma V^2}{mG_c D^2}\left[\left(\frac{k}{\alpha}\right)^2 + \left(\frac{k}{\alpha}\right)\right] = A\left[\frac{k}{\alpha} + 1\right] \leqslant \alpha^2. \qquad (31)$$

If we take $\alpha = 0.05$, and if Eq. (31) holds (i.e., $A(20k+1) \leqslant 1/400$) then the magnitude of $f(\omega)$ cannot exceed $0.1\ mG_c$ at ω^+; therefore, the value of h cannot exceed $0.1\ mG_c$ and may be considerably less. Thus for sufficiently small values of the parameter A, as determined by Eq. (31), it is probably safe to neglect $f(\omega)$ or h in the stability criterion. [see Eq. (29) for a basic expression for A.] It would always seem best in any particular case, however, to plot $f(\omega)$, determine the size of h directly, and compare it with the difference between the frequency-independent terms to be certain whether or not it can be neglected.

When h can be neglected the stability criterion becomes

$$-\tfrac{1}{2}(\mathcal{G}' + \mathcal{G}) + mG_c < 0 \text{ stable} \qquad (32)$$
$$> 0 \text{ unstable.}$$

We refer to this condition as a modified CS criterion; it may be compared with the original form of the CS criterion,[2] namely

$$-G + mG_c < 0 \text{ stable}$$
$$> 0 \text{ unstable.} \qquad (33)$$

We see that the effect of the present analysis for the special case under consideration is to replace the liquid temperature gradient by a mean of conductivity weighted gradients in the liquid and solid. A better comparison between the two criteria is obtained by using Eq. (18) and the definitions of the $\mathcal{G}$'s to rewrite Eq. (32) as

$$-(\kappa_L/\bar{\kappa})G - (L/2\bar{\kappa})V + mG_c$$
$$= -G + mG_c + [(\kappa_s - \kappa_L)/(\kappa_s + \kappa_L)]G$$
$$-[L/(\kappa_s + \kappa_L)]V < 0 \text{ stable}$$
$$> 0 \text{ unstable.} \qquad (34)$$

The term $[-L/(\kappa_L + \kappa_s)]V$ makes the interface more stable than the original CS criterion would predict; the term $[(\kappa_s - \kappa_L)/(\kappa_s + \kappa_L)]G$ makes it more stable if $\kappa_L > \kappa_s$ and less stable if $\kappa_s > \kappa_L$ (the usual case). Thus, assuming the present approximation applicable, it is possible to have instability without CS and CS without instability. The difference between the original CS criterion and our modified CS criterion, applicable when h can be neglected, becomes evident when either of the last two terms becomes comparable with say the first term, that is when either $|[(\kappa_s - \kappa_L)/(\kappa_s + \kappa_L)]G| \simeq |G|$ or $|[L/(\kappa_s + \kappa_L)]V| \simeq |G|$. The first case should occur often as usually $\kappa_s \sim 2\kappa_L$ (for metals). The second case should occur for fairly high velocities as equivalence of the terms occurs when $[L/(\kappa_s + \kappa_L)]V \simeq 100$ V $\simeq 10°$C/cm or $V \simeq 10^{-1}$ cm/sec.

The modified CS criterion resembles the original one[4] in giving a straight line when the c_∞ corresponding to breakdown is plotted as a function of G/V; thus substituting for G_c from Eq. (14) into Eq. (34), the equation for the breakdown line becomes

$$c_\infty = [kD\kappa_L/(k-1)m\bar{\kappa}](G/V) + (kDL/2(k-1)m\bar{\kappa}), \qquad (35)$$

and differs from the corresponding original CS equation in the value of the slope $[kD\kappa_L/m(k-1)\bar{\kappa}]$ and in the possession of a finite intercept $[kDL/2(k-1)m\bar{\kappa}]$ (small on the scale of a typical plot).

We reiterate that Eqs. (32)–(35) only apply when h can be neglected and that in general Eq. (26) must be used.

Finally, any physically real interface must, in general, be described by a function of two variables rather than one variable, namely, $z = \phi(x,y)$. The Fourier components of an arbitrary infinitesimal perturbation in such a surface are of the form $\delta(t) \sin\omega_x x \sin\omega_y y$. If the preceding analysis is repeated for a perturbation of this form, it is easily seen that all of the formulae we have obtained remain valid under the substitutions

$$\partial^2/\partial x^2 \rightarrow (\partial^2/\partial x^2) + (\partial^2/\partial y^2),$$
$$\omega \rightarrow (\omega_x^2 + \omega_y^2)^{\frac{1}{2}}, \qquad (36)$$
$$\lambda^{-1} \rightarrow (\lambda_x^{-2} + \lambda_y^{-2})^{\frac{1}{2}}.$$

The stability criterion and all results stemming therefrom remain the same.

III. DISCUSSION OF THE CELL SIZE

It is possible to plot $\dot{\delta}/\delta$ as a function of frequency for any particular experimental case from Eq. (20) thereby obtaining graphs similar to those appearing in Fig. 1. (Note that $\dot{\delta}/\delta$ is a considerably more complicated function of ω than is the bracket in the numerator of $\dot{\delta}/\delta$ which we have studied to determine the stability criterion.) If a plot of this type is made for typical values of the growth parameters in a cell growth experiment, it is found that the wavelength range within which $\dot{\delta}/\delta$ is positive and in particular the wavelength corresponding to the maximum of $\dot{\delta}/\delta$ is the same order of magnitude as a typical cell size, namely, $\simeq 50\ \mu$. One is tempted to press for detailed agreement between the wavelength corresponding to a maximum $\dot{\delta}/\delta$ in an unstable case and the cell size of the structure into which the unstable planar interface develops on the basis of the following rationalization: the fastest growing Fourier components of an arbitrary perturbation in the planar shape should eventually dominate causing a rippled or cellular structure with a wavelength $\sim 2\pi/\omega_M$. This procedure carried out on the basis of Eq. (20), however, fails to give detailed agreement between the theoretically predicted and the experimentally observed relationship of the cell size and growth parameters. There are probably two main reasons for this failure: first, we have used steady-state diffusion fields in the preceding calculation. As explained in the introduction this should be a good approximation for frequencies near ω_0 where the interface shape changes very slowly. For frequencies near ω_M, however, the steady-state solutions could be seriously in error due to the possibility of a rapidly changing interface shape; that is, the true value of ω_M based on the rigorous time-dependent solutions might differ considerably from the value calculated from steady-state solutions.

The second reason is that the structure which finally develops in cell growth experiments does not have a small amplitude.[1,3] Since all of our calculations are based on the assumption of small amplitude perturbations (first order in δ), a perfectly adequate approximation for the investigation of stability, they cannot in general be expected to give reliable predictions concerning the final cell size.

The preceding two difficulties should not occur in the special case of the small amplitude perturbation developing during the initial phase of the breakdown of a planar interface into corrugations under conditions of weak instability in which the value of $\dot{\delta}/\delta$ at $\omega=\omega_M$ is sufficiently small.[1] The scale or wavelength of the small amplitude corrugations might then be expected to correspond to the predicted value of $\lambda_M=2\pi/\omega_M$ determined from a plot of Eq. (20).

ACKNOWLEDGMENT

Appreciation is expressed to Dr. W. A. Tiller for a critical reading of the manuscript.

APPENDIX. THE CRITICAL POINT OF $f(\omega)$

We first prove that the function

$$f(\omega)=-T_M\Gamma\omega^2+mG_c\frac{-2k}{[1+(2\omega D/V)^2]^{\frac{1}{2}}-1+2k}$$

$$=-mG_c+[(D^2mG_c/V^2k)-T_M\Gamma]\omega^2+\cdots \qquad \text{(A1)}$$

has at the most one positive critical point (value of ω for which the derivative vanishes). Calculating $df/d\omega$ and equating it to zero one readily obtains

$$\frac{T_M\Gamma V^2}{4kmG_cD^2}\left[1+\left(\frac{2\omega D}{V}\right)^2\right]^{\frac{1}{2}}$$

$$=\left\{\left[1+\left(\frac{2\omega D}{V}\right)^2\right]^{\frac{1}{2}}+(2k-1)\right\}^{-2}. \qquad \text{(A2)}$$

Introducing the substitutions

$$A=kT_M\Gamma V^2/mG_cD^2>0 \qquad \text{(A3)}$$

and

$$u=[1+(2\omega D/V)^2]^{\frac{1}{2}}+2k-1 \qquad \text{(A4)}$$

we may rewrite Eq. (A2) as

$$(A/4k^2)u-A[(2k-1)/4k^2]=1/u^2. \qquad \text{(A5)}$$

Since ω must be real, Eq. (A4) gives the inequality

$$u-2k+1=[1+(2\omega D/V)^2]^{\frac{1}{2}}>1,$$

or

$$u>2k>0. \qquad \text{(A6)}$$

Therefore, only positive roots u of Eq. (A5) can be accepted. But there is always just one positive root of Eq. (A5) as can be seen immediately by considering the equation graphically as the intersection of the straight line of positive slope $A/4k^2$ with the hyperbola u^{-2}. Therefore, there can be at most one critical point for a positive value of ω. [Not all positive roots of Eq. (A5) give real values of ω; to do so they must exceed $2k$ according to Eq. (A6).] A straightforward calculation shows $d^2f/d\omega^2<0$ at the critical point thereby proving it to be a maximum.

Since $f(\infty)=-\infty$, there must be a maximum if $f(\omega)$ increases with ω for small ω; conversely if $f(\omega)$ decreases with ω for small ω there can be no maximum as there would first have to be a minimum contradicting the proof that there is only one critical point for $\omega>0$. Therefore, from the expanded form of Eq. (A1), we deduce that there is a maximum for $\omega>0$ if the coefficient of ω^2 is positive, i.e., if

$$A=kT_M\Gamma V^2/mG_cD^2<1, \qquad \text{(A7)}$$

whereas there is no maximum for $\omega>0$ and $f(\omega)$ is a monotone decreasing function of ω if the coefficient of ω^2 is nonpositive, i.e., if

$$A\geqslant 1. \qquad \text{(A8)}$$

Note added in proof. In another paper to appear shortly, the quantity h [Eq. (24)] is explicitly evaluated in terms of dimensionless parameters and a stability function closely related to h is tabulated numerically. In terms of this stability function, the complete stability criterion [Eq. (26)] is studied in detail.

Journal of Crystal Growth **27** (1974) 118–125 © *North-Holland Publishsing Co.*

DEFECTS IN EPITAXIAL MULTILAYERS*

I. MISFIT DISLOCATIONS

J. W. MATTHEWS and A. E. BLAKESLEE

IBM Thomas J. Watson Research Center, Yorktown Heights, New York 10598, U.S.A.

Received 6 March 1974; revised manuscript received 10 July 1974

Multilayers composed of many thin films of GaAs and $GaAs_{0.5}P_{0.5}$ were grown epitaxially on GaAs surfaces inclined at a few degrees to (001). Examination of the multilayers by transmission and scanning electron microscopy has revealed that the interfaces between layers were made up of large coherent areas separated by long straight misfit dislocations. The Burgers vectors of the dislocations were inclined at 45° to (001) and were of type $\frac{1}{2}a\langle 110\rangle$. Dislocations in adjacent interfaces were usually not independent of one another. They often lay on the same slip plane and when this was so they were clearly products of the same source. The layer thickness at which misfit dislocations were formed was in satisfactory agreement with the predicted thickness. However, the fraction of the total misfit accommodated by dislocations (once the critical thickness for dislocation generation was passed) was much smaller than predicted. This large discrepancy seems to arise from difficulties associated with the creation of misfit dislocations. Although there are many processes which can impede dislocation generation, the most important one in $GaAs/GaAs_{0.5}P_{0.5}$ multilayers appears to be the impaction of dislocations on one glide plane against dislocations in another.

1. Introduction

The accommodation of misfit across the interface between an epitaxial film and its substrate has been considered by Frank and van der Merwe[1,2]). They show that a misfit smaller than about 7 percent will be accommodated by uniform elastic strain until a critical film thickness is reached. Thereafter, it is energetically favorable for misfit to be shared between dislocations and strain. Experimental tests of these predictions have been made on many bicrystals. In the majority of these tests the agreement between predictions and experiment has been satisfactory. However, in some the fraction of misfit accommodated by elastic strain has been larger than predicted[3−5]). The discrepancies between prediction and experiment in these systems are believed to result from difficulties associated with the generation of misfit dislocations[6]).

The aim of this paper is to describe a study of misfit accomodation in epitaxial multilayers. The multilayers were made by depositing a succession of gallium arsenide and gallium arsenide–phosphide films on a gallium arsenide substrate. All layers were single crystals in the orientation of their substrate. They were accurately planar and their thickness was uniform to within a few percent. They were prepared for the 'semiconducting superlattice' device proposed by Esaki and Tsu[7]).

* A summary of this work was presented at the Conference on Vapor Growth and Epitaxy, Jerusalem, May 1973.

2. Experimental details

Alternating layers of GaAs and $GaAs_{0.5}P_{0.5}$ were grown on GaAs substrates using the Ga–AsH_3–PH_3–HCl–H_2 vapor system. In this system GaCl is formed by reaction of Ga with HCl and transported by the H_2 carrier gas, with either AsH_3 or AsH_3+PH_3, into the deposition zone. Reactive deposition produces an epitaxial layer of GaAs or Ga(As,P) on the substrate surface. The details of the apparatus used to grow the alternating layers have been described elsewhere[8]). An important feature of it is the ability to inject PH_3 into the AsH_3 vapor stream so that there is little mixing of the AsH_3 and AsH_3+PH_3 pulses as they move to the deposition zone. However, some mixing is inevitable, and as a result of it, the interfaces between layers are not perfectly sharp.

The duration of the injection of PH_3 was controlled by a solenoid valve activated by an electronic timer. The relative thicknesses of the GaAs and Ga(As,P) layers could be adjusted by varying the ratio of the off to on times. However, the on and off times were equal in all specimens described here. This ensured that the thicknesses of the GaAs and Ga(As,P) layers were approximately equal. The multilayers contained either 60 or 120 layers and the layer thickness ranged from 75 to 700 Å. Layer thickness was determined from scanning electron micrographs of the multilayers viewed from the side or from the positions of satellite peaks in X-ray diffraction patterns[9]). The resolution limit of the scanning microscope was smaller than 150 Å. This resolution enables one to determine the wavelength, or repeat distance, in a multilayer made of GaAs and Ga(As,P) layers that are each about 75 Å in thickness. All layers with the exception of the thickest were grown in 1 sec. The injection time used for the thickest (700 Å) layers was 5 sec.

The GaAs substrate surfaces were chemically polished and were inclined at between 2° and 3° to (001). The rotation away from (001) was about a ⟨110⟩ axis in (001). The density of dislocations in the substrates was always less than $5 \times 10^4/\mathrm{cm}^2$ and usually less than $1 \times 10^4/\mathrm{cm}^2$. The wafer temperature during the deposition of the multilayers was 750 °C. An epitaxial GaAs layer 10 to 20 μm in thickness was grown on the substrate surface before the deposition of the alternating layers began. This layer was doped with between 10^{17} and 10^{18} sulphur atoms per cm^3. The multilayers were sometimes doped similarly.

Samples were prepared for transmission electron microscopy in the following way. Wafers were lapped on the substrate side to a total thickness of ~ 250 μm and cleaved into small squares so as to fit into the sample holder of the microscope. The multilayer side of each square was then attached to a thin glass cover slide with a methanol-insoluble grease. The slide was mounted vertically and a fine jet of a solution containing 15 drops of Br_2 in 100 ml of CH_3OH was directed against the center of the sample. This removed GaAs at approximately 12 μm/min and produced a polished surface. Etching was stopped as soon as a small hole appeared in the sample. Specimens were removed from the slide by dissolving the grease in trichlorethylene.

3. Observations

3.1. The geometry of misfit dislocations

Specimens composed of layers 75, 160, 350, 380, 440 and 700 Å in thickness were examined. Dislocations that accommodated part of the misfit between layers were found in specimens composed of 350, 380, 440, and 700 Å layers. However, they were not present in specimens composed of thinner layers. This means that the critical thickness for the generation of misfit dislocations lay somewhere between 160 and 350 Å.

Four misfit dislocations between 700 Å layers are seen in fig. 1. A feature of these and many of the other dislocations present to accommodate misfit between individual layers is that they are paired. The Bragg reflections responsible for image contrast in fig. 1. were $\bar{2}\bar{2}0$ in (a), 040 in (b), $\bar{2}20$ in (c) and 400 in (d). Two pairs of dislocations are visible in (a) and (c), the upper pair is visible in (b), and the lower one in (d). The invisibility of the lower pair of dislocations in (b) shows that the Burgers vectors of this pair lay in (010). If we assume[10]) that stable, complete dislocations in GaAs or Ga(As,P) have Burgers vectors of type $\frac{1}{2}\,a\,\langle 110\rangle$ then the Burgers vectors of the lower pair were either $\pm\,\frac{1}{2}\,a\,[101]$ or $\pm\,\frac{1}{2}\,a\,[10\bar{1}]$. The Burgers vectors of the upper pair were either $\pm\,\frac{1}{2}\,a\,[011]$ or $\pm\,\frac{1}{2}\,a\,[01\bar{1}]$. All these possible Burgers vectors are inclined at 45° to (001) and at 60° to the dislocation lines. The misfit accommodated by dislocations with this geometry is only half that accommodated by edge dislocations with Burgers vectors in (001). The dislocations in fig. 1 are thus inefficient misfit dislocations. However, they are the most efficient complete misfit dislocations that can be made by glide to the interface on {111} slip planes. The dislocations are straight because the lines of intersection of {111} slip planes and the interface are straight.

Dislocations similar to those in fig. 1 have been found in silicon doped by diffusion[11]), in GaAs–Ga(As,P) samples[12]), and in deposits of one fcc metal on another[13,14]). The fact that the dislocations in fig. 1 go out of contrast in pairs rather than singly is consistent with the hypothesis (proved below) that paired dislocations have antiparallel Burgers vectors.

The separation, S, of paired dislocations was found, in the majority of cases, to obey the following relation:

$$S = h \cot 55^\circ, \qquad (1)$$

where h is the thickness of individual GaAs or Ga(As, P) layers, and 55° is the angle between {111} slip planes and the (almost) (001) interface between layers. Paired misfit dislocations that did not obey eq. (1) had spacings that were either three or five times the spacing given by

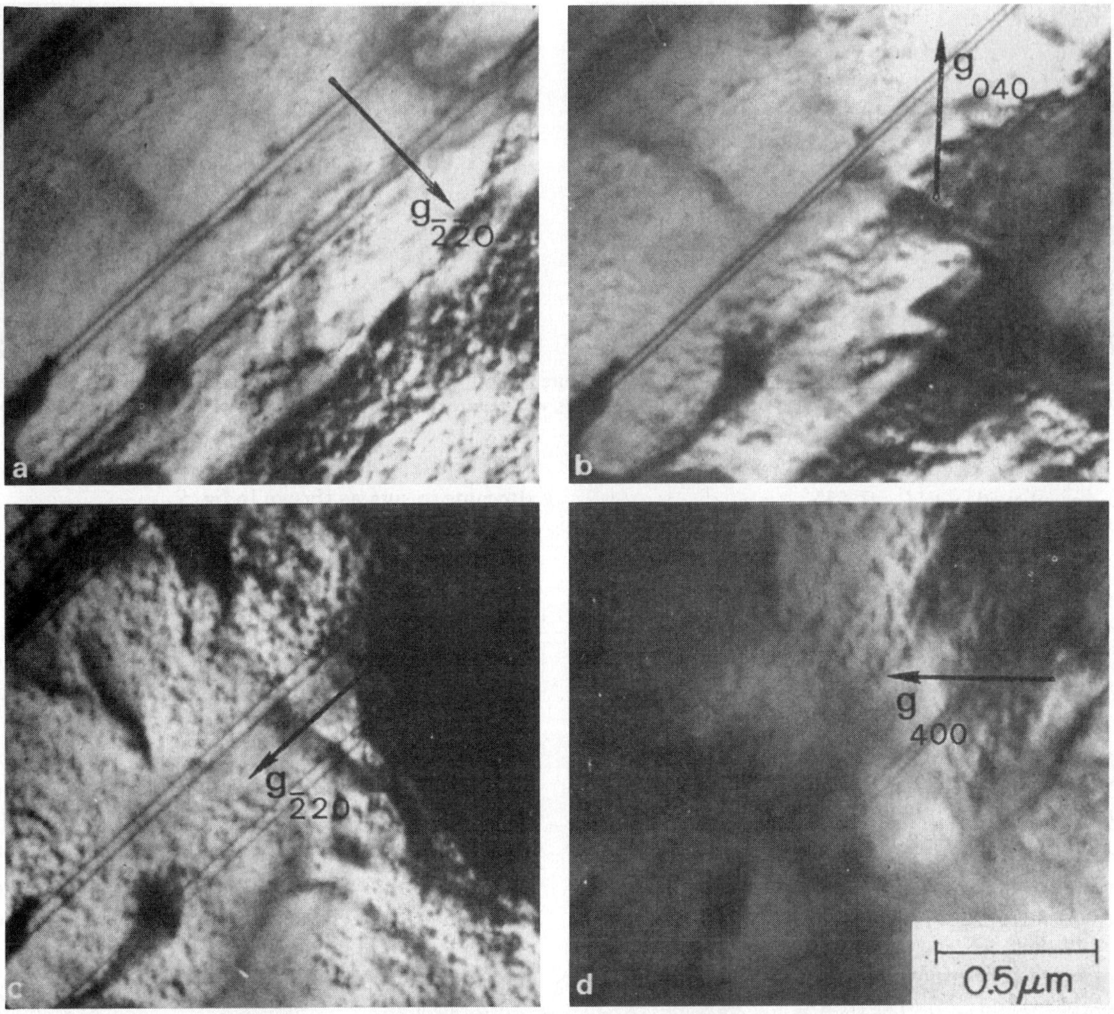

Fig. 1. Four micrographs of a specimen composed of 700 Å layers. The layers were almost perpendicular to the incident electron beam. The reflections responsible for the image contrast were $\bar{2}\bar{2}0$ in (a), 040 in (b), $\bar{2}20$ in (c) and 400 in (d).

eq. (1). These results suggest that paired dislocations lay on the same {111} plane and in interfaces that were either one, three or five layers apart.

Paired dislocations separated by three 350 Å layers are seen in the micrographs in fig. 2. An important feature revealed by this figure is that paired dislocations are joined to one another. They are portions of the same dislocation line. This means that paired dislocations have antiparallel Burgers vectors.

Although many of the misfit dislocations in samples composed of layers 350 Å or more in thickness were paired, there were many others arranged in parallel and uniformly spaced arrays. Portions of two arrays in the specimen made up of 700 Å layers are seen in fig. 3 (a, b and c). Some of the properties of the dislocation arrays are listed below.

(i) The dislocation lines were parallel to the lines of intersection of {111} slip planes and the interface. As the interface plane was close to (001) this means that the dislocation lines were approximately parallel to the [110] and [$\bar{1}$10] directions in the (001) plane.

(ii) The Burgers vectors of the dislocations were of type $\frac{1}{2}a\langle 110\rangle$ and were inclined at 45° to (001). This result follows from fig. 3 (b) if one assumes that the Burgers vectors of stable, complete dislocations in fcc crystals are of type $\frac{1}{2}a\langle 110\rangle$.

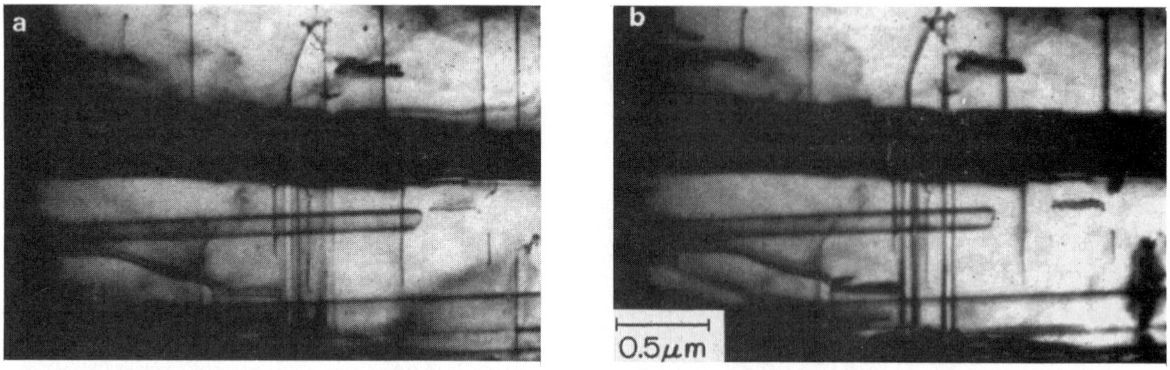

Fig. 2. Successive micrographs which show the removal of paired misfit dislocations. The dislocations were separated by three 350 Å layers and they lay on the same (111) glide plane. The layers were approximately perpendicular to the incident electron beam.

(iii) The average separation of adjacent parallel dislocations obeyed $S = h \cot 55°$.
(iv) Members of an array lay in the same or in nearby {111} planes. This result is suggested by (iii) and confirmed by fig. 3 (c) which was recorded after the sample had been tilted to bring a set of {111} planes parallel to the incident beam. It can be seen that this tilt brought the members of an array vertically above one another.
(v) Most arrays terminated against other arrays. An example of this is present in fig. 3.
(vi) The end of the visible array in fig. 3 (b) shows that the dislocations in the array were joined to one another in pairs. Examination of both ends of arrays has revealed that they consist of single dislocations that bend back and forth as illustrated in fig. 4. This means that the Burgers vectors of the parallel portions of arrays alternate in sign as shown in fig. 5.
(vii) The area occupied by individual arrays was often hundreds of square microns. The arrays in fig. 3 extended beyond the borders of the figure and, although we do not have direct evidence for this, there is little doubt that they extended to interfaces above and below those present in the thinned sample. Evidence that arrays often involved almost all the interfaces present in a multilayer is provided by micrographs like the one in fig. 6. This figure is a scanning electron image of an etched {110} cleavage surface perpendicular to the multilayer plane. The layer thickness was 440 Å. The horizontal dark and light lines are images of individual layers. The rows of pits that pass obliquely

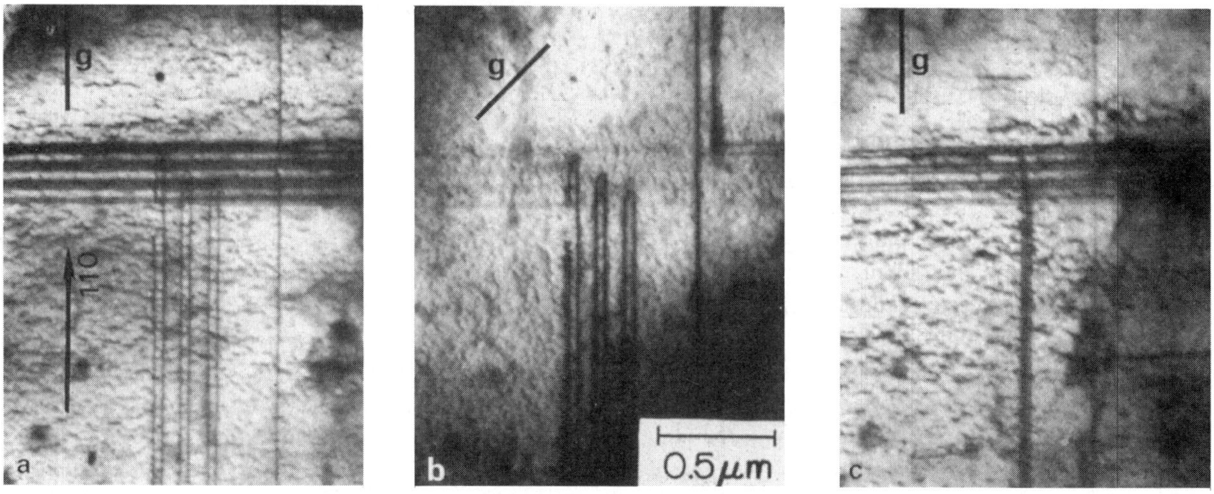

Fig. 3. Two arrays of misfit dislocations in the specimen composed of 700 Å layers. The layers were approximately perpendicular to the incident electron beam in (a) and (b). The specimen was tilted in (c) so as to view (111) planes edge on.

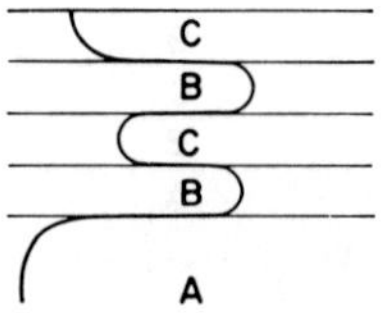

Fig. 4. An array of misfit dislocations.

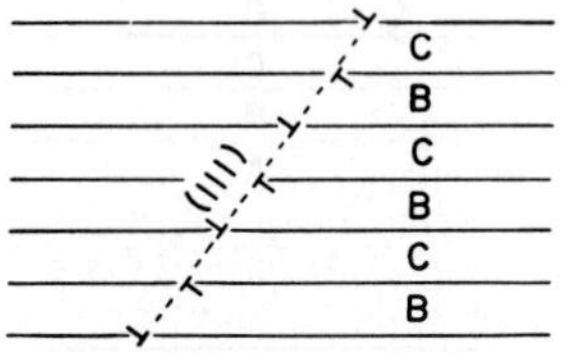

Fig. 5. A section through an array of misfit dislocations.

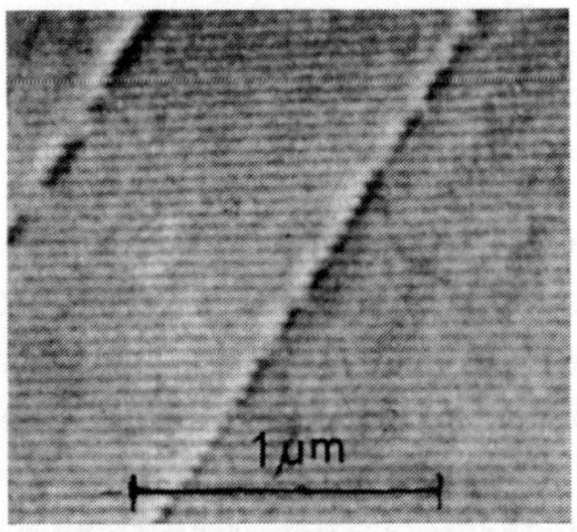

Fig. 6. Scanning electron micrograph of a multilayer seen from the side. The thickness of the layers was 440 Å. Pits mark the emergence points of dislocations in arrays on (111).

across the figure mark the emergence points of dislocations arranged in arrays on two parallel {111} planes. In addition to showing the extent of arrays this figure reveals that dislocations are sometimes absent from a few of the interfaces present.

3.2. Elimination of misfit dislocations

Creation of misfit dislocations has not been observed, but the reverse process has. Figs. 2 (a) and 2 (b) are successive electron micrographs of the sample composed of 350 Å layers. The parallel lines near the center of each micrograph are misfit dislocations that have antiparallel Burgers vectors and lines that are separated by three layers. The micrographs reveal the removal of short lengths of these dislocations by the motion of the threading dislocation that connects them.

If paired dislocations are separated by a single layer they can be destroyed by a process which is slightly different from that in fig. 2. Dislocations in adjacent interfaces can move towards one another and cancel. If

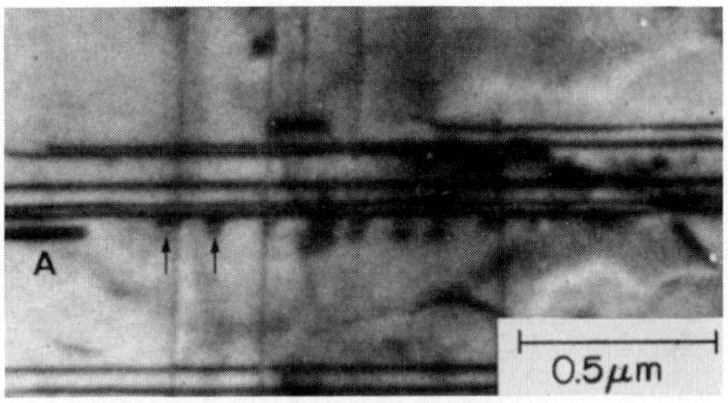

Fig. 7. Dislocation loops left after paired dislocations had annihilated one another at several points along their length. Layer thickness = 350 Å.

the dislocations lie on the same {111} plane this motion is by glide. If they lie on adjacent or nearby {111} planes their motion involves climb as well as glide. A train of dislocation loops left after cancellation had occurred at various points along the length of a pair of dislocations (A) with antiparallel Burgers vectors are present in fig. 7. Two of the loops are arrowed. The thickness of individual layers in fig. 7 was 350 Å.

The elimination of misfit dislocations from the specimen composed of 350 Å layers suggests that diffusion reduced the misfit between adjacent layers sufficiently for misfit dislocations to be unstable. (By this we mean that diffusion raised h_c from below 350 Å to above.) This is discussed further in 4.2 and 4.3.

3.3. Misfit accommodated by dislocations

The misfit accommodated by dislocations with the geometry described in 3.1 is

$$\delta_{BC} = b/2d, \tag{2}$$

where b is the strength of the dislocations, and d the average distance between dislocation lines in the same interface. Measurements of d in the specimen composed of 700 Å layers showed that $\delta_{BC} \approx 10^{-4}$. This is less than one percent of the misfit between GaAs and $GaAs_{0.5}P_{0.5}$; it is compared with the predicted value for δ_{BC} in 4.4.

4. Discussion

4.1. Dislocation formation

4.1.1. *Dislocation arrays*

One mechanism for formation of arrays is clear from fig. 4. A substrate dislocation with suitable Burgers

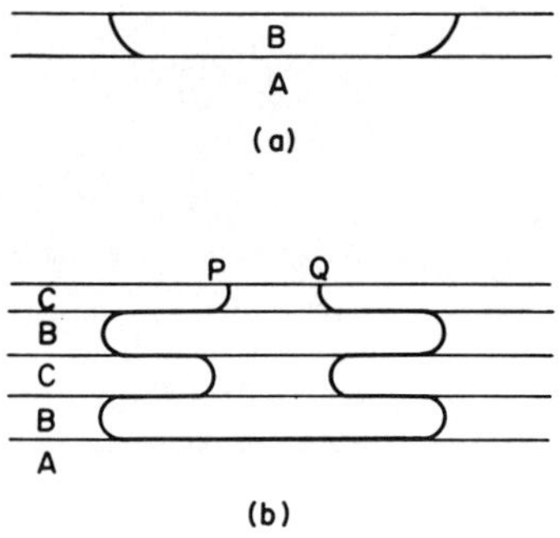

Fig. 8. Mechanism for creation of dislocation arrays.

vector is replicated in the deposit. This dislocation glides back and forth under the influence of coherency strain and generates interfacial dislocations as it does so.

Although this mechanism gives arrays with the geometry of those observed it is unable to explain the number of arrays present. The dislocations that terminate on the substrate surface can account for less than one percent of the observed arrays. From this we may conclude that many threading dislocations are created during layer growth. Comparison of the number of dislocations that terminate on the substrate surface with the number that terminate on the surface of the multilayer confirms this conclusion. The density of dislocations in the substrate surface was $< 5 \times 10^4/\text{cm}^2$. The density in the multilayer surface was $\sim 10^8/\text{cm}^2$.

A mechanism for the creation of pairs of threading dislocations, and for conversion of these threading dislocations into dislocation arrays, is illustrated in fig. 8. The misfit strain in the first B layer results in the nucleation of a dislocation half-loop on a {111} plane. This loop grows by glide to make a pair of threading dislocations and a length of misfit dislocation line in the AB interface [fig. 8(a)]. The growth of additional B and C layers is accompanied by back and forth motion of the threading dislocations to make misfit dislocations in BC and CB interfaces [fig. 8(b)]. The process is terminated if dislocations like P and Q in fig. 8(b) meet during the growth of the layer in which they lie and annihilate one another. This is an improbable event, however. This is because[15]) it is energetically favorable for δ_{AB} to exceed the dislocation content of the final BC interface when the stress-free lattice parameters of the substrate (A) and C layers are equal.

The nucleation of half-loops like the one in fig. 8(a) has been discussed elsewhere[16]). It will not begin until the thickness of the first layer is large enough for it to contain a half-loop stable under the misfit strain.

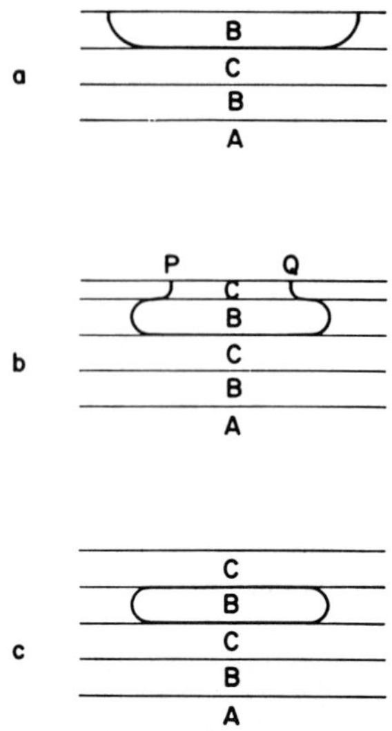

Fig. 9. Mechanism for formation of paired dislocations.

The number of threading dislocations made as in fig. 8 will only be significant if the misfit strain is large enough for dislocation nucleation to be probable at the temperature of film growth. The calculations of Frank[17]) and Hirth[18]) suggest that the 1.8% misfit between GaAs and $GaAs_{0.5}P_{0.5}$ is sufficient for this purpose.

4.1.2. *Paired dislocations*

Although paired dislocations are made when one of the loops in an array (see fig. 4) travels further than the remainder, this may not be the only mechanism for their generation. An alternative process is shown in fig. 9. A half-loop similar to that in fig. 8 (a) is created in a layer other than the first. During the growth of the next layer portions of the loop labelled P and Q move towards one another and annihilate. Annihilation is probable because, as has been shown elsewhere[15]), it is energetically favorable for the dislocation content of the final interface to exceed that of the penultimate or semifinal one.

4.2. Effects of diffusion

A realistic diffusion coefficient for GaAs–Ga(As,P) at 750 °C is believed to be 10^{-15} cm^2/sec. If we assume this value then for all specimens except the one composed of 700 Å layers the diffusion distance $[2\sqrt{(Dt)}]$ was $\sim$ 6 Å at the end of the growth of a single layer, was $\lesssim$ 70 Å after the growth of a multilayer, and was $\sim$ 130 Å by the time specimens were examined.

4.3. Critical thickness for the formation of misfit dislocations

Interface structure in multilayers can be predicted from the forces on dislocation lines[19]. Two of the important forces are F_ε, the force exerted by the misfit strain, and F_l, the tension in the dislocation line. If the elastic constants of B and C are equal and isotropic, and $h_B = h_C$, then

$$F_\varepsilon = \frac{2G(1+\nu)}{(1-\nu)} bh\varepsilon \cos\lambda . \tag{3}$$

G is the shear modulus of B and C, ν is the Poisson ratio and λ is the angle between the slip direction and that direction in the film plane which is perpendicular to the line of intersection of the slip plane and the interface. The tension in the dislocation line is approximately

$$F_l = \frac{Gb^2}{4\pi(1-\nu)}\left(1-\nu\cos^2\alpha\right)\left(\ln\frac{h}{b}+1\right), \tag{4}$$

where α is the angle between the dislocation line and its Burgers vector.

The maximum value of the strain is $\varepsilon_{max} = \frac{1}{2} f$. If $F_{\varepsilon_{max}}$, the value of F_ε at ε_{max}, is less than $2F_l$ then threading dislocations will have geometry similar to (a) in fig. 10 and the interfaces between layers will be coherent. If $F_{\varepsilon_{max}} = 2F_l$, threading dislocations will have the geometry shown by (b). If $F_{\varepsilon_{max}} > 2F_l$, dislocations will move and assume the geometry of (c). This motion reduces ε and destroys the coherence of the interfaces between layers. The layer thickness at which $F_{\varepsilon_{max}} = 2F_l$ is

$$h_C = \frac{b}{2\pi f}\,\frac{(1-\nu\cos^2\alpha)}{(1+\nu)\cos\lambda}\left(\ln\frac{h_C}{b}+1\right). \tag{5}$$

h_C for GaAs–$GaAs_{0.5}P_{0.5}$ (where $\nu = \frac{1}{3}$, $b = 4$ Å, $\cos\alpha = \frac{1}{2}$, $\cos\lambda = \frac{1}{2}$, and $f = 0.018$) is $\sim$ 250 Å. Thus, the presence of misfit dislocations in interfaces between 350, 380, 440 and 700 Å layers (see 3.1) is expected. Escape of misfit dislocations during examination of 350 Å layers (see 3.2) is also not surprising. Diffusion after layer growth (see 4.2) would be expected to increase h_C from $\sim$ 250 Å to roughly 350 Å.

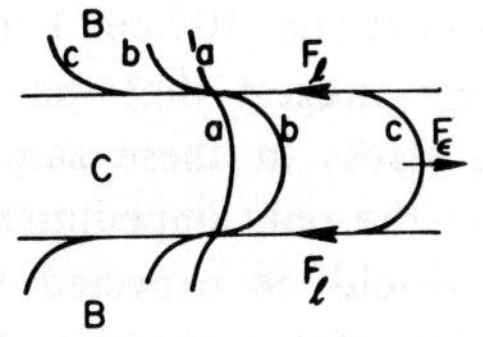

Fig. 10. Threading dislocations in coherent (a), critical (b), and incoherent (c) multilayers.

It is perhaps worth emphasizing that the calculations made above hold for *all* threading dislocations. It does not matter whether they are made by replication of dislocations present in the substrate or result from nucleation processes like the one illustrated in fig. 8.

The values of h_C predicted by eq. (5) is four times as great as the critical thickness expected in a system composed of a single epitaxial film on a substrate of infinite thickness. Half of this factor of four arises from the fact that the elastic misfit strain in a multilayer is shared between all layers. Half the layers are compressed and the other half are stretched. The remainder of the factor of four arises because the motion of a dislocation like that in fig. 10 makes two misfit dislocations. Migration of a threading dislocation in a specimen composed of a thin film on a thick substrate makes only one.

4.4. Relaxation of misfit strain

In ideal circumstances, the motion of a dislocation like (c) in fig. 10 reduces ε so as to keep $F_\varepsilon = 2F_l$. The misfit accommodated by dislocations when balance is maintained is

$$\delta_{BC} = f - \frac{b(1-\nu\cos^2\alpha)}{\pi h\,(1+\nu)\cos\lambda}\left(\ln\frac{h}{b}+1\right). \tag{6}$$

The value of δ_{BC} predicted by this equation for h = 700 Å is $\sim 10^{-2}$. This is about one hundred times the observed value (see 3.3). Discrepancies of this magnitude have been found in other systems and are believed to result from processes that impede relaxation of misfit strain[6]. Examples of these processes are the Peierls–Nabarro stress, the barrier to the nucleation of dislocations, and the interaction between dislocations.

The effect of the Peierls–Nabarro stress on the relaxation of misfit strain in semiconductors has been discussed elsewhere[16]. It is important when the substrate temperature and density of threading dislocations are low. The substrate temperature (750 °C) and the density of threading dislocations ($10^8/cm^2$) in the GaAs–Ga(As,P) multilayers suggest that the influence of the Peierls–Nabarro stress in these samples was small. Indeed, if it were the only impediment to dislocation formation, δ_{BC} would be expected to approach its optimum value [eq. (6)] in the time taken to grow a single GaAs or Ga(As,P) layer[16]).

The observation that most arrays of misfit dislocations were terminated by impaction against arrays on intersecting planes (see fig. 3) suggest that interaction between existing misfit dislocations, coupled with the barrier to the nucleation of new ones[17,18]), was largely responsible for the low value of δ_{BC}.

5. Final remarks

The multilayers described in this paper were prepared by CVD. It would be imprudent to suggest that all features of CVD multilayers would be present in specimens made by LPE or other techniques. However, there are some properties of CVD multilayers that one might expect to be quite general. The layer thickness at which the formation of misfit dislocations with the geometry described above is expected to begin is independent of preparation technique. Nucleation of dislocation half-loops is expected in all multilayers where growth temperature and misfit strain are suitably large. However, the misfit strain required for dislocation nucleation is influenced by surface steps, inclusions, and other defects that cause localized high stresses. The concentration and effectiveness of these stress raisers may depend on preparation technique. Processes that hinder the elongation of misfit dislocations are found in all systems. However, the magnitude of the effects they produce are known to vary from one epitaxial system to another[16]).

As its title implies, this paper is the first of a series of articles on defects in multilayers. Part II will be concerned with dislocation pile-ups and cracks formed in order to relieve elastic stresses present as a result of the misfit between the multilayer taken as a whole and its substrate. Part III will describe how multilayers free of misfit dislocations, threading dislocations, pile-ups, slip lines and cracks can be prepared.

Acknowledgements

We would like to thank B. K. Bischoff for his help with the growth of multilayers and with the preparation of samples for microscopy. Scanning electron micrographs were taken by C. G. Bremer, and the measurement of layer spacing by the X-ray satellite technique was performed by J. Angilello.

References

1) F. C. Frank and J. H. van der Merwe, Proc. Roy. Soc. (London) A **198** (1949) 216.
2) J. H. van der Merwe, J. Appl. Phys. **34** (1963) 117; J. H. van der Merwe, in: *Single Crystal Films* (Pergamon, New York, 1964) p. 139.
3) B. Borie, C. J. Sparks and J. V. Cathcart, Acta Met. **10** (1962) 691.
4) U. Gradmann, Ann. Physik **17** (1966) 91.
5) J. W. Matthews and E. Klokholm, Mater. Res. Bull. **7** (1972) 213.
6) N. Cabrera, Mem. Sci. Rev. Met. **62** (1965) 205.
7) L. Esaki and R. Tsu, IBM J. Res. Develop. **14** (1970) 61.
8) A. E. Blakeslee, J. Electrochem. Soc. **118** (1971) 1459.
9) A. Segmüller and A. E. Blakeslee, J. Appl. Cryst. **6** (1973) 19.
10) F. C. Frank and J. F. Nicholas, Phil. Mag. **44** (1953) 1213.
11) J. Washburn, G. Thomas and H. J. Queisser, J. Appl. Phys. **35** (1964) 1090.
12) M. S. Abrahams, J. R. Weisberg, C. J. Buiocchi and J. Blanc, J. Mater. Sci. **4** (1969) 223.
13) J. W. Matthews, Phil. Mag. **13** (1966) 1207.
14) J. W. Matthews and W. A. Jesser, Acta Met. **15** (1967) 595.
15) J. W. Matthews and A. E. Blakeslee, IBM Research Report RC 3854, May, 1972.
16) J. W. Matthews, S. Mader and T. B. Light, J. Appl. Phys. **41** (1970) 3800.
17) F. C. Frank, in: *Proc. Symp. on the Plastic Deformation of Crystalline Solids* (Carnegie Inst. of Technology, Pittsburgh, 1950) p. 89.
18) J. P. Hirth, *Relation between Structure and Strength in Metals and Alloys* (H. M. Stationery Office, London, 1963) p. 218.
19) W. A. Jesser and J. W. Matthews, Phil. Mag. **15** (1967) 1097.

Journal of Crystal Growth **24/25** (1974) 11–31 © *North-Holland Publishing Co.*

STABILITY OF FACETED SHAPES

A. A. CHERNOV

Institute of Crystallography, Academy of Sciences of the U.S.S.R., Moscow, U.S.S.R.

The present state of the stability theory of singular interfaces is reviewed. Stability, as determined by the anisotropy of the kinetic coefficient, and the absolute value of the kinetic coefficient, is discussed for solution and melt growth. The slopes of the hillocks which determine the growth rate of the faces increase with supersaturation and, therefore, a singular surface becomes less stable when the supersaturation increases. Nucleation at apexes is also of great importance for the occurrence of instability. The stability of an infinite planar interface against perturbations is considered. The criterion outlined for the growth from an impure melt contains the logarithmic derivative of the kinetic coefficient in addition to the usual parameters describing constitutional supercooling. A singular face turns out to be stable against short-range perturbations even in highly undercooled melts. The stability of polyhedra against perturbation at the apexes is also considered. Analysis of shapes of two-dimensional crystals growing on substrates is considered in connection with the dipole moments of adatoms and aggregates. The repulsion of an adatom from a two-dimensional crystal having a dipole moment of the same sign is weaker at the apexes than at the center of the facet, skeletal shapes being the result.

1. Introduction

An interface shape is stable when its arbitrary perturbation decays in time, and the interface returns to its initial form. On the other hand, when the perturbation increases, the interface is regarded as unstable. In a more global sense the shape is unstable when it cannot exist at equilibrium or during growth.

At thermodynamic equilibrium, only shapes with a minimum surface energy are stable. Other crystalline shapes are unstable, even when the crystal, on the average, neither grows nor dissolves. The creation of a macroscopically stepped interface instead of a smooth vicinal plane is an example.

During growth, the instability is caused by transport phenomena giving rise to skeletal and subsequently dendritic shapes.

In addition to spatial instability, there also exists temporal instability when the interface velocity is not constant. Temporal instability is closely related to the spatial instability but has not been studied as extensively as the latter.

Up to now the following three aspects of the spatial instability have been studied: (i) thermodynamic instability, (ii) growth instability of interfaces with isotropic interface kinetics and surface energy, (iii) growth instability of interfaces with anisotropic interface kinetics. Here we intend to discuss chiefly the third case. For completeness, however, it is useful to say a few words about the other two aspects.

1.1. Thermodynamic stability

An arbitrary crystalline surface is stable if[1])*

$$\alpha+\partial^2\alpha/\partial\varphi^2 > 0, \quad \alpha+\partial^2\alpha/\partial\vartheta^2 > 0, \tag{1}$$

where $\alpha(\varphi, \vartheta)$ is the specific surface free energy of the interface element, the crystallographic orientation of which is determined by the angles φ and ϑ. For φ and ϑ in the vicinity of a non-singular minimum of the surface energy, the second derivatives in (1) are always positive. Therefore the planes with such orientations are naturally stable, i.e. they will remain flat. In the vicinity of a very sharp (singular) surface energy minimum, the second derivatives in (1) may be negative. In that case an arbitrary plane, slightly inclined from the corresponding singular face, will decompose into facets with singular orientation. The edges and corners of equilibrium configurations are very stable[1]).

The following factors may be responsible for repulsion between elementary steps, and consequently prevent macrostep formation: attractive forces between atoms in the lattice, dipole moments of steps due to impurity adsorption, and/or a one-dimensional analog of Tamm surface state[2]), entropy repulsion between steps[3]). On the other hand, impurity adsorption and

* See also the Appendix for designations.

repulsive forces between atoms in ionic crystals may be responsible for the creation of macrosteps.

1.2. KINETIC STABILITY OF AN ISOTROPIC INTERFACE

The kinetic stability of an isotropic interface was intensively analysed during the last decade[4,5]). The only stabilizing factor for this interface is the surface energy. Weak surface energy anisotropy does not seriously affect the stability criteria[6]).

2. Kinetic coefficients and growth rate anisotropy

Let us now turn to the case of strong growth rate anisotropy, which is typical for atomically flat singular surfaces growing layer-by-layer. Suppose that the supersaturation or undercooling at the surface between the steps is lower than that necessary for sufficient surface nucleation. Then the growth rate along the z-axis normal to the singular orientation is

$$R = pv. \qquad (2)$$

Here $p = \tan \vartheta$ is the local slope of the vicinal face under consideration (fig. 1) and v is the step velocity. The kink density at the step is usually high, so that the step velocity varies linearly with supersaturation or with undercooling:

$$\rho v = \beta_{st}(c - c_e), \qquad (3)$$

or

$$v = \beta_{st}^{T}(T_0 - T), \qquad (4)$$

where c_e and c are the equilibrium and actual concentrations at the step, ρ the crystal density, and T_0 and T are the equilibrium and actual temperatures at the step. The physical meaning of the kinetic coefficients β_{st} (cm sec^{-1}) and β_{st}^{T} (cm sec^{-1} deg^{-1}) may be understood as follows.

Let the average interkink distance be λ_0, the interatomic distance a, and the frequencies of atom addition and subtraction at the kink ν_+ and ν_-, respectively. For a crystal–solution interface, the frequency ν_+ depends exponentially on the activation energy of desolvation, the frequency ν_- depends also on the heat of dissolution. For a crystal–melt interface, ν_+ and ν_- depend on the rearrangement activation energy and the latent heat. The solution concentration, c, is not constant at the step – it has minima at the kinks and maxima between them. However, if the kink density is high, these variations are negligibly small and we can suppose that the crystallizing molecules are homogeneously spread along the step, i.e. c is constant. Under this condition the probability of having an aggregate of solute in the crystallizing solution near the kink is $ca^3 \cdot a/\lambda_0$, and thus the quantity of atoms joining the crystal per unit time at the kink is

$$W_+ = \nu_+ ca^4/\lambda_0.$$

The subtraction of an atom or an aggregate from the crystal may take place if there is no crystallizing atom or complex of atoms in the solution in the vicinity of the kink. Thus, the dissolution rate is

$$W_- = \nu_-(1 - ca^3)\, a/\lambda_0 .$$

Consequently, the net flux into the crystalline phase per atomic site along the step is

$$a^2 \rho v = W_+ - W_- = \nu_+ ca^4/\lambda_0 - \nu_-(1 - ca^3)\, a/\lambda_0 . \qquad (5)$$

At equilibrium, $v = 0$, $W_+ = W_-$, and $c = c_e$, where

$$c_e = \nu_-/a^3(\nu_+ + \nu_-) \qquad (6)$$

is the equilibrium solution concentration. Making use of the identity $c = c_e + (c - c_e)$ and eq. (6), one can get instead of eq. (5):

$$\rho v = \frac{a^2}{\lambda_0}(\nu_+ + \nu_-)(c - c_e). \qquad (7)$$

From comparison of eq. (3) and eq. (7), we obtain

$$\beta_{st} = \frac{a^2}{\lambda_0}(\nu_+ + \nu_-) = \frac{\nu_-}{c_e a \lambda_0}. \qquad (8)$$

If there is one kink per atom site at the step, then $\beta_{st} = a(\nu_+ + \nu_-)$. In equilibrium, the fluxes of incorporated and leaving atoms are equal to each other and give the exchange current: $W_+ = W_-$. The first experimental data on the exchange current at steps were obtained in brilliant investigations conducted by Kaishev and Bu-

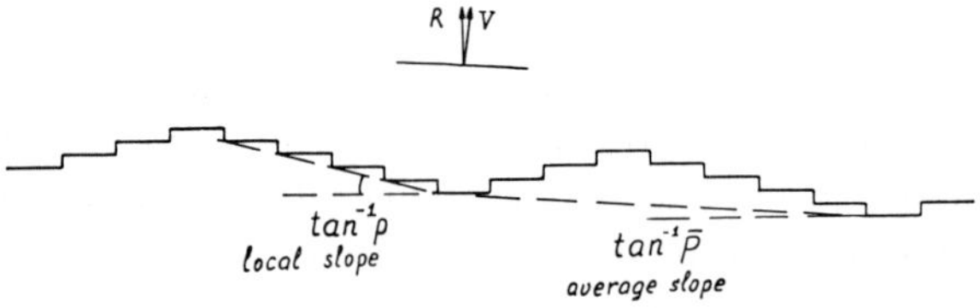

Fig. 1. Schematic cross-section of the stepped interface with two vicinal hillocks; p denotes the slope of a stepped surface and $\bar{p}$ denotes the average slope of the whole surface.

devski[7,8,10]). The experiments were performed on silver electrocrystallization from 6N $AgNO_3$ solutions. The exchange flux per atom site along a $\langle 110 \rangle$ elementary step (height $h = 2.04$ Å) turned out to be 7×10^5 addition or subtraction events per second. The specific energy of the step, found in analogous experiments[10]), appeared to be 2×10^{-6} erg cm^{-1}, i.e. the energy per crystal–solution bond $\varepsilon = 7.64 \times 10^{-14}$ erg [taking into account the step fluctuations[9]), $\varepsilon/kT = 1.74$ ($T = 318$ °K)]. Thus, according to the BCF theory,

$$a/\lambda_0 = 2[2+\exp(\varepsilon/kT)]^{-1} = 0.25,$$

For 6N $AgNO_3$ solution, $ca^3 \sim 10^{-1}$, so that from

$$W_+ = v_+ ca^4/\lambda_0 = 7\times 10^5 \text{ sec}^{-1},$$

with $a = 2\times 10^{-8}$ cm, we have $v_+ = 3\times 10^7$ sec^{-1}, $v_- = 3\times 10^6$ sec^{-1}, $\beta_{st} = 0.15$ cm se$^-$c^1. Generally, at small concentrations $ca^3 \ll 1$, and at small supersaturations $(W_+ - W_-)/W_- = (c-c_e)/c_e$, so the kinetic coefficient may be estimated quite simply:

$$a^2 \rho v = W_+ - W_- = (W_-/c_e)(c-c_e), \tag{9}$$

that is,

$$\beta_{st} = aW_-/c_e a^3 .$$

Electrocrystallization of Ag takes place primarily by exchange between the kinks and the bulk solution[10]). However, all the reasoning and formulae (8) and (9) are valid also for growth via surface diffusion, for instance, for chemical crystallization from the gas phase.

For melt growth at small undercooling $(T_0 - T)$ at the step, we have

$$W_+ - W_- = \frac{a}{\lambda_0}(v_+ - v_-) \simeq \frac{av_+}{\lambda_0}\frac{\Delta H}{kT_0^2}(T_0 - T), \tag{10}$$

where $\Delta H/kT_0$ is the entropy of fusion. Thus, we arrive at the well-known formula

$$\beta_{st}^{T} = \frac{a^2 v_+}{\lambda_0}\frac{\Delta H}{kT_0^2} \tag{11}$$

Accepting $v_+ \simeq 10^{13} \exp(-E/kT_0)$ sec^{-1} and an activation energy $E \simeq \frac{1}{3}\Delta H$, we obtain for silicon ($\Delta H = 8.3\times 10^{-13}$ erg, $T_0 = 1690$ °K, $\Delta H/kT_0 = 3.55$, $a = 2.7\times 10^{-8}$ cm): $a/\lambda_0 \simeq 0.25$, $v_+ \simeq 3.3\times 10^{12}$ sec^{-1}, and $\beta_{st}^{T} = 50$ cm sec^{-1} deg^{-1}.

Experimentally, the kinetic coefficient at a single step on a $\{111\}$ face of silicon growing from the melt was found from facet sizes for crystals with and without dislocations[11]) to be: $\beta_{st}^{T} = 60$ cm sec^{-1} deg^{-1}.

Let us now turn to the kinetic coefficient of the vicinal face as a whole. We have to bear in mind that the diffusion field over the growing surface is a result of the overlapping of the diffusion fields of the steps. If growth is determined only by volume diffusion, then the concentration over the vicinal surface containing parallel steps is[1]):

$$c(x', z') = A' \ln\left(\sin^2\frac{\pi x'}{\lambda} + \sinh^2\frac{\pi z'}{\lambda}\right)^{\frac{1}{2}} + B', \tag{12}$$

where the z'-axis is perpendicular to the vicinal (not to the singular) face, and the x'-axis lies within this plane and is normal to the steps; A' and B' are integration constants, and λ is the interstep distance. At $z' \gg \lambda$,

$$c(x', z') = c(z') = \frac{A'\pi z'}{\lambda} + B', \tag{13}$$

i.e., the concentration is the same as over a homogeneously adsorbing surface. For such a surface the kinetic coefficient β can be introduced in the following manner:

$$\rho V = \beta(c - c_e), \tag{14}$$

where V is the normal growth velocity (along the z' direction, fig. 1), and $c - c_e$ is the supersaturation at the surface. At the surface $z' = 0$:

$$D\frac{\partial c}{\partial z'} = (\rho - c)V. \tag{15}$$

If the concentration over the "efficient" surface under consideration satisfies the Laplace equation, then, using the boundary conditions (14) and (15), one obtains:

$$c(z') = \frac{(\rho - c)V}{D} z' + \frac{(\rho - c)V}{\beta} + c_e . \tag{16}$$

This distribution should be compared with (13) using A' and B' found from the following two conditions: (i) the flux far from the surface must satisfy eq. (15); (ii) the total flux to a step of height h is equal to the total flux to a cylinder of radius h/π, the specific flux to the cylinder surface being

$$D\frac{\partial c}{\partial r} = \beta_{st}(c - c_e). \tag{17}$$

Here $\partial c/\partial r$ is the derivative with respect to the cylinder radius. With A' and B' determined by these conditions, eq. (13) transforms into

$$c(z') = \frac{(\rho - c)V}{D} z' + \frac{(\rho - c)V\lambda}{D}\left(\ln\frac{\lambda}{h} + \frac{\pi D}{\beta_{st} h}\right) + c_e. \quad (18)$$

The distributions (16) and (18) are identical if

$$\beta = \beta(p) = \frac{|p|\beta_{st}}{1 - (\beta_{st}h/D)\ln|p|}, \quad (19)$$

where $|p| = h/\lambda \ll 1$ is the absolute value of the vicinal surface slope. For $\beta_{st} = 1$ to 10^{-1} cm sec^{-1}, $D = 10^{-5}$ cm^2 sec^{-1}, $h = 10^{-7}$ cm, and $-\ln|p| < 10$, one has

$$-(\beta_{st}h/D)\ln|p| \lesssim 10^{-1} \text{ to } 10^{-2}.$$

Under these conditions

$$\beta = |p|\beta_{st}, \quad (20)$$

i.e., the surface kinetic coefficient may be obtained simply by "spreading" the steps over the surface. This model is not valid for very large values of

$$-(\beta_{st}h/D)\ln|p|.$$

It is necessary to emphasize that the real field $c(x', z')$ may be approximated by (16) or (18) only if evaluated far from the surface ($z' \gg \lambda$). At the surface itself, according to eq. (13), the approximate concentration $c(0) = B' = c(\frac{1}{2}\lambda, 0)$, i.e., it is equal to the maximum concentration achieved between the steps. The average concentration along the surface is less than $c(0)$:

$$\lambda^{-1}\int_{-\frac{1}{2}\lambda_0}^{\frac{1}{2}\lambda_0} c(x', 0)\,\mathrm{d}x' = B' - A'\ln 2 < c(0),$$

However, the relative error,

$$(A'\ln 2)/(B' - c_e) \approx \beta_{st}h/D,$$

is small for the above-mentioned parameters.

The $\beta(p)$ dependence of the type given by eq. (20) corresponds to a sharp singular minimum at $p = 0$. At $p \approx 1$ there are other close-packed faces corresponding to other minima as is shown in fig. 2 as a solid line for the function

$$b(p) = \beta(p)(1 + p^2)^{\frac{1}{2}}.$$

The kinetic coefficient $b(p)$ is the coefficient of proportionality between the surface supersaturation and the growth rate along the normal z to the singular (not vicinal) orientation:

$$\rho R = b(p)(c - c_e). \quad (21)$$

The singular orientations for $\beta(p)$ are also the singular orientations for $b(p)$; however, at $p \to \infty$, we have $b(p) \to \infty$, whereas $\beta(p)$ is finite.

The concentration gradient along the normal $\hat{n}$ to the interface may be represented in the form:

$$\frac{\partial c}{\partial n} = \nabla c \cdot \hat{n} = \frac{\partial c}{\partial x}\frac{\partial x}{\partial n} + \frac{\partial c}{\partial y}\frac{\partial y}{\partial n} + \frac{\partial c}{\partial z}\frac{\partial z}{\partial n}. \quad (22)$$

At small p the first two terms in the right-hand side of eq. (22) are small, and eqs. (21) and (22) give:

$$D\frac{\partial c}{\partial z} = b(p)(1 - \Omega c)(c - c_e), \quad (23)$$

where $\Omega c = c/\rho$ is small for dilute solutions.

For each point on the surface, the local step density p/a is involved in the boundary condition (23). This density is determined by the step source (for instance, by a screw dislocation) and therefore increases with supersaturation. Therefore eq. (23) does include a nonlinear dependence of the rate on the supersaturation, i.e. eq. (23) is quite general. The boundary condition (23) may be averaged not only with respect to distances which are large compared to the interstep distances λ, it may also be averaged with respect to distances which are large compared to the size of vicinal hillocks. If the slope p_0 of these hillocks (which is equal to p in fig. 1) exceeds the average slope $\bar{p}$ of the surface (fig. 1), then, if we use (23) for the face as a whole, we can insert $p = p_0$. This means that within the region $p < p_0$ there is a weak dependence or no dependence of the kinetic coefficient on orientation. Thus, the sharp

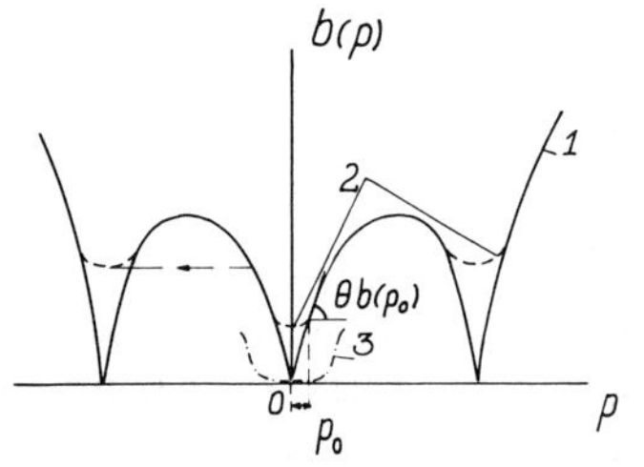

Fig. 2. Anisotropy of the kinetic coefficient. (1) Ideal interface without step generators; (2) interface with hillocks of slope p_0; (3) anisotropy in the presence of time-dependent impurity adsorption and/or quasiepitaxial adsorbed solution layer.

minima in $b(p)$ (fig. 2) must be rounded within the regions $p < p_0$ around each minimum (fig. 2, dashed line). This leads also to the conclusion that the kinetic coefficient as a function of the average slope $\bar{p}$ is not zero at $\bar{p} = 0$ for faces with defects even at small supersaturations. For supersaturations generally used in solution growth, $p_0 < 10^{-1}$.

On the other hand, when the average inclinations are large, $\bar{p} > p_0$, the local orientation $p = \bar{p}$ should be inserted into the boundary condition. We will not discuss here the possible changes in b due to step bunching and macrosteps.

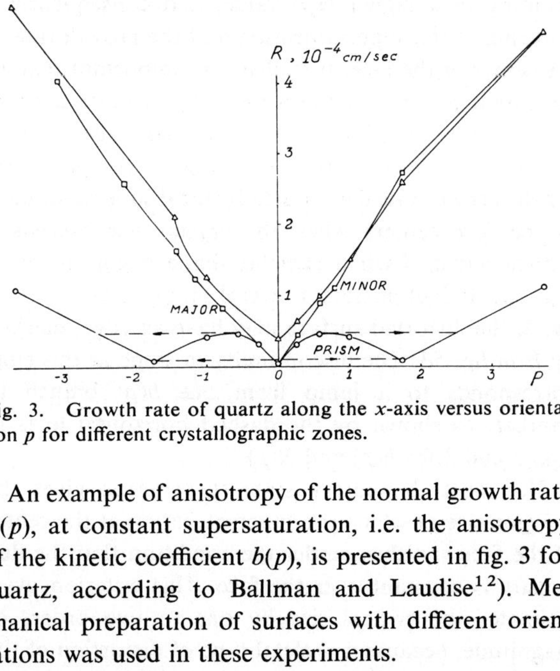

Fig. 3. Growth rate of quartz along the x-axis versus orientation p for different crystallographic zones.

An example of anisotropy of the normal growth rate $R(p)$, at constant supersaturation, i.e. the anisotropy of the kinetic coefficient $b(p)$, is presented in fig. 3 for quartz, according to Ballman and Laudise[12]). Mechanical preparation of surfaces with different orientations was used in these experiments.

The anisotropy of the kinetic coefficient and growth rate may be measured by the logarithmic derivative, θ, of $b(p)$ or $R(p)$:

$$\theta = \frac{1}{b}\frac{\partial b}{\partial p} = \frac{1}{R}\frac{\partial R}{\partial p}. \tag{24}$$

If p is so small that the step velocity does not depend on p, then $R \propto p$ and

$$\theta = 1/p. \tag{25}$$

Experimentally, the growth rate anisotropy for very small p may be reconstructed from the dependencies of the hillock slope p_0 and the normal growth rate R on supersaturation, provided that the rate R is determined by the hillock under consideration[13]). In such a fashion the effective kinetic coefficient $\mathscr{B}(p)$, defined by the equation

$$R = \mathscr{B}(p)\,(c_\infty - c_e)/c_e,$$

may be found, where c_∞ is the concentration in the *bulk* of the stirred solution. The $\mathscr{B}(p)$ dependence is presented in fig. 4 and gives $\theta = 3\times 10^2$ at $p = 10^{-2}$, $\theta = 25$ at $p = 2\times 10^{-2}$.

For quartz, according to Ballman and Laudise[12]), $\theta = 7$, $\theta = 60$, and $\theta = 22$ for small rhombohedra, for big rhombohedra, and for prisms, respectively.

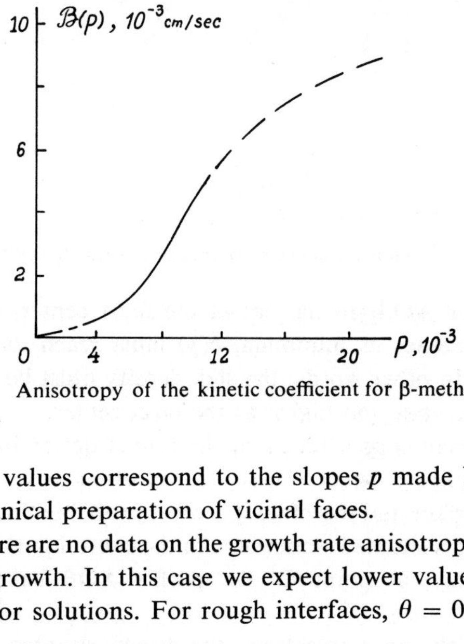

Fig. 4. Anisotropy of the kinetic coefficient for β-methylnaphthalene.

These values correspond to the slopes p made by the mechanical preparation of vicinal faces.

There are no data on the growth rate anisotropy θ for melt growth. In this case we expect lower values of θ than for solutions. For rough interfaces, $\theta = 0$.

3. When do polyhedra grow, remaining similar to themselves in shape?

Strong growth rate anisotropy permits the conservation of a polyhedral crystal shape even though the supersaturation is higher at the apexes than near the center of the faces[14]).

The concentration distribution over the growing face as determined by diffusion for a constant flux to the surface, is shown schematically in fig. 5b. Thus, the supersaturation $c - c_e$ in eq. (23) is not constant for different points on the surface. Nevertheless the face can grow remaining parallel to itself if this inhomogeneity in supersaturation is compensated by the variability of the kinetic coefficient, i.e. if the slope p satisfies the condition

$$b(p) = \frac{b(p_1)\,(c_1 - c_e)}{c - c_e}. \tag{26}$$

Here p_1 (fig. 5d) and c_1 are the slope and concentration at the point which determines the growth rate normal to the facet. According to (26), the distortion of the face AB (fig. 5) must be of the type represented by

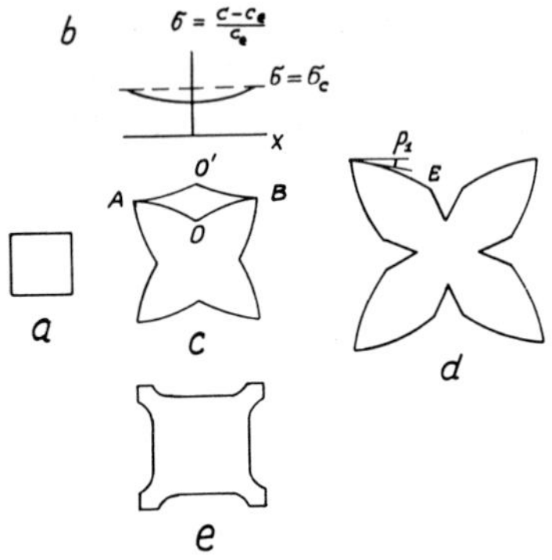

Fig. 5. Time sequence of shapes of a growing crystal.

AOB or AO′B in fig. 5c: at the facet center, where $c - c_e$ reaches its minimum, $b(p)$ must reach its maximum. In other words, the step density must be lower near the apex and higher at the facet center.

At small supersaturation, the rate is determined by the strongest defect. These defects often arise on the seed surface and therefore it is most probable that such a defect is situated somewhere in the central part of the facet, say, at point O′ the profile AOB being the result.

At high supersaturations, the defects situated in the region with the largest supersaturation will be most important, i.e. those near the apexes. It is also very probable that steps are generated at the apexes by nucleation. (It should be mentioned that the barrier to two-dimensional nucleation is $\sim 25\%$ lower at the apex than that on the flat face.) The third reason for the higher activity of the apexes is their atomic roughness, which results from the weak cooperative interaction along the edges or at the corners which may be considered as a one-dimensional ensemble or small two-dimensional ensemble.

If c_0 and p_0 are the concentration and slope near the center of the face, then the relative inhomogeneity in supersaturation over the face $(c_1 - c_0)/(c_0 - c_e)$ can be compensated by distortion:

$$p_0 - p_1 = (c_1 - c_0)/\theta(c_0 - c_e).$$

For $\theta = 10$, small distortions $p_0 - p_1 \simeq 2 \times 10^{-2}$ (i.e. of the order of one degree) may compensate $\sim 20\%$ inhomogeneity in supersaturation.

The inhomogeneity in supersaturation is proportional to $b(p)L/D$, where L is the crystal size and $b(p)$ corresponding to the slope p is determined by the strongest step source at the given supersaturation. The larger the crystal, the higher the inhomogeneity in supersaturation; this implies a larger slope of the face resulting in a higher $b(p)$ value, and consequently a lowering of the supersaturation and the growth rate at the center of the face. It is also very important that an increase in p leads to a lowering of $\theta(p)$, i.e., the average face "rigidity" diminishes with increasing distortion of the face. As a result, there is inadequate compensation for the growth rate determined by local supersaturation in the face centers when the crystal size exceeds a critical value. Then a skeletal shape begins to grow (fig. 5d). If $b(p)$ possesses several minima, as shown in fig. 2, the distorted surface may have an edge, marked by E in fig. 5d. The discontinuity in slope at this edge corresponds to a jump from one $b(p)$ branch to another, as shown by the dashed horizontal lines in figs. 2 and 3 for $b(p)$ and $R(p)$.

The most elementary stability criterion gives the polygon size at which the supersaturation at the center of the face vanishes, under the condition that the flux density is constant over the face. This criterion overestimates the critical size by one to two orders of magnitude, because a skeletal type of distortion of the polygon takes place much before growth stops at the center of the face.

A more precise criterion makes it possible to determine the crystal size for which the slope at the center of the face reaches a critical value p_c that could be detected, and beyond which the distortion rapidly increases. For solution growth[14])

$$L_c = (M\theta)\,(p_c - p_1)D/b. \tag{27}$$

For melt growth of an isolated, isothermal crystal growing from a pure supercooled melt, we have

$$L_c = M(\theta)\,(p_c - p_1)a_L/b^T T_Q. \tag{28}$$

Here D and a_L are the mass and thermal diffusivities in the liquid, T_Q is the ratio of the heat of fusion to the specific heat (the latter taken to be equal for the solid and liquid), and b^T is the kinetic coefficient for melt growth determined analogously to $b(p)$ by

$$R = b^T(p)\,\Delta T,$$

ΔT being the undercooling at the interface.

The lower the supersaturation, the lower the p values of the surface ($p_1 < p < p_c$), and the higher is $\theta(p)$. For $\theta(p) \gg 1$, $M(\theta) \simeq 2.5\,\theta$; for $\theta = 1$, $M(\theta) = 1$. Thus at $p_c - p_1 = 2\times 10^{-2}$, $\theta = 5$, $D = 10^{-5}$ cm^2 sec^{-1}, $b \simeq 10^{-3}$ to 10^{-4} cm sec^{-1}, we have $L_c \simeq 10^{-2}$ to 10^{-3} cm, which is in agreement with the experimental data.

When the supersaturation $\sigma \to 0$, then $p \to 0$, $\theta \to \infty$ and $L_c \to \infty$, i.e., the critical size increases with decreasing supersaturation. If p_1 is proportional to σ and $\theta = 1/p_1$, then $L_c \propto \sigma^{-1}$. In addition, at small supersaturations, the apexes are not the main step sources, and faces will be "broken" in the sense of fig. 5d only when the supersaturation at the centers vanishes.

For $\theta \ll 1$, the stability is determined not by the anisotropy of the growth kinetics, but by the surface energy according to the Mullins–Sekerka theory. A general approach which takes both factors into account has not yet been developed.

The decisive role of diffusion in the instability of growing polygons has been directly demonstrated by Nanev and Ivanov[15]). In their experiments, the basal plane of Zn was not flat only when the inert gas (argon) pressure and, consequently, the diffusivity in the gas phase reached a definite value. The critical size increased with decreasing gas pressure. However, the initial stage of instability in their experiments was characterized by the creation of kinematic waves, i.e. the profile had the shape of fig. 5e, but not of fig. 5c. Due to this reason, as well as to the absence of a value for the kinetic coefficient, the disagreement in absolute value of the critical size as estimated by Nanev and Ivanov[15]) from rough criteria seems not to be disappointing.

Skeletal shapes in solutions corresponding to fig. 5c have been observed by Yamamoto[23]) (fig. 6a), Papapetrou[24]) (fig. 6b), Milnikova, Bokov and Klija (fig. 6c), and many others.

The role of impurities. An important role in the stability of singular faces is also played by impurities,

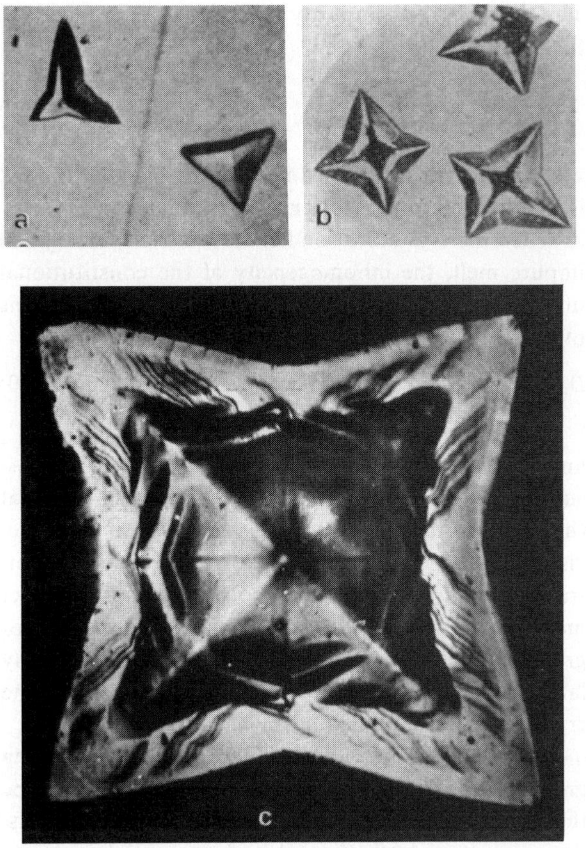

Fig. 6. Stationary skeletal shapes: (a) $Pb(NO_3)_2$[23]); (b) KCl in the presence of 1:500 Bi^{3+}[24]); (c) $Pb_3NiNb_2O_9$.

which will not be uniformly distributed over the surface. If the impurity is rejected by the growing crystal, its concentration is highest at the centers of the facets. Such a distribution leads to a distortion of the facet planes for both thermodynamic and kinetic reasons.

Thermodynamically, the higher impurity concentration at the centers of the faces may result in lower supersaturation or undercooling there. The thermodynamic effect is of special importance for melt growth[16]): the undercooling even at a singular interface is not very high in comparison with the change in melting point due to impurities. Let us estimate the condition when both factors are of comparable importance. If c_i and $m = \partial T/\partial c_i$ are the impurity concentration and the liquidus slope, respectively, then the growth rate is:

$$R = b^T(p)\,(T_0 - T - mc_i).$$

The condition for impurity balance on each facet has the form:

$$-D_i \frac{\partial c_i}{\partial z} = (1-K)c_i R, \qquad (29)$$

where D_i is the impurity diffusivity in the melt, and K is the distribution coefficient.

When the crystallization heat is removed through an impure melt, the inhomogeneity of the constitutional undercooling for small crystals ($L < b^T T_Q/a_L$) prevails over the thermal one when

$$D_i T_Q / a_L m c_{i\infty}(1-K) \ll 1. \qquad (30)$$

For bismuth, $T_Q = 420$ °C, $a_L = 8\times10^{-2}$ cm^2 sec^{-1}, and in the system Bi–Pb, $m = 3$ deg/%, $K = 0.2$. Assuming $D_i = 10^{-5}$ cm^2 sec^{-1}, we have from (30) that the concentration inhomogeneity turns out to be decisive if $c_{i\infty} > 3\times10^{-2}$ %. At lower impurity concentrations, constitutional undercooling along the facet may also be significant, but only during later stages of growth and for larger crystal sizes when a sufficiently large amount of impurities has been rejected by the crystal and accumulated near the surface.

The layers generated at the apexes and edges during growth from the melt with impurities, will also scrape the impurities toward the central parts of the facets. As a result of both normal and tangential impurity repulsion, the undercooling and growth rate will be lower at the centers of the facets, giving rise to skeletal shapes.

Making use of the approach discussed above for pure substances, we obtain a stability criterion for a cube growing from the melt with impurities:

$$L_c = \frac{M_i(\theta)\, D_i(p_c - p_1)}{(1-K)b^T m c_{i\infty}}, \qquad (31)$$

where $M_i(\theta) = 2.5\,\theta$ for $\theta \gg 1$ and $M_i(\theta) \simeq 1$ for $\theta \simeq 1$ [16]).

The criterion (31) was obtained from the supposition that the latent heat from the growing crystal is evacuated through the melt and that the impurity concentration and the temperature in the melt satisfy the Laplace equation.

The diffusion of impurities from the center of the facet takes place much slower than the evacuation of the latent heat ($D_i \ll a_L$). Therefore the layers on the same level but moving together in opposite directions and generated by the countervailing apexes and edges will in practice not join at the center of the facet. As a result, a flat-bottomed pit will appear at the center of the face (fig. 5e).

Kinetically, the adsorbed impurity lowers the kinetic coefficient and the growth rate. Again, the growth rate in the middle of each face is less than at the apexes. Kinetic effects are of special importance during solution growth.

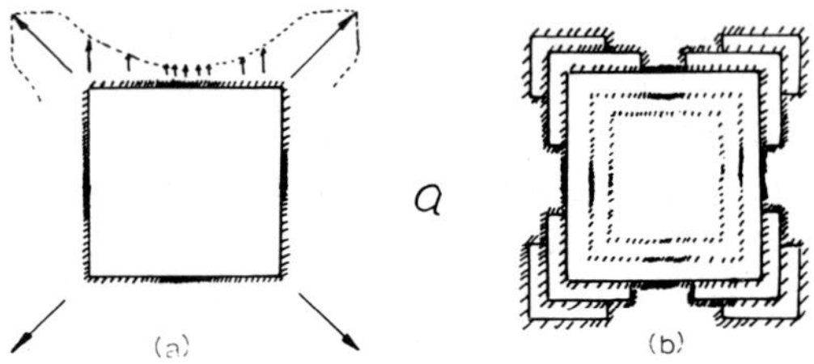

Fig. 7. Distribution of adsorbed impurities and growth rates (a) and corresponding striations and growth slopes (b).

A strongly adsorbed impurity changes the growth rate anisotropy as shown in fig. 2 by the dash-dotted line. This may cause bunching of the elementary steps and creation of macrosteps or kinematic waves. The macrosteps and kinematic waves may form also as a result of instability at the apex, when the crystalline needle "pierces" the impurity-rich layer (fig. 7). Further growth of the needle, both along its axis and perpendicular to its axis, depletes the solution near the needle and leads to impurity accumulation. This, in its turn, may stop the elongation of the needle, giving rise to a macrostep growing tangentially towards the center of the facet (fig. 7b). If the impurity concentration is relatively low, steps from countervailing apexes and edges will annihilate in the center (possibly creating inclusions). If the impurity concentration is high, the steps will not join at the centers. Again, a flat-bottomed pit in the center of the face will result (fig. 5e).

Thus, both thermodynamic and kinetic arguments can explain the well-known box-like shapes presented in fig. 8.

In chemically complex systems, the role of impurities may be played by a quasiepitaxial, partly ordered, adsorbed layer whose composition and structure are different from those of the bulk solution. This "coat of mail" (similar to the impurity "coat of mail") may be the main reason for growth rate fluctuations and the

Fig. 8. Box-like shapes: (a) Bi; (b) Mg–Al spinel.

critical supersaturation necessary for the growth, for irregular surface morphology and macrosteps instead of the regular tangential growth of very smooth surfaces possessing few vicinal hillocks. These spatial and temporal instabilities cause mosaic structures, inclusions, internal stresses, striations and other signs of "poor growth".

It is necessary to mention in concluding this section that we have considered here the conditions [in particular the critical size criteria (26), (27) and (31)] under which a polygonal shape can exist as a stationary shape, without considering arbitrary perturbations. Stability in the rigorous sense, i.e. with respect to perturbations, will be discussed in sections 4 and 5.

4. Stability of the infinite singular face

If molecular attachment kinetics are isotropic, then a planar interface is unstable in a supersaturated solution or supercooled melt. The situation is, however, quite different in the anisotropic case. This may be easily understood as follows (for simplicity we begin with solution growth).

Consider a singular interface, the growth rate of which is determined by (dislocational) shallow vicinal hillocks with slopes p_0, i.e., whose kinetic coefficient is $b(p_0)$. Let us approximate the initial, unperturbed interface by a plane with a kinetic coefficient $b(p_0)$. Assume now that this initial interface is perturbed, for instance, that one of the hillocks becomes steeper and higher than the others. Thus, the perturbed surface may be presented as a plane with an isolated hillock (fig. 9a) or a pit.

Naturally, other perturbations may occur, e.g., simultaneous steepening of all the hillocks, their arbitrary shape change, etc. These perturbations will be discussed below.

The slope p of this perturbed hillock is higher than p_0 and therefore $b(p) > b(p_0)$, since $b = 0$ for the singular orientation $p = 0$. In other words, the "absorption ability" of the hillock becomes higher than that of the remaining interface. This leads to a lowering of the supersaturation in the vicinity of the hillock, including its tip where the step generation takes place. The lines of equal concentration are shown schematically in fig. 9b by the dashed lines, the solid curves showing the flux. On the other hand, the supersaturation at the tip increases since the tip penetrates into the solution where the supersaturation is greater. This phenomenon is responsible for instability in the isotropic case. In the anisotropic case, the instability or stability of the tip depends on the relative importance of the two factors. If the instability occurs, multi-apex growth will result, which is the anisotropic analog of cellular growth. The same reasoning may be followed

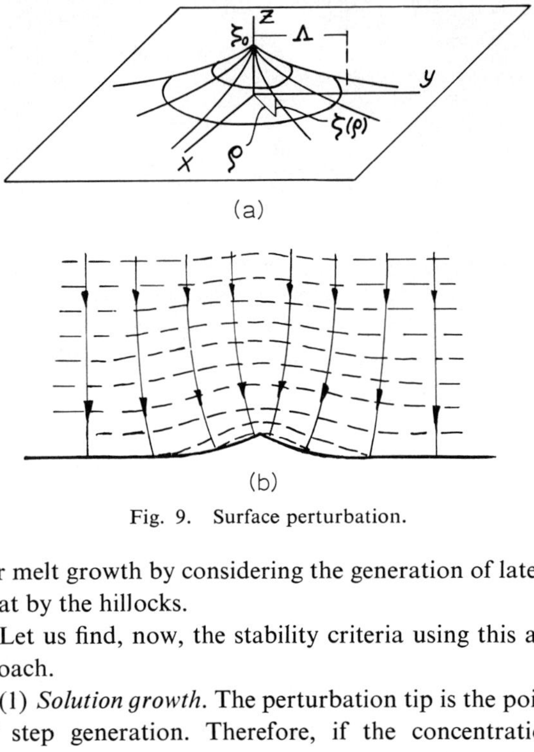

Fig. 9. Surface perturbation.

for melt growth by considering the generation of latent heat by the hillocks.

Let us find, now, the stability criteria using this approach.

(1) *Solution growth.* The perturbation tip is the point of step generation. Therefore, if the concentration change at the tip $\delta c > 0$, then the perturbation will increase with time, and the interface is unstable. Thus, the condition $\delta c < 0$ provides the stability criterion. In order to find this criterion we have to calculate the concentration change δc at the perturbation tip. The calculations were actually performed for a perturbation of the form (fig. 9a)

$$\tilde{z} = \zeta_0 \exp(-\varrho/\Lambda), \tag{32}$$

where $\varrho = (x^2+y^2)^{\frac{1}{2}}$, x and y are measured in the singular plane, and ζ_0 is the perturbation height. The concentration is distributed over the unperturbed plane according to

$$c(z) = c_e + qz + Dq/b(p_0).$$

If $\tilde{c}(\varrho, z)$ is the change in the concentration field due to the perturbation, then the concentration change at the perturbation tip ($\varrho = 0$, $z = 0$) is

$$\delta c = q\zeta_0 + \tilde{c}(0, 0), \tag{33}$$

Dq being the flux to the unperturbed interface. Now we have to find $\tilde{c}(0,0)$.

The concentration over the perturbed and unperturbed growing interface satisfies the equation

$$D\nabla^2 c + R\, \partial c/\partial z = 0. \tag{34}$$

At large distances from the interface, the change of concentration due to the perturbation vanishes: $\tilde{c}(\varrho, z) \to 0$ when $\varrho \to \infty$ and $z \to \infty$. The boundary condition at the growing interface may be obtained by expansion of (23) with respect to $\tilde{c}$ and $\tilde{z}$. In such a manner one obtains the following boundary condition for $\tilde{c}(\varrho, z)$ at the plane $z = 0$:

$$D\frac{\partial \tilde{c}}{\partial z} = b^*\tilde{c} + b^* q\tilde{z} + Dq\theta\tilde{p}, \tag{35}$$

where

$$b^* = b(p_0)\,[1-\Omega(2\bar{c}-c_e)].$$

The slope for the specific perturbation (32) is

$$\tilde{p} = \partial\tilde{z}/\partial\varrho = -\tilde{z}/\Lambda.$$

The solution of the problem (34), (35) was found by expansion of $\tilde{c}$ via a double Fourier integral in x and y. As a result, the concentration perturbation at the tip of the perturbation hillock is found to be

$$\tilde{c}(0,0) = q\zeta_0\,(1+\theta/\mu) \times \int_0^\infty \frac{x\,\mathrm{d}x}{(1+x^2)^{\frac{3}{2}}\,\{1+\frac{1}{2}s+[(\frac{1}{2}s)^2+(x/\mu)^2]^{\frac{1}{2}}\}}, \tag{36}$$

with

$$s = R/b^* = \Omega(\bar{c}-c_e)/[1-\Omega(2\bar{c}-c_e)],$$

$$\mu = b^*\Lambda/D.$$

Substitution of (36) into (33) gives the stability condition

$$\frac{\delta c}{q\zeta_0} = 1 + \frac{\theta\mu(1+s)}{1+\mu^2(1+s)}$$
$$\times \left\{1+\mu+\frac{\mu+\frac{1}{2}s}{[1+\mu^2(1+s)]^{\frac{1}{2}}}\right.$$
$$\times \ln\{\mu(1+s)\,[(1+\mu^2(1+s))^{\frac{1}{2}}-\mu(1+\tfrac{1}{2}s)]$$
$$\left.\times\,[(1+\mu^2(1+s))^{\frac{1}{2}}+1-\tfrac{1}{2}\mu^2 s(1+s)]^{-1}\}\right\} > 0. \quad (37)$$

This function of μ is plotted in fig. 10 for $\theta = 2$ and $s = 0.2$, 0.4 and 0.8 as solid lines. The parameter s is proportional to the supersaturation $(c-c_e)$ at the unperturbed interface. For moderate solubilities (say, $\Omega c_e < 0.2$, i.e. a solubility less than $\sim 20\%$), the parameter s is expressed by

$$s = (c-c_e)\Omega = \Omega c_e \sigma, \quad (38)$$

where

$$\sigma \equiv (c-c_e)/c_e$$

is usually small. For localized perturbations, when $\mu = b^*\Lambda/D \ll 1$:

$$\delta c/q\zeta_0 = 1-\theta. \quad (39)$$

Thus singular faces (possessing $\theta > 1$) are stable with respect to short-range perturbations which appear, for instance, as a result of rapid fluctuations of supersaturation or temperature at the interface. It is necessary to emphasize that the calculations are valid when $\zeta_0 \ll \Lambda$, i.e. for gently sloped perturbation hillocks. This condition remains valid also for the region $\mu \ll 1$ because ζ_0 is an arbitrary small parameter.

For extended perturbations, $\Lambda \gg D/b^*$ $(\mu \gg 1)$:

$$\frac{\delta c}{q\zeta_0} = -\frac{1}{\mu}\left(1+\frac{\theta}{1+s} - \ln\frac{4\mu}{2+\mu s}\right). \quad (40)$$

This function of μ is shown in fig. 10a,b by dashed lines for the same values of s and θ as were used for the solid lines. Comparison of the lines shows that the approximation (40) is satisfactory when $\mu \gg 1$.

The interface is stable when $\delta c < 0$, i.e. if

$$\mu > \mu_c = 2\left\{4\exp\left[-\left(1+\frac{\theta}{1+s}\right)\right]-s\right\}^{-1}. \quad (41)$$

The dimensionless critical size of the perturbation μ_c depends on supersaturation via the anisotropy parameter $\theta = \theta(s)$. The latter function is determined by

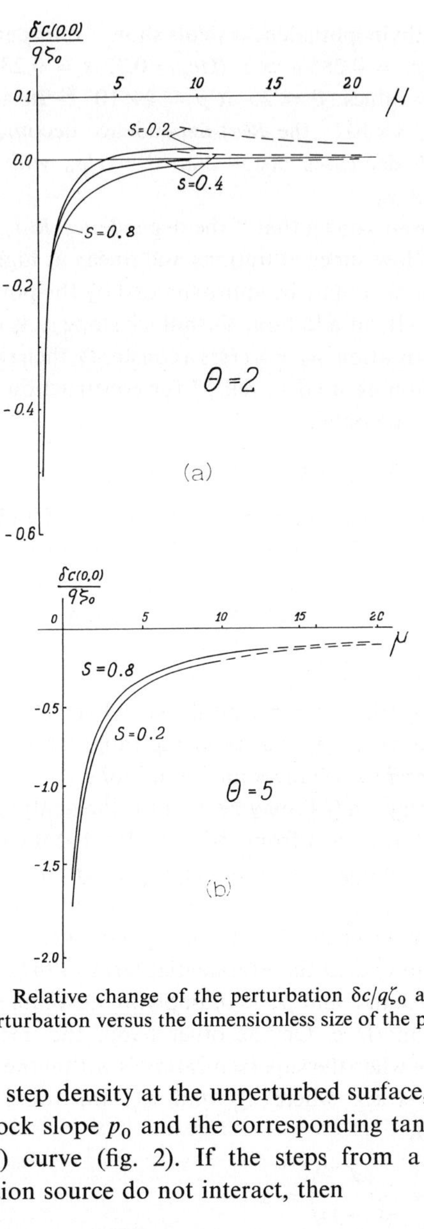

Fig. 10. Relative change of the perturbation $\delta c/q\zeta_0$ at the tip of the perturbation versus the dimensionless size of the perturbation.

the real step density at the unperturbed surface, i.e. by the hillock slope p_0 and the corresponding tangent of the $b(p)$ curve (fig. 2). If the steps from a screw-dislocation source do not interact, then

$$\theta = \frac{1}{p_0} = \frac{\lambda}{a} = \frac{19\,\Omega\alpha}{kTa\sigma}$$
$$= \frac{19\,\Omega^2 c_e \alpha}{kTas}. \quad (42)$$

When $\Omega = 3\times10^{-23}$ cm^3, $\alpha = 10^2$ erg cm^{-2}, $kT = 4\times10^{-14}$ erg, $a = 3\times10^{-8}$ cm, $\Omega c_e = 10^{-1}$, eq. (42) gives $\theta = 5/s$. Thus, for $s = 10^{-2}$ $(\sigma = 10\%)$, θ (s) 500 and $p_0 = 0.2\,s = 2\times10^{-3}$.

β-methylnaphthalene crystals show[13]) steeper hillock slopes $p_0 = 0.285\,\sigma \simeq s$ ($\Omega c_e = 0.2$, $s = 0.23\,\sigma$) and lower θ values: $\theta = 25$ at $p = 2\times10^{-2}$. In addition, for $\sigma \gtrsim 3\times10^{-2}$ the $R(\sigma)$ dependence becomes linear where θ decreases faster than $\theta = 1/p_0$ with the increase of p_0.

It is well known that if the dependence $R(\sigma)$ is parabolic at low supersaturations and linear at high supersaturations, it may be approximated by the power law: $R \propto \sigma^m$. If, in addition, the hillock slope p_0 is linear in supersaturation, $p_0 = r\sigma$ (r is a constant), then repeating the reasoning used in ref. 13 for construction of $\mathscr{B}(p)$ (fig. 4), one obtains

$$\theta = (m-1)/p_0 = (m-1)/r\sigma. \tag{43}$$

For β-methylnaphthalene crystals, $m = 1.5$ and at $p_0 = 2\times10^{-2}$, eq. (43) gives $\theta = 25$, in agreement with the value calculated directly from the $\mathscr{B}(p)$ curve. Replacement of σ by s in (43) gives the function

$$\theta = \mathscr{A}/s, \tag{44}$$

which is valid for the typical case where $R \propto \sigma^m$. The constant $\mathscr{A}$ in (44) varies in the range of 10^{-1} to 10 for different substances and conditions.

The relation (44) may be used for the analysis of (40) and (41). It is clear from (40) and (41) that the interface loses its stability only at supersaturation for which $\mu_c > 0$. The $\mu_c(s)$ dependence for different values of $\mathscr{A}$ is presented in fig. 11. If the supersaturation is sufficiently low, then the exponential term in (41) is much smaller than s and $\mu_c < 0$, implying absolute stability of the interface. On the other hand, the interface is unstable when the supersaturation is within the interval $s_{c_1} < s < s_{c_2}$, where s_{c_1} and s_{c_2} are roots of the equation:

$$\frac{4}{e}\exp\left(-\frac{\mathscr{A}}{s(s+1)}\right) = s. \tag{45}$$

At $s > s_{c_2}$ the value of μ_c is negative and the interface is absolutely stable again.

The function $\exp(-\mathscr{A}/s)$ increases rapidly at $s \simeq \mathscr{A}$ and tends to unity when $s \to \infty$. Thus the smaller critical supersaturation, s_{c_1}, must be of the order of magnitude of $\mathscr{A}$; s_{c_2} is of order unity. Consequently, instability occurs only at rather high supersaturations. The width of the instability region $s_{c_1} < s < s_{c_2}$ decreases with increasing $\mathscr{A}$ and becomes equal to zero at a definite value of $\mathscr{A} = \mathscr{A}_c$. As a rough approximation, we can neglect s in comparison with unity in eq. (45), which gives

$$\mathscr{A}_c = s_{c_1} = s_{c_2} = 4/e^2 = 0.54. \tag{46}$$

Numerical solution of eq. (45) gives $\mathscr{A}_c = s_{c_1} = s_{c_2} = 0.9$. Interfaces with $\mathscr{A} > \mathscr{A}_c$ must be stable at any supersaturation – naturally, within the framework of this model.

It is evident from (42) that $\mathscr{A}$ increases with increasing specific step energy α, and decreases with the crystallization temperature. The same situation is to be expected for nucleation step sources. It is worth emphasizing that interfaces with more active step sources are less stable.

The actual values of s are lower for the less concentrated solutions, i.e. $s \to 0$ when $\Omega c_e \to 0$. Thus, the interfaces in very dilute solutions are always unstable, the critical size of the perturbation being

$$\mu_c = 0.5\exp(1+\theta) = 1.35\exp\theta. \tag{47}$$

However, even a relatively low anisotropy $\theta = 7$ gives a critical perturbation size $\Lambda_c = 10^3\,D/b = 10$ cm [for $D = 10^{-5}$ cm^2 sec^{-1}, $b(p_0) = 10^{-3}$ cm sec^{-1}]. Consequently, facets with smaller dimensions are stable (effects connected with the apexes will be discussed in section 5).

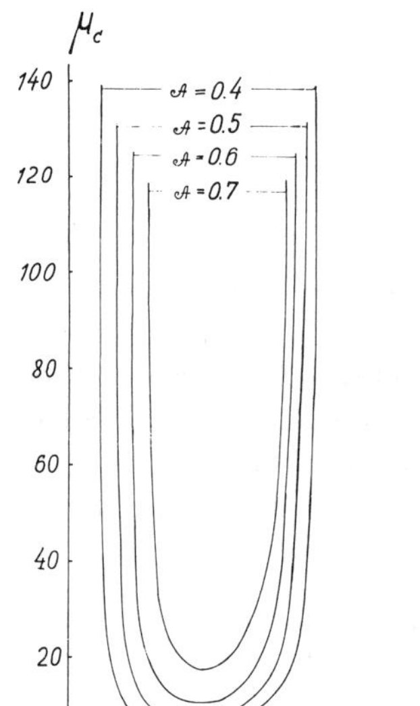

Fig. 11. Dimensionless critical size μ_c versus supersaturation s.

Again, an increase in supersaturation causes a decrease in θ, which in turn leads to instability with respect to short-range perturbations.

(2) *Melt growth.* Consider now growth from the melt containing an impurity. The temperatures of the liquid and solid phases, T_L and T_S, and the impurity concentration c_i, satisfy equations of the type (34) and also satisfy the standard boundary conditions for heat and impurity mass balance. The growth rate is related to the undercooling at the surface as in eq. (4). To find the stability criterion we again introduce a perturbation $\tilde{z}(\varrho)$ in the form of (32) and calculate the corresponding changes, $\tilde{T}_L$, $\tilde{T}_S$ and $\tilde{c}_i$, in the initial temperature and concentration fields, $\bar{T}_L$, $\bar{T}_S$ and $\bar{c}_i$.

Expansion of the boundary conditions gives:

$$\tilde{T}_S - \tilde{T}_L = \left(\frac{\partial \bar{T}_L}{\partial z} - \frac{\partial \bar{T}_S}{\partial z}\right)\tilde{z}, \tag{48a}$$

$$a_S \frac{\partial \tilde{T}_S}{\partial z} - a_L \frac{\partial \tilde{T}_L}{\partial z} + T_Q b^T (\tilde{T}_S + m\tilde{c}_i)$$
$$= + T_Q b^T \left[\frac{(1-K)m\bar{c}_i R}{D_i} - \frac{\partial \bar{T}_S}{\partial z}\right]\tilde{z} - T_Q R\theta \frac{\partial \tilde{z}}{\partial \varrho}, \tag{48b}$$

$$D_i \frac{\partial \tilde{c}_i}{\partial z} + (1-K)(R - b^T m\bar{c}_i)\tilde{c}_i$$
$$-(1-K)b^T \bar{c}_i \tilde{T}_S$$
$$= -(1-K)\left[\frac{\bar{c}R}{D}[b^T m\bar{c}_i + K(R - b^T m\bar{c}_i)]\right.$$
$$\left. - b^T \bar{c}_i \frac{\partial \bar{T}_S}{\partial z}\right]\tilde{z} + (1-K)R\theta\bar{c}_i \frac{\partial \tilde{z}}{\partial \varrho}, \tag{48c}$$

where $b^T = b^T(p_0)$, R is the growth rate of the unperturbed interface, and K is the distribution coefficient. The unknown quantities $\tilde{T}_S$, $\tilde{T}_L$ and $\tilde{c}_i$ may be found by the Fourier transform method:

$$\tilde{c}_i = \frac{1}{2\pi}\iint_{-\infty}^{\infty} A(\boldsymbol{k}) \exp(-k_z z - \mathrm{i}\boldsymbol{k}\cdot\boldsymbol{\rho})\, \mathrm{d}\boldsymbol{k}, \tag{49a}$$

$$\tilde{T}_S = \frac{1}{2\pi}\iint_{-\infty}^{\infty} B_S(\boldsymbol{k}) \exp(-k_z^{(S)} z - \mathrm{i}\boldsymbol{k}\cdot\boldsymbol{\rho})\, \mathrm{d}\boldsymbol{k}, \tag{49b}$$

$$\tilde{T}_L = \frac{1}{2\pi}\iint_{-\infty}^{\infty} B_L(\boldsymbol{k}) \exp(-k_z^{(L)} z - \mathrm{i}\boldsymbol{k}\cdot\boldsymbol{\rho})\, \mathrm{d}\boldsymbol{k}, \tag{49c}$$

$$k_z = \frac{R}{2D_i} + \frac{R}{2D_i}\left(1 + \frac{4k^2 D_i^2}{R^2}\right)^{\frac{1}{2}}, \tag{49d}$$

$$k_z^{(S)} = \frac{R}{2a_S} - \frac{R}{2a_S}\left(1 + \frac{4k^2 a_S^2}{R^2}\right)^{\frac{1}{2}}, \tag{49e}$$

$$k_z^{(L)} = \frac{R}{2a_L} + \frac{R}{2a_L}\left(1 + \frac{4k^2 a_L^2}{R^2}\right)^{\frac{1}{2}}. \tag{49f}$$

Positive values of z correspond to the liquid phase, and negative values of z correspond to the solid phase. Substitution of (49) and the Fourier transform of the perturbation z into (48) gives a linear system of equations for A, B_S and B_L. The solution, together with (49), represents the complete temperature and concentration around the perturbation.

The interface is stable when the change in undercooling at the perturbation tip is negative:

$$-\delta(T_0 - T - mc_i)$$
$$= \left[m\tilde{c}_i + m\frac{\partial \bar{c}_i}{\partial z}\tilde{z} + \tilde{T}_S + \frac{\partial \bar{T}_S}{\partial z}\tilde{z}\right]_{\rho=0,\, z=0}$$
$$= \int_0^{\infty} (mB_S + A)\, k\, \mathrm{d}k$$
$$+ \left[\frac{\partial \bar{T}_S}{\partial z} - \frac{m\bar{c}_i(1-K)R}{D_i}\right]\zeta_0 > 0. \tag{50}$$

Analysis of (50) has been performed to date only for localized perturbations, for which

$T_Q b^T A/(a_S + a_L) \ll 1$.

The corresponding stability criterion is as follows:

$$\frac{G}{R} > \frac{(1-K)mc_{i\infty}}{D_i K}(1-\theta) - \frac{T_Q\theta}{a_L + a_S}, \tag{51}$$

where

$$G = \frac{a_L \partial \bar{T}_L/\partial z + a_S \partial \bar{T}_S/\partial z}{a_L + a_S}, \tag{52}$$

and $c_{i\infty}$ is the impurity concentration in the bulk melt. At $\theta = 0$, criterion (51) transforms into the conventional constitutional undercooling criterion. For $m = 3$ deg/%, $T_Q = 400$ °C, $c_i = 10^{-2}$ %, $D_i = 10^{-5}$ cm^2 sec^{-1}, $a_S = a_L = 10^{-2}$ cm^2 sec^{-1}, $K = 0.1$, eq. (51) takes the form (in deg sec cm^{-2}):

$G/R > 3\times 10^4(1-\theta) - 10^4\theta$,

i.e. the interface in the undercooled melt is stable if $\theta > 0.75$. Interface stability increases with θ, i.e. it is greater with smaller undercooling at the growth front. Conversely, an increase in the undercooling at the growing interface, say, due to increase of R, causes a lowering of the θ values and thus leads to instability, i.e. to cellular and dendritic growth.

(3) *Other types of perturbations*. The criteria (39) and (51) show interface stability with respect to a specific exponential perturbation (32). Rigorously speaking, these criteria cannot be taken as general. Thus it remains to clarify whether there exist other perturbations which are more dangerous for the interface than (32) and which cause instability at lower values of θ, R/G or supersaturation. To answer this question, one has to analyze the stability with respect to a perturbation of an arbitrary shape as was done in the Mullins–Sekerka theory for the isotropic case. However, the singularity in the kinetic coefficient makes the problem substantially non-linear. Therefore complete harmonic analysis in its ordinary form is impossible and we have restricted ourselves until now to several perturbation forms different from (32).

It has already been mentioned that vicinal hillock perturbations can occur as a result of macroscopic supersaturation or undercooling fluctuations at the interface. In this case the steepening or lowering of all the hillocks occurs simultaneously. Thus we come to a perturbation of the type shown in fig. 12.

In this model, the perturbation was chosen to be sharp-apexed alternating positive and negative pyramids with the purpose of excluding a shifting of the interface as a whole. The calculations for this case (A. A. Chernov and M. A. Sarkisyan) were performed as follows.

The perturbation may be written in the form:

$$\tilde{z} = \zeta_0 \left(1 - \frac{|x-2q\Lambda_1|}{\Lambda_1} - \frac{|y-2r\Lambda_2|}{\Lambda_2}\right), \quad (53)$$

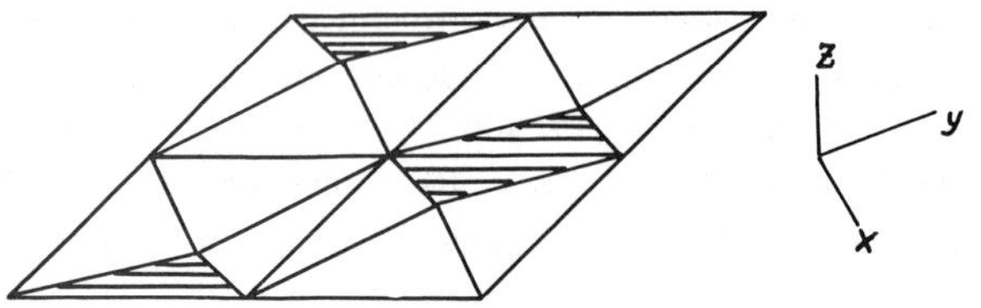

Fig. 12. Multiple surface perturbation.

where

$$|x-2q\Lambda_1| < 2\Lambda_1, \quad |y-2r\Lambda_2| < 2\Lambda_2,$$

$$q = 0, \pm 1, \pm 2, \ldots, \quad r = 0, \pm 1, \pm 2, \ldots,$$

and where x and y lie in the unperturbed singular plane. Thus the apexes are situated at the points $2q\Lambda_1$, $2r\Lambda_2$ for the positive pyramids, and at the points $(2q+1)\Lambda_1$, $(2r+1)\Lambda_2$ for the negative pyramids.

For *solution growth*, only the case of a dilute solution was considered ($\Omega c_e \ll 1$). In this case, the concentration satisfies the Laplace equation. The concentration change is:

$$\tilde{c}(x, y, z) = \sum_{m,n} A_{m,n} \exp(-k_{m,n} z) \times \cos\left(\frac{\pi m}{\Lambda_1} x\right) \cos\left(\frac{\pi n}{\Lambda_2} y\right), \quad (54)$$

where

$$k_{m,n} = \left[\left(\frac{\pi m}{\Lambda_1}\right)^2 + \left(\frac{\pi n}{\Lambda_2}\right)^2\right]^{\frac{1}{2}}.$$

The coefficients $A_{m,n}$ have been determined from the boundary condition (35) with $b^* = b$ and

$$|\tilde{p}| = \zeta_0(\Lambda_1^{-2} + \Lambda_2^{-2})^{\frac{1}{2}}.$$

Namely

$$A_{m,n} = -q \frac{b\tilde{z}_{m,n} + D\theta\tilde{p}_{m,n}}{Dk_{m,n} + b}, \quad (55)$$

$\tilde{z}_{m,n}$ and $\tilde{p}_{m,n}$ being the Fourier components of the perturbation $\tilde{z}$ and its slope $\tilde{p}$. It is appropriate to note here that at constant $|\tilde{p}|$ there is just a uniform value of the new kinetic coefficient for the whole interface. The concentration change at the apexes of the pyramids was calculated giving the following result:

$$\frac{\delta c}{q\zeta_0} = \frac{2}{\pi^2}\left\{\frac{1}{\mu_1}[\Psi(\tfrac{1}{2}+\tfrac{1}{2}\mu_1) - \Psi(\tfrac{1}{2})] + \frac{1}{\mu_2}[\Psi(\tfrac{1}{2}+\tfrac{1}{2}\mu_2) - \Psi(\tfrac{1}{2})]\right\} - \frac{\theta}{\pi}\left(\frac{1}{\mu_1^2} + \frac{1}{\mu_2^2}\right)^{\frac{1}{2}}, \quad (56)$$

with

$$\mu_1 = b\Lambda_1/D, \quad \mu_2 = b\Lambda_2/D,$$

$$\Psi(z) = \mathrm{d} \ln \Gamma(z)/\mathrm{d}z,$$

where $\Gamma(z)$ is the gamma-function.

For $\mu_1 \to 0$ and $\mu_2 \to 0$, the relative concentration change $\delta c/q\zeta_0 \to -\infty$, i.e. the surface is stable with respect to short-range perturbations at any finite anisotropy θ, not only when $\theta > 1$, as it was in the case of an isolated perturbation hillock [see eq. (39)]. In other words, the multiple perturbation (53) is less dangerous than the single one as given by (32).

For $\mu_1 \gg 1$, $\mu_2 \gg 1$, the behavior of (56) is analogous to the behavior of (37) at $s = 0$. In particular, for a square perturbation net, when $\mu_1 = \mu_2 = \mu$:

$$\frac{\delta c}{q\zeta_0} = \frac{4}{\pi^2 \mu}\left[\Psi(\tfrac{1}{2}+\tfrac{1}{2}\mu) - \Psi(\tfrac{1}{2}) - 2^{-\frac{1}{2}}\pi\theta\right]. \tag{57}$$

Taking into account that $\Psi(\frac{1}{2}) = 0.036$ and that $\Psi(z) = \ln z$ when $z \gg 1$, one obtains the following critical perturbation period:

$$\mu_c = 2\exp(2^{-\frac{1}{2}}\pi\,\theta). \tag{58}$$

Thus the critical perturbation size increases exponentially with increasing θ, as in the case of the isolated perturbation [of eq. (32)]. This rise, however, is greater by a factor $\frac{1}{2}\pi$. Consequently the multiple perturbation is also less dangerous for the interface for long-range perturbations, $\mu \gg 1$.

As for *melt growth in the presence of impurities*, calculation for $\Lambda_1 = \Lambda_2 = \Lambda$ and

$$\mu = b^{\mathrm{T}} T_{\mathrm{Q}} \Lambda/(a_{\mathrm{L}} + a_{\mathrm{S}}) \ll 1$$

gives a stability criterion in the form:

$$\frac{G}{R} > \frac{(1-K)mc_{\mathrm{i}\infty}}{D_{\mathrm{i}}K} - \frac{2^{\frac{1}{2}}T_{\mathrm{Q}}}{a_{\mathrm{L}}+a_{\mathrm{S}}}\frac{\theta}{\mu}. \tag{59}$$

This result shows that the interface is stable against short-range perturbations for arbitrary positive θ and demonstrates once again that the multiple perturbation is less dangerous.

Finally, a perturbation was considered in the form of an isolated ledge on the surface:

$$\tilde{z} = \zeta_0 \exp(-x/\Lambda).$$

For solution growth in the Laplace approximation ($s = 0$):

$$\frac{\delta c}{q\zeta_0} = 1 + \frac{2(\theta+\mu)}{(1+\mu^2)}(\ln\mu - \tfrac{1}{2}\pi\mu), \tag{60}$$

i.e. the interface is stable with respect to the creation of a sharp edge (or pit, when $\zeta_0 < 0$) at arbitrary positive θ. The critical perturbation width causing instability is

$$\mu_c = \exp(\tfrac{1}{2}\pi\theta). \tag{61}$$

This coincides with the critical size (58) of the pyramid in the multiple perturbation within a factor of 2, and again μ_c appears to be greater than the critical size for an isolated hillock.

Thus, the most dangerous perturbation among all that have been considered is the isolated hillock. The physical reason is quite clear – for the other two perturbations the kinetic coefficient increases either on the whole surface (fig. 12) or along an infinite strip (fig. 13), i.e. on an area which is substantially larger than that for the isolated hillock. Consequently, the decrease in concentration ($\tilde{c}$ is always negative) is minimal for the hillock and maximal for the multiple perturbation. The one-dimensional perturbation (edge) is intermediate.

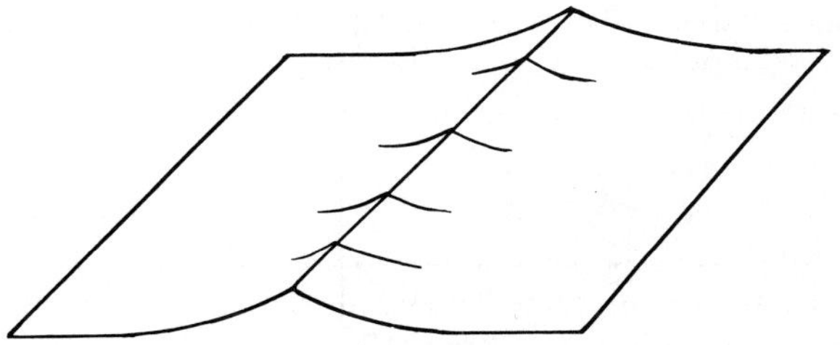

Fig. 13. Edge-like perturbation.

On these grounds, one can conclude that the criteria (37) and (51) are probably very near to the actual ones. The minimization of $-\tilde{c}$ by varying the class of functions which describes the isolated perturbation is a problem to be solved in future.

5. Polyhedron stability

In section 3 we found the conditions under which a polyhedral crystal may or may not grow without a change in shape. Now we are going to analyze whether the perturbations may cause transformation of a polyhedron to a skeletal or dendritic form, or cause other macroscopic changes in its shape at the earlier stages of growth.

Consider a polyhedron in an unstirred solution. The size of the polyhedron is assumed to be less than the critical size (26), i.e. the inhomogeneity in concentration over the crystal faces is compensated by the anisotropy of the kinetic coefficient. The supersaturation is maximal at the apexes and therefore perturbations at these places seem to be most probable. A crystal apex with a perturbation is shown in fig. 14. To find the stability criterion, we have to calculate, as before, the change in concentration at the tip of the perturbation. Only the two-dimensional case has been considered up to now (A. A. Chernov, A. M. Melnikova, J. Adolfi).

A perturbation was taken in the form (fig. 14):

$$\tilde{Y}' = \zeta_0 \exp(-|X'|/\Lambda). \tag{62}$$

Here the Y'-axis coincides with the diagonal of the regular polygon under consideration, X' is perpendicular to Y' in the corner of the polygon and $\tilde{Y}'$ is the interface shift along the Y'-axis due to the perturbation. The perturbation amplitude ζ_0 and width Λ are assumed to be much smaller than the edge L of the polygon. The slope of the perturbed surface with respect to the singular edge orientation which coincides with the x-axis (fig. 14) is:

$$p = (\zeta_0/\Lambda)\sin^2\psi \exp[-\tfrac{1}{2}(L-2x)\sin\psi] \times \{1+(\zeta_0/\Lambda)\sin\psi\cos\psi \times \exp[-\tfrac{1}{2}(L-2x)\sin\psi]\}^{-1}, \tag{63}$$

where

$$\psi = \tfrac{1}{2}\pi - \pi/n,$$

and where n is the number of edges of the polygon. For perturbations with gentle slope, that is, for $\zeta_0/\Lambda \ll 1$, the denominator of (63) is equal to unity.

The tip of the perturbation penetrates into a region of higher concentration so that the change in concentration at the tip due to the penetration is

$$\frac{\partial\bar{c}}{\partial Y'}\zeta_0 = \frac{\partial\bar{c}}{\partial y}\frac{\partial y}{\partial Y'}\zeta_0 = \frac{q\zeta_0}{\cos(\pi/n)}, \tag{64}$$

where $q = \partial\bar{c}/\partial y$, $\bar{c}(x,y)$ being the unperturbed concentration distribution around the polygon. The perturbation of this distribution, $\tilde{c}(x,y)$ is assumed to satisfy the Laplace equation and the boundary condition, analogous to (35):

$$D\frac{\partial\tilde{c}}{\partial y} = b\tilde{c} + bq\tilde{y} - D\frac{\partial^2 c}{\partial y^2}\tilde{y} + Dq\theta\tilde{p}. \tag{65}$$

As before, this condition is applied on the absolutely straight edge $y = 0$. Since $bL/D < 1$ for the unperturbed polygon, the inequalities $b\Lambda/D \ll 1$ and $b\zeta_0/D \ll 1$ are also valid.

The first, second and third terms on the right-hand side of eq. (65) are either of the order of $b\Lambda/D$ or $b\zeta_0/D$ or Λ/L in comparison with the fourth and therefore may be neglected in the approximation under consideration. Thus, we come to the following problem. There exists a regular polygon whose edges absorb the dissolved substance only within the regions of length Λ near the corners of each edge. The power of these sinks is $Dq\theta\tilde{p}$. The concentration perturbation $\tilde{c}(x,y)$ at the tip is to be found. This quantity can be roughly estimated if we neglect the influence of the polygon on the diffusion field. Within this approximation, assuming

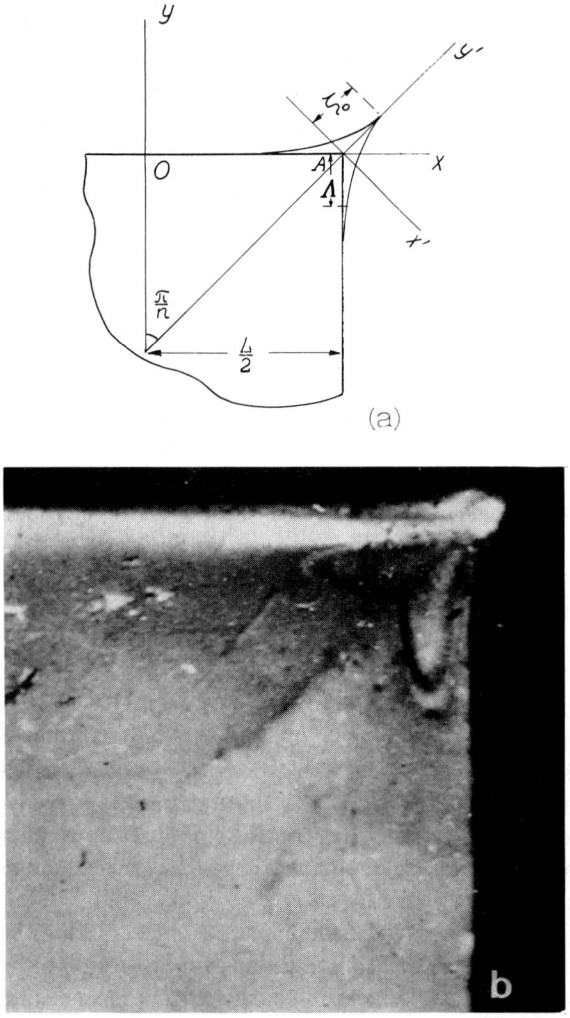

Fig. 14. Initial apex perturbations: (a) schematically in two dimensions; (b) three-dimensional $Pb_3NiNb_2O_9$ apex.

$|\tilde{p}| \simeq \zeta_0/\Lambda$ and taking into account eq. (64):

$$\frac{\delta c}{q\zeta_0} \simeq \frac{1}{\cos(\pi/n)} + \theta \ln \frac{\Lambda}{L}. \tag{66}$$

Therefore the polygon is unstable if the length of the perturbation exceeds the critical length Λ_c:

$$\frac{\Lambda_c}{L} \simeq \exp\left[-\frac{1}{\theta \cos(\pi/n)}\right]. \tag{67}$$

A rigorous solution of the problem stated above was found by making use of a conformal transformation[17]). Namely, the region $yOAy'$ in the $z = (x,y)$ plane was transformed into the upper half of the $w = (u,v)$ plane by the function

$$z = l \int_0^w (1-t^2)^{1/n-\frac{1}{2}}\, dt, \tag{68}$$

where

$$l = L\Gamma(1+n^{-1})/\Gamma(\tfrac{1}{2}+n^{-1})\,\Gamma(\tfrac{1}{2}).$$

The concentration perturbation in the w-plane is of the form

$$c(u,v) = \frac{\theta q l}{\pi} \int_0^1 p \left.\frac{dy}{dv}\right|_{v=0} \ln|w^2-u^2|\, du$$

$$= \frac{\theta q}{\pi} \int_0^{\frac{1}{2}L} \tilde{p} \ln|w^2-u^2|\, dx, \tag{69}$$

where $u = u(x)$ and $p = p(x)$. At the tip of the perturbation, i.e. at the point ($x = \frac{1}{2}L$, $y = 0$) in the z-plane or ($u = 1$, $v = 0$) in the w-plane,

$$c(1,0) = \frac{\theta q}{\pi} \int_0^{\frac{1}{2}L} \tilde{p} \ln|1-u^2|\, dx. \tag{70}$$

The function $u(x)$ and the integral (70) may be calculated making use of the expansion of (68) in the vicinity of the corners:

$$z \simeq \tfrac{1}{2}L - \frac{2^{1/n+\frac{1}{2}}\, nl}{n+2} (1-w)^{1/n-\frac{1}{2}}. \tag{71}$$

This approximation is sufficient because $\tilde{p}(x)$ has substantial values only near the corner ($2\Lambda \ll L$). Calculations for a square [$n = 4$, $\cos(\pi/n) = 2^{-\frac{1}{2}}$] give:

$$\frac{\delta c}{q\zeta_0} = 2^{\frac{1}{2}} + \frac{2^{\frac{3}{2}}}{3\pi}\left[\frac{2\Lambda}{\zeta_0} \ln\left(1+\frac{\zeta_0}{\Lambda}\right) \ln\left(\frac{\Lambda}{L}+1.6\right) + \int_0^\infty \frac{\ln z\, dz}{\exp(z)+\frac{1}{2}\zeta_0}\right]. \tag{72}$$

For perturbations with gentle slope, for which $\zeta_0/2\Lambda \ll 1$,

$$\frac{\delta c}{q\zeta_0} = 2^{\frac{1}{2}} - 0.58 + 0.3\,\theta\left(\ln\frac{\Lambda}{L}+1.6\right), \tag{73}$$

where the Euler constant 0.58 arises from the integral in (72). Thus, the critical perturbation size is determined by the relationship:

$$\Lambda_c/L = 0.2 \exp(-2.8/\theta). \tag{74}$$

If $\Lambda > \Lambda_c$, the polygon is unstable. This criterion was obtained under the supposition that the unperturbed shape is a polygon, so that the small values of θ are incompatible with (74). If the dependence $\beta(\vartheta)$ may be approximated by circles in the polar coordinates (β,ϑ) [like the surface energy anisotropy[18,19])], then the stationary shape is a polygon only when $\theta > \tan(\pi/n)$. Thus, $\theta > 1$ for a square and the ratio Λ_c/L changes from 0.2 (when $\theta \to \infty$) to 0.012 (when $\theta = 1$). Taking into account that the solution is valid for small values of $2\Lambda/L$, we may consider only the region $0.01 < \Lambda_c/L < 0.1$. This region corresponds to $\theta \gtrsim 4$.

Criterion (74) shows that the localized perturbations with small Λ, which are perhaps created by rapid fluctuations, heal with time and cannot cause instability. The healing process consists of the propagation of steps [of height $\zeta_0 \cos(\pi/n)$] from the corners towards the center of the edge. When the steps reach each other they annihilate, probably giving rise to inclusions.

Perturbations of width $\Lambda > \Lambda_c$ ($\Lambda \ll L$) cause instability, showing that even small crystals are not stable with respect to long perturbations (surface energy was not taken into account!). This instability, however, does not necessarily cause dendritic growth. Indeed, the growing perturbation will acquire a steeper slope and a greater kinetic coefficient. The latter, in turn, will cause a decrease in supersaturation at the tip. This decrease may stop the generation of steps at the apex if the generation occurs by nucleation. As a result, a macrostep will form. The diffusion field of the step reaches the apex and lowers the supersaturation there, for the same reasons that apply to the perturbation slope. The macrostep moves away from the apex, its influence on the supersaturation at the apex weakens, and the conditions for instability due to the next fluctuation arise again. Consequently, the development of such instability will generate macrosteps at the apexes and cause a temporal instability of the facet growth rate (fig. 7).

A similar situation may be expected when the perturbation at the apex has the form of a "needle" ($\Lambda \ll \zeta_0$). The lateral needle surface may possess a small kinetic coefficient corresponding to one of the $b(p)$ minima. Consequently, the concentration field perturbation $\tilde{c}$ will be small, the supersaturation change δc at the tip will be positive, thus bringing about instability. Further thickening of the whisker will be more intensive at its bottom, giving rise to an increase of the kinetic coefficient and to a decrease of supersaturation at the tip. Again elongation of the whisker may be stopped and a macrostep appears.

The same reasoning also applies to growth in the presence of impurities which form a "shell" covering the polygon (or a flat interface). The needle piercing the shell will turn into a macrostep according to the suggested mechanism (see also section 3). This macrostep will bury the impurity-rich layer, giving rise to a striation in the crystal (perpendicular to the growth direction) and to growth rate oscillations. Their amplitude may be higher than the amplitude caused by the external fluctuations alone. In this case, instability of the interface amplifies the external fluctuations of temperature and concentration.

Quantitative analysis of stability with respect to needle-shaped perturbations (probably taking into account the surface energy) and of the later stages of instability have not yet been performed.

6. Stability of plates, steps and two-dimensional crystals on substrates

The details of the stability of these shapes arise from the character of their heat and diffusion fields and the structure of their lateral surfaces.

If the step height or plate thickness is comparable with interatomic distances, then the lateral surfaces will be atomically rough and the kinetic coefficients will be large and isotropic. The stability of thin discs growing on a substrate via surface diffusion was considered by Avignon[20]. The stability of a disc in the bulk melt was analysed recently by Fujioka and Sekerka[25].

In the case of both surface and three-dimensional volume diffusion, thin plates and step contours are more stable than a cylinder of corresponding cross-section, because changes in feeding to the perturbation tip from different sides will substantially compensate each other[14].

An isolated thin plate growing via surface diffusion on *both* basal planes is stable due to diffusion itself, independent of the kinetic coefficient anisotropy or surface energy. Indeed, the feeding is poorer for a positive perturbation (bump) and better for a negative perturbation (pit).

In the case of plates and steps of macroscopic thickness, the lateral surfaces may be atomically flat. Therefore these lateral surfaces will be more stable both in the basal cross-section and in the cross-section perpendicular to the substrate or the plate (axial cross-section). However, if the parameter bh/D reaches a definite critical value[14,28], the latarel surface may not remain flat. As a result, the plate can split into two parallel plates of smaller thickness, with the macrostep transforming into an overhanging layer.

Increasing the height of plates or steps can also cause instability of the lateral surface in the basal cross-section. That is why the heights of surface dendrites must be greater than a definite critical value.

Another cause of instability may be the repulsion between the dipole moments of adsorbed atoms and crystallites. The origin of this is connected with adatom ionization. For instance, Na adatoms on a W substrate are negative and possess dipole moments $p_1 = 4$–5 Debye units for (110) W at a relative coverage ≈ 0.2[21], and $p_1 \simeq 4$ D and $p_1 \simeq 2.5$ D for (100) W and (111) W, respectively. The dipole moments diminish with the density of the coverage and strongly influence the thermodynamics[22] and kinetics[9] of monolayer condensation.

The dipole moment p_2 per crystalline aggregate or atom is, roughly speaking, proportional to the contact potential difference between the crystallite and the substrate. For estimation, we will use $p_2 \simeq p_1$.

During condensation on the substrate, the atoms have to overcome not only the surface energy barrier, but also the dipole–dipole repulsion barrier[9].

The repulsion energy between an isolated atom and a two-dimensional crystalline aggregate is equal to

$$\frac{p_1 p_2}{a^2} \iint \frac{\mathrm{d}x\,\mathrm{d}y}{(x^2+y^2)^{\frac{3}{2}}},$$

where the origin of the coordinate system (x,y) within the substrate plane is at the adatom, and the integration is performed over the whole crystalline aggregate.

If the atom is located at the edge of an aggregate, this repulsion energy reaches its maximum

$$\frac{p_1 p_2}{a^2}\int_a^L \frac{\varphi(\varrho)\,\mathrm{d}\varrho}{\varrho^2},$$

where $\varphi(\varrho)$ is the contour of the aggregate in polar coordinates (ϱ, φ), with $\varrho = (x^2+y^2)^{\frac{1}{2}}$, $\tan\varphi = y/x$, a being the interatomic distance and L the aggregate size. Thus, the aggregate shape near the point where the new atom is added to the aggregate strongly influences the repulsive energy. In particular, the repulsive energy at the polygon apex at $L \gg a$ equals

$$\pi p_1 p_2(1-2/n)/a^3.$$

Thus, the barrier for an adatom to join the aggregate at its apex is $(1-2/n)$ times lower than that at the edge. This effect may be quite substantial: if $p_1 \simeq p_2 \simeq 3D = 3\times 10^{-18}$ cgs, the repulsive energy from the edge is $p_1 p_2/a^3 \simeq 0.5$ eV, i.e. it is comparable with two-dimensional heats of condensation for metals. If p_1 and p_2 are of opposite sign, the electrostatic effects will stabilize the growing islands.

Acknowledgements

It is a great pleasure for the author to thank R. F. Sekerka and K. A. Jackson whose help was very important in the improvement of the text.

Appendix. List of symbols

a	Interatomic distance
a_L, a_S	Thermal diffusivities ($cm^2\ sec^{-1}$)
A'	Integration constant, eq. (12)
$A(\boldsymbol{k})$	Fourier transform of the perturbation in the concentration field
$A_{m,n}$	Fourier coefficients of the change in concentration
$\mathscr{A}$	Constant relating anisotropy to supersaturation: $\theta = \mathscr{A}/S$
b	Kinetic coefficient ($cm\ sec^{-1}$), eq. (21)
b^*	$= b[1-\Omega(2\bar{c}-c_e)]$ $cm\ sec^{-1}$
b^T	Kinetic coefficient ($cm\ sec^{-1}\ deg^{-1}$)
B'	Integration constant, eq. (12)
$B_S(\boldsymbol{k})$, $B_L(\boldsymbol{k})$	Fourier transforms of the perturbation in the temperature fields in the solid and liquid, respectively
$\mathscr{B}$	Effective kinetic coefficient
c	Concentration
$\bar{c}$	Unperturbed concentration field
$\tilde{c}$	Change in concentration field due to a perturbation
c_0	Concentration near the center of a face
c_1	Concentration at the point which determines the growth rate normal to the facet
c_∞	Concentration in the bulk
c_e	Equilibrium concentration
c_i	Impurity concentration
$\bar{c}_i$	Unperturbed impurity concentration
$\tilde{c}_i$	Change in impurity concentration due to perturbation
$c_{i\infty}$	Bulk concentration of impurity
δc	Concentration change at perturbation tip
D	Mass diffusivity ($cm^2\ sec^{-1}$)
D_i	Impurity diffusivity
E	Activation energy for atom addition at a kink
G	Averaged temperature gradient
h	Step height (cm)
ΔH	Enthalpy of fusion (latent heat)
k	Boltzmann's constant
$\boldsymbol{k}$	Wave number
k_z	Wave number in z direction for composition field
k_z^S, k_z^L	Wave numbers in z direction for thermal fields in solid and liquid
$k_{m,n}$	Wave number
K	Distribution coefficient
l	$= L\Gamma(1+1/n)/\Gamma(\frac{1}{2}+1/n)\Gamma(\frac{1}{2})$
L, L_c	Crystal size, critical crystal size
m	Liquidus slope
m	Exponent in a power law relating growth rate to supersaturation $R \propto \sigma^m$, eq. (43)
M	Anisotropy parameter relating to the critical stable crystal size
M_i	As above, but for an instability caused by an impurity
$\hat{n}$, n	Vector normal to the interface
n	Number of edges of the polygon, eqs. (63)–(71)
p	Local slope of the interface

$\bar{p}$	Average slope of the interface
$\tilde{p}$	Slope of surface at perturbation
p_0	Slope of surface near center of face
p_1	Slope of surface at the point which determines the growth rate normal to the facet
p_c	Critical value of slope at the center of a face
$\tilde{p}_{m,n}$	Fourier components of the slope of the surface at a perturbation
q	Concentration gradient at the interface
r	Radius in cylindrical coordinates
R	Growth rate normal to singular surfaces
s	$= \Omega(\bar{c}-c_e)/[1-\Omega(2\bar{c}-c_e)]$ supersaturation parameter
s_{c_1}, s_{c_2}	Two critical values of s
t	Time
T	Temperature
T_0	Equilibrium temperature
T_L, T_S	Temperatures of liquid and solid
$\bar{T}_L$, $\bar{T}_S$	Unperturbed temperatures in liquid and solid
$\tilde{T}_L$, $\tilde{T}_S$	Change in temperature of liquid and solid due to perturbation
T_Q	Ratio: (heat of fusion)/(specific heat)
ΔT	Undercooling at the interface
u, v	Coordinates in w-plane
v	Step velocity
V	Growth velocity normal to average (stepped) interface
$w(u, v)$	Mapping plane in conformal transformation
W_+, W_-	Quantity of atoms joining and leaving crystal per unit time per one atomic site at the step
x	Axis in the singular plane
x'	Axis in vicinal surface normal to steps
X'	Normal to Y'
y	Axis in the singular plane
$\tilde{y}$	y component of perturbation
$\tilde{y}'$	y' component of perturbation
Y'	Diagonal of polyhedron
z	Normal to singular plane
z'	Axis normal to vicinal surface
$\tilde{z}$	z component of perturbation
$\tilde{z}_{m,n}$	Fourier components of perturbation
α	Specific surface free energy (erg cm^{-2})
β	Kinetic coefficient relating normal growth rate V to supersaturation
β_{st}	Kinetic coefficient relating step velocity to supersaturation
β_{st}^{T}	Kinetic coefficient relating step velocity to undercooling
Γ	Gamma function
ε	Bond energy
ζ_0	Perturbation height
ϑ	Angle of interface normal
θ	Anisotropy of kinetic coefficient
λ	Interstep distance
λ_0	Interkink distance
Λ	Characteristic length of perturbation
Λ_c	Critical perturbation size
μ	$b^*\Lambda/D$, dimensionless size of perturbation
μ_c	Critical value of μ
ν_+, ν_-	Frequencies of atom addition and subtraction at kink
ρ	Crystal density
ϱ	Radius in cylindrical coordinates
σ	Supersaturation ratio
φ	Angle of interface normal
$\Psi(z)$	$= \mathrm{d} \ln \Gamma(z)/\mathrm{d}z$
Ω	Atomic volume

References

1) A. A. Chernov, Soviet Phys.-Usp. **4** (1961) 129.
2) S. G. Davison and J. D. Levine, Surface States, in: *Solid State Physics*, Vol. 25 (Academic Press, New York, 1970).
3) V. V. Voronkov, Kristallografiya **12** (1967) 831.
4) R. F. Sekerka, J. Crystal Growth **3/4** (1968) 71.
5) R. L. Parker, Crystal Growth Mechanisms, in: *Solid State Physics*, Vol. 25 (Academic Press, New York, 1970).
6) J. W. Cahn, in: *Crystal Growth*, Ed. H. S. Peiser (Pergamon, Oxford, 1967) p. 681.
7) R. Kaischev and E. Budevski, Contem. Phys. **8** (1967) 489.
8) V. Bostanov, G. Staikov, E. Budevski and R. Kaischev, Commun. Dept. Chem., Bulgarian Acad. Sci. **4** (1971) 311.
9) A. A. Chernov, Crystallization, in: *Annual Review of Materials Science*, Vol. 3 (1973).
10) V. Bostanov, R. Rusinova and E. Budevski, Mechanism and Kinetics of Crystallization, Part II, in: *IV All-Union Conf. on Crystal Growth*, Erevan (Akad. Nauk Arm. SSR, 1972) p. 11.
11) V. V. Voronkov, Kristallografiya **17** (1972) 909.
12) A. A. Ballman and R. A. Laudise, Hydrothermal Growth, in: *The Art and Science of Growing Crystals*, Ed. J. J. Gilman (Wiley, New York, 1963) p. 231.
13) A. A. Chernov and E. D. Dukova, Kristallografiya **14** (1969) 169.
14) A. A. Chernov, Kristallografiya **16** (1971) 842.

15) C. Nanev and D. Ivanov, J. Crystal Growth **3/4** (1968) 530.
16) A. A. Chernov, Kristall und Technik **6** (1971) 577.
17) A. Seeger, Phil. Mag. **44** (1953) 348.
18) C. Herring, in: *Structure and Properties of Solid Surfaces*, Eds. R. Gomer and C. S. Smith (Chicago Univ Press, 1953) ch. 1.
19) C. Herring, Phys. Rev. **82** (1951) 87.
20) M. Avignon, J. Crystal Growth **13/14** (1971) 113.
21) E. V. Klimenko and A. G. Naumovets, Surface Sci. **14** (1969) 141.
22) L. A. Bol'shov, Soviet Phys.-Solid State **13** (1971) 1679.
23) T. Yamamoto, Bull. Inst. Phys. Chem. Res. **11** (1932) 1083; **12** (1933) 506; **13** (1934) 1108; **14** (1935) 61.
24) A. Papapetrou, Z. Krist. **92** (1935) 89.
25) T. Fujioka and R. F. Sekerka, J. Crystal Growth **24/25** (1974) 84.